D1104799

Thermal Regimes of Combustion

Thermal Regimes of Combustion

Lev Abramovich Vulis

Kazakh State University, U.S.S.R

Literal Translation from the Russian by
Morris D. Friedman

Translating Editor
Glenn C. Williams
Massachusetts Institute of Technology

This translation was sponsored, in part, by
Project Squid, which is supported by the Office
of Naval Research, Department of the Navy,
under contract Nonr-1858(25), NR-098-038.
Reproduction in full or in part is permitted for
any purpose of the United States government.

McGRAW-HILL BOOK COMPANY, INC.
New York   Toronto   London
1961

M541.36
V9X6t
E1961

THERMAL REGIMES OF COMBUSTION

Copyright © 1961 by the McGraw-Hill Book Company, Inc. Printed in the United Stated of America. All rights reserved. This book, or parts thereof, may not be reproduced in any form without permission of the publishers. Library of Congress Catalog Card Number 61-12951.

67620

THE PENNSYLVANIA STATE
UNIVERSITY LIBRARY

Foreword

This book is devoted to exposition of the elementary thermal
theory of combustion. Major attention is focused on the thermal
phenomena, and the treatment of chemical kinetics is highly simplified. By examples of the combustion of homogeneous gas mixtures, carbon (coke), and unmixed gases, there are shown the peculiarities of exothermic reactions: the possibility of stationary-
state processes, critical occurrence of ignition and extinction,
heat loss from the flame, process stability, etc. The influence of
various parameters is examined: gas velocity, mixture composition, heating value, initial temperature, etc. The valuable results
obtained are coordinated with scientific and practical conclusions
concerning stable, steady-flow combustion. A minimum space is
devoted to some discussion of the gas-dynamic aspects of combustion: steady-flame fronts and the role of turbulence, the concept
of detonation.

The book is intended to inform workers, engineers, and students
in technical institutes.

The author, Lev Abramovich Vulis, is a professor at the Kazakh
State University and a member of the Academy of Science of
Kazakh.

He has published a number of articles on thermodynamics in
Soviet technical journals, and in 1959 was editor of a series of
articles on gas dynamics published by the Academy of Science of
Kazakh, and author of two of them.

Preface

The practical utility of the combustion process in various branches of engineering is exceptionally large. Despite the considerable progress of domestic science in developing combustion theory, at the present time the solution of engineering problems depends primarily on the results of experimental investigations conducted in specific furnaces or under conditions as close as possible to the engineering conditions.

The role of combustion theory lies basically in the creation of general physical concepts, in a qualitative analysis of the influence of separate factors, in seeking methods of generalizing experimental results, and in a rational direction of experimental work.

This book is an attempt to explain the elementary thermal-combustion theory, limited by an approximate consideration of the physical bases of the simplest phenomena of which the complex technical combustion process is composed.

Particular attention is paid to the thermal aspect of the process, with a considerable idealization of the phenomenon as a whole and, in particular, the conceptions of chemical kinetics. In substance, these conceptions are limited to the most general properties of simple exothermal reactions whose rates depend on the concentrations of the initial substances and whose acceleration mechanism is related to a rise in temperature.

Considered in most detail are peculiarities of the steady-state thermal region of the combustion process, the physical meaning of the critical phenomena of ignition and extinction, the influence of mixing and heat emission, the most simple considerations on the stability and "inertia" of combustion, etc. The method of investigating these questions is a development of the classical methods of Academician N. N. Semenov, explained in his works on the thermal explosion of combustible mixtures which underlie modern thermal-combustion theory. The problem of flame propagation, the theory of normal and turbulent combustion, the most simple information on detonations, etc., are explained in a comparatively brief space from the viewpoint of analyzing the thermal-combustion process in a steady flow.

When discussing the solutions of the separate problems, an attempt is made to relate them qualitatively to engineering problems and to conditions of the combustion process in stationary furnaces; the writer was influenced by this inclination to approximate the results of combustion theory to the requirements of fuel consumption practice in preparing this monograph. The full-valued solution of this mature problem is possible only in the future and it requires the combined efforts of various specialists. However, it is to be hoped that the first systematic steps in this direction will be of great advantage to Soviet thermal physicists and thermal engineers.

The desire to make the book and the methods of investigation used in the thermal theory of combustion more easily understood by students stimulated the writer to give a comparatively detailed explanation not only of the physical substance of the separate problems but of the mathematical side of the questions, as well as providing a maximum illustration of the computational results by graphical constructions. Missing from the book are an explanation of experimental results, an analysis of specific furnace designs and constructions, as well as peculiarities of the behavior of various fuels in the combustion process. Not discussed herein are questions which are specific to the combustion of liquid fuels (the processes of jet breakdown, evaporation, etc.), and the actual mechanism of the gas or coal combustion reaction (the problem of primary products, secondary reaction on the coal surface and in the gaseous phase, the behavior of light ashes and cinders, etc.) is not considered. The single example of an engineering computation in the book (muffle burner), although carried through to numerical results, is only of methodological value.

The last chapter of the book, Elements of Gas Dynamic Combustion, is explained sketchily and a very limited number of questions are considered therein. A detailed discussion of the question of gas dynamics as applied to combustion processes must be the subject of a special monograph.

The book as a whole is based on the thermal combustion theory investigations conducted by Soviet scientists; Academician N. N. Semenov and his school (Corr.-Memb. AN USSR Ia. B. Zel'dovich, D. A. Frank-Kamenetskii, K. I. Shchelkin et al.), Academician L. D. Landau, Corr.-Memb. AN USSR A. S. Predvoditelev and his colleagues (L. N. Khitrin et al.), V. I. Blinov, G. F. Knorre, Corr.-Memb. AN USSR Z. F. Chikhanov, et al. Explained herein (especially in the first five chapters) are results obtained by the author and frequently published earlier. A detailed explanation of these results was contained in a number of lecture courses read by the author in 1945-1950 (in particular, in a course on combustion theory for aspirants of the Moscow Aviation Institute named for Ordzhonikidze).[1]

---

[1]In this connection, the manuscript of the book was completed at the end of 1950 and later investigations are not used therein and, as a rule, are not listed in the bibliography.

The preliminary information needed by the reader is a basic knowledge of questions of heat transmission and a general acquaintance with furnace technique. Some very simple information on the rate of chemical reactions, characteristics of turbulent motion, etc., is given in the text for the convenience of the reader.

The mathematics used in the first five chapters is simple and well-known to a wide circle of readers; the last two chapters require an acquaintance with the equations of mathematical physics and can be of some difficulty for an unprepared reader. However, their explanation is accompanied by comparatively detailed physical explanations.

The author is grateful to Doctor of Engineering Science G. F. Knorre for reviewing the manuscript and offering suggestions.

Lev Abramovich Vulis

Editor's Introduction

Professor Vulis presents a rather complete discussion of combustion on the basis of the interaction of simple first-order chemical kinetics, molecular diffusion, and heat transfer in perfectly stirred reaction zones. The discussion is illustrated by numerous graphical presentations of the variation in performance characteristics, such as fractional completion of combustion, ignition and extinction temperatures, and compositions as affected by various operating parameters and characteristics of the fuel-oxidant mixtures. To my knowledge, Professor Vulis' treatment is the most comprehensive of the "well-stirred" reactor and considerably antedates similar discussions of high-output combustion in the Western literature.

Professor Vulis' text uses quite involved sentences, seemingly more Germanic than Russian in structure. Although much of the apparent awkwardness resulting from a literal translation has been removed in the final translation, it is hoped that enough has been retained to give the reader a feeling of the original expression. Where it was felt that a literal translation would introduce no ambiguity, it has been used. An example is the use of "stay time" as the equivalent of the term "residence time" more commonly used in the English literature.

I wish to acknowledge my indebtedness to my associate, Mr. W. Paul Jensen, for extensive assistance in the preparation of the manuscript and figures, and for the careful reading of proof.

Glenn C. Williams

Contents

Notation

Symbol	Dimensions	Designation
T	°K	Temperature
P	kg/m^2	Pressure
γ	kg/m^3	Specific weight
v	m^3/kg; m^3	Specific volume; chamber volume
ρ	kg(sec)^2/m^4	Density
I	kcal/kg	Enthalpy (sensible enthalpy)
h	kcal/kg	Chemical enthalpy
H	kcal/kg	Total enthalpy ($H = h + I$)
T_*	°K	Stagnation temperature
w	m/sec	Velocity
τ	sec	Time
G	kg/sec	Weight flow rate of mixture
l	m	Length, turbulence scale
R	kg(m)/kg(°K)	Gas constant [universal gas constant $R = 1.986$ kcal/mol(°K)]
E	kcal/mol	Activation energy
W	kg/m^3(sec)	Reaction rate per unit volume
V	kg/kg (sec)	Reaction rate per kg of mixture
k	(sec)$^{-1}$; m^3/sec	Reaction rate constant (first order)
k_0	(sec)$^{-1}$; m^3/sec	Constant in Arhennius equation
k_{eff}	(sec)$^{-1}$; m^3/sec	Effective reaction rate constant
c'	kg/m^3	Concentration per unit volume
c	kg/kg	Relative weight concentration
Q	kcal/m^3(sec)	Rate of heat production (heat loading)
q	kcal/kg; kcal/m^3	Heat of reaction; heat release of mixture
x, y, n, t	m	Coordinates

Symbol	Dimensions	Designation
α	$kcal/m^2(sec)(°K)$	Heat transfer coefficient
α_D	$m^3/m^2(sec)$	Diffusion coefficient (gas)
c_p	$kcal/kg(°K)$	Specific heat at constant pressure
c_v	$kcal/kg(°K)$	Specific heat at constant volume
λ	$kcal/m(°K)$	Thermal conductivity
a	m^2/sec	Thermal diffusivity
D	m^2/sec	Diffusivity
μ	$kg\ sec/m^2$	Viscosity
ν	m^2/sec	Kinematic viscosity
C_{ir}	$kcal/(sec)m^2(°K)^4$	Effective radiation coefficient
$\delta,\ d,\ r,\ R$	m	Characteristic dimension
α	—	Coefficient of excess air
χ_0	—	Stoichiometric ratio of reactants
χ	—	Weight ratio of oxidizer to fuel in a mixture
k_T	—	Thermal diffusion constant
k	—	Adiabatic exponent ($k = C_p/C_o$)
$\theta = RT/E$	—	Dimensionless temperature
$\vartheta = R_q c_0/E_{c_p}$	—	Dimensionless characteristic production
$\varphi = 1 - \dfrac{c}{c_0}$	—	Fractional completion of combustion
$\beta = a E/c_p k_0$	—	Reduced coefficient of heat transfer (convection)
$\sigma = E^3 C_{ir}/R^3 C_p k_0$	—	Reduced coefficient of heat transfer (radiation)
$\tau_{ij} = \tau_i/\tau_j$	—	Dimensionless time
$\chi = \dfrac{k_{eff}}{k_0}$	—	Reduced reaction velocity
Re	—	Reynolds number: $Re = wd/\nu$ (criterion of flow regime)
M	—	Mach number: $w/a(a = \sqrt{kgRT}$, sound velocity)
λ	—	Reduced velocity: $= w/a_{cr}$ ($a_{cr} = \sqrt{2gkRT_*/(k+1)}$ – critical velocity)

Thermal Regimes of Combustion

Chapter 1

Introduction

1-1. PRELIMINARY REMARKS

The book is devoted to the study of the stationary thermal region[1] of combustion. Despite the fact that combustion refers to a number of nonstationary phenomena, the basic conception of the thermal region of the process and many substantial conclusions on the mechanism of the phenomenon can be obtained from investigations of a stationary scheme. Just as the method of studying flows in Eulerian coordinates has received widespread usage in hydrodynamics, so, in investigations of combustion it is expedient in many cases to desist from observations on the fate of the separate particles of fuel or of the combustible mixture and to concentrate attention on the phenomena occurring in a definite part of the furnace space. In this case, for a steady region of operation of the combustion chamber as a whole, the state of the combustible mixture at any point of the space can be characterized by time-constant values of the temperature, concentration, etc.

In view of the turbulent character of the motion, these values (for example, of the temperature) are considered as certain average values in a time interval sufficiently large in comparison with the period of the turbulent pulsations.

The assumption of the stationarity of the combustion excludes substantially nonstationary processes as, for example, burning in a piston engine or pulsating motor, from consideration in this book.

The substance of the fundamental problem considered below in detail can be explained briefly by the following consideration. It appears at first glance that combustion can be realized for any arbitrarily chosen values of the region parameters—temperature in the chamber, velocity of gas motion, etc. The simplest observations of the process in any furnace apparatus show, however, that such an assumption does not correspond to reality. The combustion process in every concrete case is included in a certain more-or-less narrow interval of parametric values dependent on internal relations inherent in the phenomenon itself; at first glance, by the

[1]There does not appear to be a satisfactory short translation of the word режим as used here by Vulis. A combination of "regime" and "region" is what Vulis is trying to express, i.e., the range of independent parameters in which thermal processes (temperature) may be considered to control the rate of combustion. Ed.

1

relation between the quantity of heat to be liberated [by combustion, Ed.] and [that, Ed.] given off [from the combustion volume. Ed.]. Limiting values of the parameters (for example, the rate of air intake, its abundance, etc.) exist for each apparatus, beyond which a stable region cannot possibly be realized. The variation of one of these parameters (an excess of one of the components of the combustible mixture, say) within certain limits leads to a smooth change in the performance; and in certain other cases, as is known, to an abrupt, practically spasmodic transition to another level. In conformance with this, the problems of the investigation are, first of all, to look for stationary levels of the process which are possible in principle, to explain their stability depending on various "external" parameters and, finally, to determine the conditions for the transition of the process from one level to another.

In the general case, the problem formulated should be solved by taking into account the spatial distribution of all the parameters within the combustion chamber and on its boundaries. Mathematically, this would mean the solution of a three-dimensional problem (in a particular case of axisymmetric or approximately plane flow, of a two-dimensional problem). Without speaking of the complexity of the analysis leading to the integration of a system of nonlinear partial differential equations (i.e., to a problem whose solution is most often obtained successfully by numerical methods for specific conditions), a detailed investigation can very rarely be carried out because of the impossibility of assigning the boundary conditions exactly. Usually, a detailed picture of the fuel and air distribution at the chamber intake sections, the exact values of the spatial velocity, etc., at the system boundaries are unknown. This fact, in addition to (1) the inadequacy of information on the mechanism of the combustion reaction and its dependence on the temperature and concentration; (2) ignorance of the mixing laws; and (3) the complexity of the configuration of the combustion chamber and of the real picture of the fuel and air motion therein, necessitates reliance on significant simplifications in order to explain the physical picture of the phenomena.

In this connection, approximate solutions based on the transformation to a one-dimensional linear model have been widely used. Use of a one-dimensional scheme (usually called hydraulic in contrast to the hydrodynamic scheme taking into account the distribution of parameters over two or three space coordinates) corresponds to the introduction of values of the variables averaged over the chamber cross-section into the computations while retaining the single space coordinate, the length. Mathematically, this simplification reduces to a transformation from partial differential equations to ordinary nonlinear differential equations.

Use of the one-dimensional model of the process led to useful qualitative results in a number of cases. However, it should be noted that the assumption that all the variables are constant over the chamber cross section is generally very far from reality. Still more important, perhaps, is the fact that the location of the coordinate axes in real furnaces often remains indefinite. Finally, it is essential that a considerable equilibration of the temperature and concentration usually occurs over the whole furnace space or in certain of its parts in the real process. This is caused by the mixture of the fresh fuel with the products of combustion and by heat exchange within the chamber.

These considerations make the use of the one-dimensional model difficult to a considerable degree and oblige us to look for a diagrammatization of the phenomenon which is more simple and not too far removed from actual conditions.

In attempting to reduce the number of space coordinates it is natural to turn finally to a "zero-dimensional" or point scheme, i.e., to a complete rejection of taking into account the distribution of the variables within the furnace space and to the introduction into the computation of average values of the parameters for the chamber as a whole or for a certain region isolated for the investigation. In addition to the obvious mathematical simplification of the problem related to transforming from nonlinear differential equations to algebraic, this scheme (substantially, the method of finite differences) is interesting from the physical viewpoint inasmuch as it corresponds to the limit case of the complete mixing of fresh fuel with the combustion products in the chamber and, correspondingly, to the complete equilibration of the temperature and concentration in the furnace space. In many cases, the introduction into the computation of temperature and concentration values averaged over the whole space corresponds well to actual conditions of the progress of the process; perhaps not in the whole chamber but at least in separate sections, in particular, in the flame zone of the fresh fuel. We speak of such widely used combustion chamber constructions in which a considerable mixing of the fresh fuel with the products of combustion occurs and in which it is practically impossible to show the trajectories of the motion of the individual particles because of the complex and intricate character of the mixture motion within the chamber. Let us also note that it is specifically the mixing of the fresh products with the combustion products which makes continuous ignition of the fresh fuel possible in many cases in practice and therefore the very existence of a steady process. A great deal of attention will be paid to this question below. The finite difference method ("zero-dimensional" model) is common to the first four chapters of the book.

Brief facts on the rate of chemical reactions are cited in the first (introductory) chapter and the theory of thermal explosions of a combustible mixture due to N. N. Semenov (44) is considered. This substantially introduces a graphico-analytic method of investigation used in the three succeeding chapters.

A progressive analysis of the simplest phenomena (the "elements" of a complex technical process) which permits general physical laws of combustion to be established and the role of individual factors to be explained, is made in the later chapters with problems of gradually increasing complexity considered. Thus, adiabatic combustion of a well-mixed gas mixture is considered in Chapter 2, heterogeneous combustion on an isolated element of the surface of the solid phase in Chapter 3, the influence of the heat supply and heat emission (radiant and convective) on the thermal combustion region in Chapter 4.

The choice of the two simplest schemes, combustion of a well-mixed mixture and heterogeneous combustion (with diffusion of the reacting phase to the surface of the solid phase) appears to be particularly convenient also because the development of the analogy between them in this book permitted the mathematical relations for both cases to be completely identified. Actually, as will be shown below, the same formulas and expressions are suitable to describe both processes. It is understood that this agreement is not accidental; it is based on the physical closeness of the phenomena under consideration. This closeness becomes obvious if attention is concentrated on the burning out of the gas phase in both cases and if the laws of the chemical kinetics are diagrammed uniformly (reaction rate as a function of temperature and concentration). The last point requires special explanation.

Only very general concepts of chemical kinetics, unique for all exothermal reactions, are used to solve the problems of the thermal combustion region herein. The interpretation of the actual mechanism of concrete chemical combustion reactions, the role of the intermediate products, "active centers," and similar questions making up the subject studied as chemical kinetics does not enter into the problems of the book; the purpose of the book is a detailed explanation of the thermal side of the process. Consequently, only two completely indisputable statements from chemical-kinetics concepts will be introduced into the considerations; first, rapid increase in the reaction rate with increase in temperature and second, the inevitability of its dropping in the long run as the mixture burns out. Relying upon the detailed apparatus of kinetics to analyze a technical process would not permit the question to be considered in general form and, what is very important, is not possible at present. As Ia. B. Zel'dovich (14) indicates, for example "the

problem of using combustion as a kinetic experiment is successful
in a preliminary evaluation of the kinetics of the combustion process with a subsequent interpretation of its results. A direct pre-
calculation of the combustion rate on the basis of chemical-kinetic
results is as yet still a problem of the future."

This statement, in addition to the complexity of the combustible
mixtures with which furnace engineering deals, is explained also
by the manifold physical and physicochemical phenomena entering
as component parts into the complex, total combustion process.
The failures are well known which have attended the attempts to
create a theoretically based technical computation of combustion
by starting from purely kinetic relations. The viewpoint that the
"secondary phenomena"—the material and energy transport—accompanying combustion are only unpleasant distortions in the
course of the chemical reaction seems naive now. In addition, the
opposite conception, that the chemical reaction rate has no part in
the total combustion process, has not been developed. All these
questions, in particular the interaction of the reaction rate and the
physical phenomena in the combustion process (heat exchange,
diffusion, etc.), appear with special clarity in investigating the
thermal combustion region.

Let us turn to a brief survey of the contents of the book. Its
fifth chapter is like a transition from the "zero-dimensional" to
the one-dimensional model of the process. The simplest one-dimensional problems are considered briefly there and it is shown
that the transition from differential to finite-difference equations
leads to the zero-dimensional model. Hence, the latter plays the
part of the usual approximate method of investigating the problem.
Moreover, certain general considerations on the rate of flame
propagation are given in the fifth chapter together with a comparatively detailed example of a schematic computation of the simplest
technical process (combustion of a carbon-air mixture in a muffle
burner). This example is carried out to numerical calculations
which are mainly of methodological value. Essential in this computation is the analysis of the optimum ("step-by-step") scheme of
air supply which is apparently of more general interest.

Chapter 6 is devoted to an analysis of the normal combustion of
a well-mixed mixture and also of the laminar combustion of unmixed gases. In addition to the general concepts and the choice of
the most complete theory of Ia. B. Zel'dovich (18) on thermal flame
propagation, special attention is paid here to the similarity conditions of the temperature and concentration fields in normal and
diffuse combustion; qualitative reasoning on the stability limits of
the process is also given.

The last chapter, Chapter 7, contains an explanation of the

theory of L. D. Landau (27) on "self-turbulization" of the flame front as well as brief information on turbulent combustion and gas-dynamic relations in a flame front and a detonation wave; also cited for the latter is a gas-dynamic scheme for selecting the stationary wave velocity which is based on an analogy to the motion of gases with preheating in a cylindrical pipe (2).

It should be noted that a comparatively detailed mathematical analysis of the problem of normal flame propagation, of the combustion of unmixed gases, and of the stability of a plane front is carried out not only for the sake of final conclusions from this theory but in order to acquaint the reader with exact methods of the theoretical investigation of combustion processes.

The general conclusion which results from all the contents of the book reduces to the possibility of separating the problems of applied combustion theory into two groups. Among the first is the investigation of stable stationary combustion in assigned (experimentally confirmed) limits of variation of the variables. The reaction rate in such a formulation of the problem can be considered as infinitely large in practice, i.e., it can be eliminated from the computation.

Among the second group are questions related to the establishment of the limit of the existence of stable stationary combustion, conditions for collapse of the process (extinction) or for its origination (ignition). In order to solve these problems, it is necessary to draw upon the fundamental information on the chemical reaction rate in addition to taking the transport phenomenon into account. It is essential that the physical mechanism of the ignition and extinction phenomena should vary very slightly in making the transition from one case to the other; this even refers to such a process as detonation, which differs sharply from the usual combustion in the nature of its progress.

We shall also dwell on the fundamental assumptions used in deriving the equations and in performing the computations. In addition to the above mentioned assumptions (simplified representations of the reaction rate), they are the following: The whole investigation has been limited to low values of the velocity (more exactly, of the Mach number $M = w/a$) for which the process can be considered as practically isobaric and kinetic energy of the gases can be neglected in comparison with the heat content. In specific cases, an estimate can be made of the error by using the formulas and relations given in Chapter 7 (section 7-3, "Gas Motion with Heat Supply").

Furthermore, all the computations are carried out, for simplicity, for constant (the average in the computational interval) values of the physical constants: heat capacity, diffusion coefficient, etc. In particular, the latter corresponds to failure to take into account the thermal dissociation at high temperatures. The exception is the analysis of the differential equations of heat propagation and diffusion in Chapter 6 (section 6-2) and also the solution of the problem of the normal combustion rate (section 6-3), which is carried out for the general case of variable constants in order to show a more exact computational method.

Both the assumptions (low values of the motion velocity and the introduction of average values of the physical constants in the computations) detract little from the qualitative conclusions of the investigation for the majority of results given in the book which were not computed.

Finally, a common limitation for the whole book is, as already remarked, the investigation of stationary processes. The latter corresponds to the assumption of the quasi-stationary character of the process, i.e., to the possibility of its approximate representation as a continuous mixing of a state which differs slightly from equilibrium, when applied to such an explicitly nonstationary phenomenon as, for example, the combustion of coal particles, etc.

These general remarks should be kept in mind when studying the separate sections of the book; more exact assumptions impede the path of the explanation.

1-2. SIMPLEST INFORMATION ON REACTION RATE

Referring the reader interested in studying the rate of chemical reactions to the special literature on chemical kinetics and its application to combustion processes (13a, 24, 25, 30, 35, 43, 46, 50, 53), let us limit ourselves to recalling certain elementary information required for the subsequent explanation.

In this book, we shall speak only of simple exothermal reactions whose rate depends on the concentration of the initial material and whose acceleration mechanism is related to the liberation of heat and the increase in the temperature.

Following the concepts of chemical kinetics, let us first introduce the concept of reaction rate. Let us define the latter as the quantity of substance which reacts in unit time per unit volume and let us denote it by the symbol W (kg/m³ sec). As is known, the reaction rate depends on the temperature and the concentration of the substances participating in the reaction (the initial, intermediate and final materials in the general case; but only on the initial materials in the limitation to simple reactions assumed). We represent this dependence as

$$W = -\frac{dc'}{d\tau} = W(T, c')$$ (1-1)

where c' (kg/m³) is the concentration of initial material;[2] τ (sec) is time; T (°abs.) is the temperature.

It is customary to represent the function $W(T,c')$ as the product of two functions, of the temperature and of the concentration separately:

$$W = W_T (T) \cdot W_c (c') \tag{1-2}$$

Let us analyze both functions individually by paying special attention to the temperature dependence of the reaction rate.

As is usual, let us represent the first of the functions in (1-2) which is called the reaction rate constant and is usually denoted by $k = k(T)$, as an exponential dependent on the temperature (the so-called Arrhenius law)

$$W_T = k(T) = k_0 e^{-E/RT} \tag{1-3}$$

where k_0 is a constant (the factor before the exponential), which is not temperature dependent in the first approximation (we do not mention the dimensionality of the constants k and k_0 since it is related to the form of the function $W_c(c)$ in (1-2)); E (kcal/mole) is the activation energy; $R = 1.986$ (cal/mole deg) is the universal gas constant.

Furthermore, let us consider (1-3) as an approximate empirical relation and k_0 and E as certain experimental constants. Such an interpretation of this equation is most valid at the present time when applied to the total technical combustion process. In addition, it is useful to cite certain information from kinetics also which would illustrate the physical meaning of k_0 and E for simple chemical reactions.

Equation (1-3) is empiric in origin; it arose in the treatment of experimental data in a $\ln W = f(1/T)$ coordinate system. When experimental results are superposed in such coordinates (with the concentration of the reacting substances remaining invariant), the slope of the line drawn through the experimental points corresponds to the temperature coefficient of the reaction rate E, the activation energy; the constant k_0 is also easily determined from the same graph.

The first attempts to give Eq. (1-3) a theoretical foundation were thermodynamic in nature. For example, it can be derived from the known thermodynamic equations for the equilibrium constant K of a reversible chemical reaction under additional assumptions:

---

[2]Later, it will be advantageous to use the relative concentration c (kg/kg) related to the quantity c' by means of $dc' = \gamma dc$; $c' = \gamma c$, where γ (kg/m³) is the specific gravity. See section 6-2 also about this, where the errors related to the incorrect use of c and c' are mentioned in detail.

$$\frac{d \ln K}{dT} = \frac{q}{RT^2}$$

where q is the heat of the reaction.

Keeping in mind that by definition the equilibrium constant is the ratio of the reaction rate constants for forward and reverse reactions occurring in a certain system (according to the equation $A + B + \ldots \rightarrow C + D + \ldots + q$, say), the cited equation can be rewritten as

$$\frac{d \ln K}{dT} = \frac{d \ln \vec{k}}{dT} - \frac{d \ln \overleftarrow{k}}{dT} = \frac{\vec{E}}{RT^2} - \frac{\overleftarrow{E}}{RT^2}$$

where $\vec{k}, \vec{E}$ and $\overleftarrow{k}, \overleftarrow{E}$ are the k and E values for the forward and reverse reactions (according to the arrow direction), respectively, where

$$q = \vec{E} - \overleftarrow{E} \tag{1-4}$$

Now, if the unknown function of the temperature $A(T)$ in the equation for any of the quantities $k(T)$ is equated to zero (arbitrarily, substantially)

$$\frac{d \ln k}{dT} = \frac{E}{RT^2} + A(T)$$

then integrating it will lead to (1-3). It is of definite interest to relate the activation energy to the thermal effect of the reaction (1-4) in this attempt to derive (1-3). In conformance with the modern viewpoint, it can be illustrated by using the concept of "energy barrier." Let us visualize (Figure 1-1) two energy levels (I) and (II) of a certain system corresponding to the stoichiometric equation of a reversible reaction:

$$(I) \rightleftarrows (II) + q$$

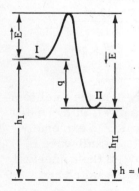

The transition from the state (I) into the state (II) from left to right on Figure 1-1 is possible with the initial expenditure of the energy $\vec{E}$; the reverse transition (II)-(I), with the initial expenditure of the energy $\overleftarrow{E}$, respectively. Consequently, the quantity of energy

Fig. 1-1. Relation between the activation energy and the heat of reaction.

$$q = \vec{E} - \overleftarrow{E}$$

is liberated (I $\rightarrow$ II) or absorbed (II $\rightarrow$ I) as the reaction is performed. Let us also note that this quantity q equals the difference of the chemical energies (or the enthalpy for a reaction at constant pressure) of the initial and final reaction products according to the law of the well-known Russian scientist, G. I. Hess:

$$q = h_I - h_{II}$$

measured from a certain level $h = 0$ on Figure 1-1.

Hence, the energy barrier concept very graphically relates the activation energy and the heat of reaction concepts and also the first law of thermodynamics in its application to chemical reactions.

Equation (1-3) also has a direct statistical interpretation which corresponds most to the modern viewpoint. It is known from statistics that the quantity $\exp(-E/RT)$ is the fraction of the molecules possessing the energy $E' \geqslant E$ at the temperature T. If it is assumed that only the collisions of the energy-rich "active" molecules (moving, say, with velocity not less than a certain minimum value $w_{min} \approx \sqrt{2E}$), then k_0 and E have a simple interpretation. The value of k_0 in this simplified scheme corresponds to the total number of collisions,[3] and the value of E to the minimum value of the molecule energy which guarantees the effectiveness of the collisions (reaction realization). This latter graphically explains the origin of the term "activation energy."

The reasoning cited illustrates the meaning of k_0 and E; however, as already mentioned, they should be considered later as certain, re-

Table 1-1. Influence of Temperature on Reaction Rate

Temperature	Values of $\dfrac{k}{k_0} = \exp\left(\dfrac{-E}{RT}\right)$			
$T°K$	For $E = 20,000$		For $E = 40,000$	
500	2×10^{-9}	1	4×10^{-18}	1
1000	4×10^{-5}	2×10^4	2×10^{-9}	5×10^8
2000	6×10^{-3}	3×10^6	4×10^{-5}	1×10^{13}

ferred, empiric constants which approximately reflect the total temperature dependence of the reaction rate. Let us dwell in more detail on the quantitative side of this dependence which is extremely important for what follows. The exceptionally strong influence of the temperature on the reaction rate is seen, say, in the numerical values given in Table 1-1 for the activation energies which are

[3]Actually, the quantity k_0 still contains a factor related to the three-dimensional orientation of the colliding molecules (a spatial factor), etc. Consequently, the value of k_0 for even comparatively simple reactions can differ by several orders of magnitude from the number of collisions per unit time.

usual for simple chemical reactions (approximately of the order
of 20,000 to 40,000 cal/mole).

As is seen from this table, a twofold increase in the temperature leads to a 20,000-fold increase in the function $\exp(-E/RT)$ for
$E = 20,000$ cal/mole for a transition from 500 to 1000°K and to a
500-million-fold increase for $E = 40,000$ cal/mole and the same
values of the temperature. A similar rise in the temperature (from
1000 to 2000°K) causes an increase of 150 times in the reaction rate
for the first and of 20,000 times for the second value of the activation energy. The example cited shows how large is the influence of
the temperature on the chemical reaction rate; it also shows the
possibility of neglecting weaker (power) temperature dependencies
in the quantitative computations in comparison with the exponential
(if they occur in a product with the factor $\exp(-E/RT)$.

It is also seen from the example in Table 1-1 that the influence
of the factor $\exp(-E/RT)$ on the reaction rate diminishes as the
absolute temperature increases. Shown in Figure 1-2 is a curve of
the dependence of the function $\exp(-E/RT)$ on the group RT/E
(called "nondimensional temperature" later). It is essential that
only the initial part of the curve, plotted on Figure 1-2 to a larger
scale, i.e., the region where the function grows abruptly, should
be taken into account in all practical computations. Actually, the

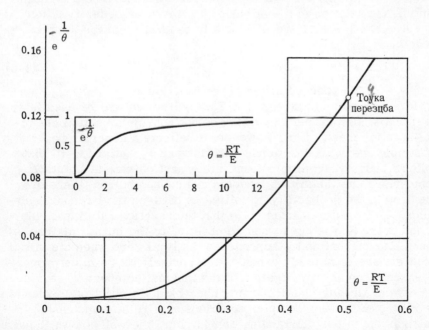

Fig. 1-2. Graph of function $\exp(-E/RT)$. (Inflection point on curve.) °

inflection point of this curve, on the basis of the equality

$$y'' = e^{-1/\theta}\left(\frac{1 - 2\theta}{\theta^4}\right) = 0$$

(the following notations are used here for brevity: $y = \exp(-E/RT)$; $\theta = RT/E$; $y'' = d^2y/d\theta^2$) corresponds to the value

$$\theta_{inf} = 1/2; \quad T_{inf} = \frac{E}{2R} \quad (R = 1.986 \approx 2 \text{ cal/mole degree})$$

Therefore for $E \approx 20,000$ to $40,000$ cal/mole, the value of T_{inf} lies in the 5000 to 10,000°K temperature range, values which are inadmissible in combustion chambers. Hence, the abrupt retardation of the growth of the curve of $\exp(-E/RT)$ and the asymptotic tendency of the values of this function to unity as $T \to \infty$, which occurs after the inflection point of the curve $y = y(\theta)$ on Figure 1-2, are of little practical significance.

Let us also dwell briefly on the concentration dependence of the reaction rate. According to formal kinetics, the function $W(c')$ in Eq. (1-2) can be represented as a power dependence of the concentration of initial substances for the simplest reactions. Thus, for example, $W(c') = c_A'$ for a first-order reaction proceeding according to the equation $A \to B$, where c_A' is the concentration of A. $W(c') = c_A' \cdot c_B' \approx c_A'^2$ (if the substances A and B are in a stoichiometric relation in the mixture) for a second-order reaction $A + B \to C + D + \dots$. We will have in general form for simple reactions:

$$W(c') \approx c'^n = (\gamma c)^n \tag{1-5}$$

where n is the reduced order of the reaction and $c = c'/\gamma$.

It is necessary to stress that Eq. (1-5) which will be used later in its most simple form $(n = 1)$ does not convey the actual chemical reaction mechanism. However, it reflects a general property of simple chemical reactions which is very essential for all that follows, namely, the diminution in the reaction rate at constant temperature as the initial products are consumed and, therefore, the drop in the probability of collisions between the reacting molecules. It also follows from (1-5) that the reaction rate inevitably drops in the final stages when combustion of the initial mixture is taken into account and it approaches the limit zero when the initial products are completely exhausted. Precisely this simple property is essential to an investigation of the thermal combustion region.

As was already mentioned, the actual kinetic reaction mechanism is described by very complex equations as a rule. Remarkable investigations of our outstanding compatriots, the well-known Russian chemist N. A. Menshutkin, who studied the chemical reaction rate for approximately 10 years before foreign scientists (Van't Hoff, Arrhenius, Ostwald, etc.), N. Ia. Bach, N. A. Shilov, and others, and finally, the foremost school of N. N. Semenov and other Soviet scientists, have advanced the science of chemical kinetics considerably and in particular have led to the creation of a modern theory of chain reactions (39, 44). At the present time, the progress of the reaction in a number of the most simple systems (oxygen-carbon monoxide, oxygen-hydrogen, etc.) has been studied in detail (13a, 30, 35, 43). It has been established that the majority of reactions corresponds to a very complicated mechanism related to the formation of active intermediate products (atoms and "scraps" of molecules, radicals). For example, the hydrogen oxidation reaction, whose complete stoichiometric equation is

$$2H_2 + O_2 = 2H_2O$$

actually progresses approximately as follows (13a):

The first act therein is the formation of atomic hydrogen because of the collision of the H_2 molecule with some other molecule

$$H_2 + M = 2H + M$$

Following this is

$$H + O_2 = OH + O$$

$$O + H_2 = OH + H$$

$$OH + H_2 = H_2O + H, \text{ etc.}$$

Active centers (the H and O and the hydroxyl OH atoms) form continuously because of these elementary chemical acts, where the entrance of one hydrogen atom into reaction leads to the formation of several active centers.[4]

It is natural to assume that the formation of intermediate products plays a large part in the complex combustion reactions which proceed under furnace conditions. In support of this assumption is that the activation energy of the primary acts is always much less than for the direct reaction between complex molecules (direct spectroscopic investigations disclose significant (nonequilibrium) atom and radical concentrations in the flame zone (24 and others)). However, the quantitative side of the question for complex mixtures is completely unclear. Moreover, experimental facts from furnace technique in which the influence of the active centers would have been separated indisputably from the influence of a temperature rise (or drop because of heat emission) are apparently unknown at

[4]An example of a so-called branched chain reaction (see (44)); for details on the reaction of hydrogen with oxygen see (35).

present and the number of facts whose explanation is not within the scope of heat theory is negligibly small (and, in addition, decreases continuously). Consequently, the tendency to limit the interpretation of phenomena observed in combustion chambers by simple and physically evident reasoning resulting from the heat mechanism is natural.[5]

Hence the expression for the reaction rate which reflects the basic properties for the investigation of the thermal region will be written, taking (1-3) and (1-5) into account, as

$$W = k_0 e^{-E/RT} c'^n$$

(1-6)

and for the case which is most simple and, consequently, most convenient for qualitative computations, $n = 1$:

$$W = k_0 e^{-E/RT} c'$$

(1-7)

Later, it will be more convenient to transform to weight concentrations $c = c'/\gamma$ (kg/kg) and correspondingly to the reaction rate referred to 1 kg of mixture. We will denote this latter by the symbol V where

$$V = W/\gamma \text{ (kg/kg sec)}$$

Hence, Eq. (1-7) does not change outwardly

$$V = k_0 e^{-E/RT} c$$

(1-7')

The quantities k and k_0 will have the dimensionality of reciprocal time for first-order reactions: k (1/sec); k_0 (1/sec).

It is seen from (1-6) that the reaction rate to consume a combustible mixture varies from a certain initial value (at $c = c_0$) to zero for total combustion ($c = 0$). The character of the variation of the quantity V in the combustion process is determined by the heat-exchange conditions. Shown schematically on Figure 1-3 are the curves of $V = V(c)$ for the two limiting cases of the process: the isothermal (for intense heat emission) when V drops as c decreases (linearly for $n = 1$) and the adiabatic[6] when the reaction rate increases abruptly as the temperature rises, attaining a maximum near total combustion (here the value $V = V_{max}$ is several orders higher than the initial value) and then drops to zero very steeply. This dependence will be analyzed in more detail later.

Additional conditions relative to the magnitude of the concentration c must be introduced for subsequent use. Let us agree to call the weight content of a stoichiometric mixture per kg of mix-

---

[5]In addition, a number of phenomena (cool flames, the effect of anti-detonators, etc.) is usually explained by the diffusion of active centers.

[6]That is, heat insulation.

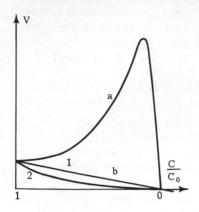

ture (or, in particular cases, of one of the components inadequately contained in the mixture) the concentration of reacting (initial) material c (kg/kg). For example, if we speak of a mixture consisting of 1 kg of the first conpoment (fuel, say) and χ kg of the second (oxidizer, say) and if the stoichiometric relation between them is $1 : \chi_0$ according to the reaction equation, then denoting the coefficient of surplus air (oxidizer in the general case) in thermal engineering, by the symbol

Fig. 1-3. Variation of the combustion rate during the reaction. a—exothermal process; b—isothermal process; 1—$n = 1$; 2—$n > 1$.

$$\alpha = \frac{\chi}{\chi_0}$$

the quantity c should be defined by means of the formula

$$c = \frac{1 + \chi_0}{1 + \chi} = \frac{1 + \chi_0}{1 + \alpha \chi_0} \qquad (1\text{-}8)$$

for the $\alpha > 1$ case, and by the formula

$$c = \alpha \frac{1 + \chi_0}{1 + \chi} = \alpha \frac{1 + \chi_0}{1 + \alpha \chi_0} \qquad (1\text{-}9)$$

for the $\alpha < 1$ case.

For example, for $\alpha = 1$, the initial value of the concentration is $c_0 = 1$ in a stoichiometric mixture of hydrogen and oxygen for which $\chi_0 = 32$ from the reaction equation

$$2H_2 + O_2 = 2H_2O.$$

For $\alpha = 2$, i.e., $H_2:O_2 = 1:64$. $c_0 = \dfrac{1 + 32}{1 + 64} \approx 0.51$ and for

$\alpha = 0.5$, i.e., $H_2:O_2 = 1:16$, $c_0 = 0.5 \dfrac{1 + 32}{1 + 16} \approx 0.97$; etc.[7]

[7]The values of c_0 for this same example of hydrogen reacting with the oxygen of air for $\chi_0 = 32(1 + 3.33) \approx 138.7$ kg/kg would equal, respectively, for $\alpha = 1, 2, 0.5$: $c_0 = 1$ for $\alpha = 1$; $c_0 = (1 + 138.7)/(1 + 277.4) = 0.5$ for $\alpha = 2$; $c_0 = 0.5(1 + 138.7)/(1 + 69.35) = 0.99$ for $\alpha = 0.5$, etc. The inclusion of the nitrogen from the air in the combustible mixture is not compulsory, it is understood; using only the combustible elements (H and O) for the computation in this same example yields $c_0 = 0.24$; 0.12 and 0.23 for $\alpha = 1, 2$ and 0.5, respectively.

Consequently, if q_0 is the heat production of a stoichiometric ($\alpha = 1$) mixture, i.e., the thermal efficiency of the reaction, per kg stoichiometric mixture, then the actual value of the heat production of the working mixture ($\alpha \neq 1$) will equal the product qc_0.

1-3. THE N. N. SEMENOV THEORY OF THE "THERMAL EXPLOSION" OF A COMBUSTIBLE MIXTURE

As an introductory problem which would permit the substance of the method of investigating stationary levels of the combustion process to be explained, let us consider the classical theory of the thermal explosion of a combustible mixture proposed by N. N. Semenov (44, 45, 13a, 50).

Let us imagine a certain closed vessel filled with a combustible mixture. Let us characterize the state of the mixture by the average (by volume) values of the temperature and the concentration c. Let us also assume that the vessel and the mixture give off heat during the reaction to the ambient medium which is at a temperature T_0.

Let us try to explain the possible quasi-stationary states of the mixture as the reaction progresses in the vessel. In connection with our speaking of comparatively low temperatures and very low reaction rates, correspondingly, let us neglect the change in the concentration because of the reaction. As will be shown below, such an approximation is accurate enough in the region of slight mixture heating near the ignition temperature. In order to solve the problem by following Semenov, let us turn to the diagram shown on Figure 1-4. Here, the temperature is plotted along the horizontal axis, the quantity of heat being liberated or going out of the vessel in unit time, along the ordinate.

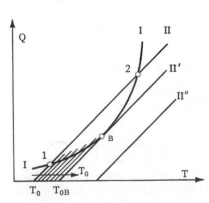

Fig. 1-4. I—Curve of heat liberation; II—curve of heat loss.

Let us note that the first of these quantities (heat liberation) is the product of the reaction rate and its thermal effect in a computation in a unit volume; therefore, the heat-liberation curve in Figure 1-4 is similar to the curve of the temperature dependence of the reaction rate and differs from it only by the ordinate scale. Let us superpose two curves separately on the Q-T diagram on Figure 1-4: the adiabatic liberation of heat because of the chemical reaction (I) and the heat discharge (II). As follows from the reasoning mentioned in the preceding paragraph, the first is an exponential curve which rises sharply as the temperature increases. The second can be mapped by a straight line in a first approximation; even taking into account heat emission by radiation proportional to the difference in the fourth powers of the temperature T and T_0, the heat emission curve will have considerably less curvature than the curve $Q_1 \exp(-E/RT)$ and can be replaced by a straight line approximately, on comparatively small sections.

The quantity of heat being liberated per unit time in a stationary process must evidently equal the quantity of heat given off in unit time by the vessel to the ambient medium; graphically this condition corresponds to the points of intersection of curves (I) and (II). As is seen from Figure 1-4, there are two such points of intersection (for a curve and a line) in certain cases (line II), sometimes one (tangent, line II') and sometimes none (line II'').

The possibility, in principle, of the existence of two independent stationary regions (points 1 and 2) corresponds to the first of these cases, only one stationary region (point B) corresponds to the second case, the transition between the first and third cases and, finally, the impossibility of a stationary region corresponds to the third. The transition from a line of type (II) to (II') and, furthermore, to (II'') can be accomplished, as is seen from this same Figure 1-4, by raising the temperature of the ambient medium T_0, say (the parallel translation of the line (II) toward increasing temperature; the value of T_0 corresponds to the intersection of the heat elimination line with the horizontal axis).

Let us first investigate the state of the system corresponding to the two points of intersection (1 and 2) of the curve I and the line II. In the interests of clarity, the intersection of the curves in these points is shown separately on Figure 1-5a and b. It is not difficult to establish by means of a simple analysis that only the first of these points, in the region of lesser values of the temperature and the reaction rate (point 1, Figure 1-5a) corresponds to stable equilibrium; the second point, in the region of higher values of the temperature and reaction rate (point 2, Figure 1-5b), on the contrary corresponds to an unstable equilibrium state, practically impossible to realize.

In order to be convinced, let us resort to the usual method of investigating the stability of equilibrium states of any system. Let us assume that insignificant (more exactly, infinitesimal) deviations from the equilibrium state have occurred in a system in equilibrium and let us trace the character of the further changes in the state. If we start from region 1 of the intersection of curves I and II, then, as is seen in Figure 1-5a, a deviation toward lower tem-

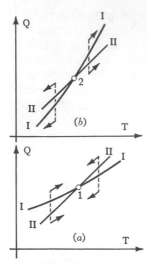

Fig. 1-5. Stationary reaction state. I-I—Heat-liberation curve; II-II—heat-loss curve; (*a*) stable state; (*b*) unstable state.

peratures leads to a state for which the quantity of heat being liberated I exceeds the quantity being eliminated II. Therefore, the system is again heated and returns to the equilibrium state 1. Such a nonequilibrium state occurs for a rise in the temperature relative to the same equilibrium state such that the quantity of heat being eliminated will be larger than the quantity being liberated; therefore the system is cooled and again returns to equilibrium. Hence, random deviations in both cases create conditions for the system to return to equilibrium. Therefore, the stationary region 1 is stable.

Similar reasoning for region 2, which corresponds to the intersection of the curves shown on Figure 1-5*b*, leads to the progressive growth of infinitesimal deviations from equilibrium because of the excess of heat liberation over elimination as the temperature rises or the converse (the excess of heat emission over heat liberation) as the temperature drops. Nonstationary heating will occur in the system in the first case, cooling in the second. Inevitable random deviations in this and other cases lead to the progressively increasing withdrawal of the system from equilibrium. In this connection, region 2 is unstable and can be eliminated from the reasoning.

Now, let us trace the change in the stable quasi-stationary state of a system as the temperature of the ambient medium rises successively (graphically, the displacement of the line II to the right on Figure 1-4). The values of the stationary temperature will increase continuously just so long as the lines II intersect the curve I. However, such a character of the change in the stationary temperature is retained only up to the point of contact B of curves I and II, which is the limiting (last) point for the existence of a stationary reaction region. An infinitesimal excess in the value of the parameter T_0 over its value T_{0B}, corresponding to the tangent point (line II′ on Figure 1-4), is sufficient for a stationary process to become impossible; curves I and II would have no common points. Physically, this corresponds to the transition to abrupt nonstationary burning up of the mixture under the conditions of increasing heat accumulation, rising temperature, accelerating reaction, etc.

This phenomenon, the transition from a slow, quasi-stationary reaction accompanied by insignificant heating to an explosive, nonstationary, progressively accelerating burning up of the mixture has been called "thermal explosion."[8]

It is customary to designate the boundary stationary region of the tangent to the heat-liberation and -elimination curves (point B) as the ignition point and the corresponding temperature as the ignition temperature. The condition to which the state at the point B corresponds is usually called the "critical ignition condition" since an abrupt, critical change of state for an infinitesimal change in the parameter (the medium temperature T_0 and others) is characteristic for the region at point B (so to speak, the region of unilateral stability, that is, stable with respect to its temperature reduction and unstable with respect to its temperature rise, see Figure 1-6).

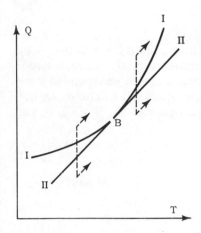

Fig. 1-6. Critical ignition region B. I-I—Heat-liberation curve; II-II—heat-elimination curve.

Let us summarize briefly. The analysis carried out explains first the presence of special, critical phenomena (in this case, ignition) in an exothermal process. Physically, the critical ignition condition characterizes the limiting region beyond which the rate of heat liberation in the system always surpasses its rate of elimination; in this connection the stationary process becomes unstable. It is extremely important, and this is fundamental for all modern thermal theories of combustion, that the dynamic character of the ignition phenomenon and therefore the ignition temperature be established clearly in the Semenov theory considered here. It becomes clear that the interpretation, prevalent earlier and encountered up to now (particularly in the foreign literature), of the ignition temperature of a combustible mixture as a certain physicochemical constant (similar to the viscosity coefficient, heat conduction, etc.) is incorrect in principle. Actually, it follows from the Semenov theory that the ignition conditions (in particular, the ignition temperature) are determined by all the conditions for the progress of the process in a system rather than by single properties of the mixture, i.e., by the properties of the mixture, the character of the heat

[8]The reaction rate increases because of the temperature rise, i.e., the intensity of heat liberation increases, which again leads to a temperature rise, etc., up to complete burn-up of the mixture.

exchange with the ambient medium, its temperature, the size and shape of the vessel, etc. This singularity of the ignition phenomenon (later, the extinction) is retained under very complex conditions for the progress of the process and is of great value both in investigating the thermal region and for the whole thermal theory of combustion.

1-4. IGNITION TEMPERATURE

Let us analyze the simplest quantitative relations characterizing the thermal explosion phenomenon.

The quantity of heat being liberated per unit time in a vessel with a combustible mixture as a result of a chemical reaction can be represented as

$$Q_I = W \cdot q \cdot v = k_0 e^{-E/RT} W_c(c') q \cdot v \tag{1-10}$$

where, in addition to the preceding notation, v is the volume of the vessel; the function $W_c(c')$ is an expression for the concentration dependence of the reaction rate which we leave in unexpanded form in connection with neglecting the burning up of the mixture. Combining all the constant factors in (1-10), namely: k_0, $W_c(c')$, q, and v, let us rewrite it as

$$Q_I = A e^{-E/RT} \tag{1-11}$$

Let us also write the expression for the quantity of heat given off by the vessel to the ambient medium in unit time

$$Q_{II} = \alpha \cdot F \cdot (T - T_0) \tag{1-12}$$

where α and F are the total heat emission coefficient and the vessel surface, respectively. Replacing the product αF by the constant B, we obtain

$$Q_{II} = B(T - T_0) \tag{1-13}$$

The condition for the existence of a stationary region for the reaction progress, i.e., the equality of the heat being liberated and that which can be eliminated, will be

$$Q_I = Q_{II} \tag{1-14}$$

or, taking (1-11) and (1-13) into account

$$A e^{-E/RT} = B(T - T_0) \tag{1-15}$$

The graphical solution of this transcendental equation was shown above on Figure 1-4.

Now, let us turn to the critical ignition condition. We have the following system of equations for the point B, the tangent of the heat-liberation and heat-elimination curves:

$$Q_I = Q_{II}; \quad \frac{dQ_I}{dT} = \frac{dQ_{II}}{dT} \tag{1-16}$$

or, in expanded form

$$Ae^{-E/RT} = B(T - T_0); \quad \frac{AE}{RT^2} e^{-E/RT} = B \tag{1-17}$$

Substituting the expression $A \exp(-E/RT)$ from the first expression into the second, we arrive at a quadratic equation in the temperature at the point of tangency of curves I and II

$$E/RT^2 (T - T_0) = 1$$

or

$$T^2 - ET/R + ET_0/R = 0 \tag{1-18}$$

The value of the ignition temperature, T_B, corresponding to the minus sign before the radical,[9] i.e., the smaller root of Eq. (1-18), equals from the last equation

$$T_B = E/2R \left(1 - \sqrt{1 - 4RT_0/E}\right) \tag{1-19}$$

This expression, which we shall later call the N. N. Semenov formula, shows in particular that the ignition phenomenon in the problem analyzed of the thermal explosion can exist only in a bounded region of ambient medium temperatures:

$$0 \leqslant T_0 \leqslant E/4R \approx E/R$$

From (1-19), the maximum value of the ignition temperature at $T_0 = E/4R$ will be $T_{B\ max} = E/2R \approx E/4$, i.e., corresponds to the point of inflection of the curve $\exp(-E/RT)$ shown on Figure 1-2.

The "thermal explosion" region, i.e., the region in which a stationary reaction is impossible, is located in the whole theoretically unbounded range of values of the temperature of the ambient medium above $T_{0\ max} = E/4R$ for any heat emission conditions.

Formula (1-19) can be given a simpler, approximate form for low values of the temperature of the ambient medium $T_0 \ll E/4R$. To do this, let us expand the radicand in (1-19) into series

$$T_B = (E/2R)\left[1 - (1 - 2RT_0/E - 2R^2T_0^2/E \dots)\right]$$

[9]The larger root of (1-18) for the positive radical corresponds to the tangency of a heat-elimination line and a heat-liberation curve in a high temperature region already discarded by physical considerations (beyond the inflection of the curve $\exp(-E/RT)$ on Figure 1-2).

The first approximation yields

$$T_B \approx T_0 \tag{1-20}$$

The second approximation yields correspondingly

$$T_B \approx T_0 + RT_0^2/E \tag{1-21}$$

Hence, the relative heating of the system which corresponds to the critical ignition region is comparatively small; approximately for low values of RT_0/E

$$(T_B - T_0)/T_0 = (T_B/T_0) - 1 \approx RT_0/E \tag{1-22}$$

while, in the general case, the ratio of the ignition temperature T_B to the initial temperature T_0 is included within the limits

$$1 < T_B/T_0 < 2$$

or $0 < (T_B - T_0) < T_0$

This means that the maximum value of the ignition temperature $(T_{BM} = E/2R$ for $T_{0M} = E/4R)$ is twice T_0

$$T_{B\ max} = 2T_0 \tag{1-23}$$

All these relations are encountered later. Let us note in conclusion that it does not at all follow from (1-19), as could be shown at first sight, that the continuous variation of the parameter T_0 will lead to a continuous change in the ignition temperature T_B, other conditions being equal. Actually, the latter is possible only under the condition that at least one of the quantities which characterizes the intersection of curves I and II, i.e., the conditions for the progress of the process (the slope of the heat-elimination line II, say, i.e., the value of the heat emission coefficient α, etc.) should change simultaneously with T_0. Only one critical value of the ignition temperature T_B is possible at a completely specific value of T_0 when the values of all the variable quantities, speaking generally, in the system (1-17), i.e., the values of A, B, and E, are given. Actually, the critical value of the ignition temperature can be expressed from the system (1-17) in terms of A, B, and E (by solving the second equation graphically, say) after which the magnitude of T_0 appears to be determined uniquely by the first of these equations. Hence in substance (1-19) seems to contain the set of all possible values of the ignition temperature T_B depending on the temperature of the ambient medium, where realization of each of the values of T_B is possible for appropriate values of the remaining parameters.

This remark again shows the complex nature of the ignition temperature which is dependent on all the conditions of the proc-

ess.[10] This remark is particularly essential in the subsequent
paragraphs in which the number of variables in the heat balance
equations or in the critical conditions equations similar to the
Eqs. (1-14) and (1-16) in the problem of the thermal explosion of
a combustible mixture is increased when more complex problems
are investigated.

Expanding the relations mentioned in this section, Semenov related the values of the mixture temperature and pressure in the
ignition state (44, 45). The expression he obtained was subsequently
verified experimentally by Zagulin and others (13a, 45, 50).

The theory of thermal explosions was analyzed in more exact
form by Frank-Kamenetskii (50), who obtained the solution of the
problem taking the temperature distribution within the vessel (because of heat conduction) into account. In particular, the critical
ignition conditions for vessels of various shapes, also verified by
experiment, were derived in this solution. Finally, Todes and
others (47) developed the nonstationary theory of the thermal explosion in which an expression was obtained for the period of induction (ignition lag) of a combustible mixture. All these investigations, considered in detail in the literature (13a, 50) showed the
validity of the fundamental assumptions and the fruitfulness of the
investigation method proposed by Semenov. Since the majority of
these works are related principally to laboratory experiment in outlook, and supplement the physical content and make more precise
the problem considered above, we will limit ourselves to references
to the sources and we will turn to an investigation of the stationary
thermal region of the combustion of a well-mixed mixture in an
adiabatic combustion chamber.

[10]Mathematically this means that the ignition temperature is a function
of three variables $(T_0, E,$ and $A,$ say) and not of two as, apparently, results
from (1-19) since the initial system of two equations (1-17) contains five
[four independent, Ed.] variables and, therefore only one can be eliminated.

Chapter 2

Stationary Combustion Region of a Well-mixed Mixture

2-1. HEAT-BALANCE EQUATION FOR AN ADIABATIC PROCESS

Let us consider the simplest diagram of a combustion chamber (Figure 2-1). Let us assume that a well-mixed mixture continuously enters the chamber at the temperature T_0 and the concentration c_0 and its combustion products leave just as continuously at temperature T and a concentration of unburned [fuel] in the hot mixture, c. Let us denote the mixture stay time in the chamber by the symbol τ_s.

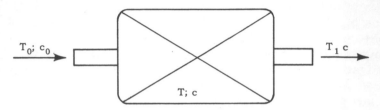

Fig. 2-1. Diagram of a combustion chamber.

If the chamber volume is v_c and the density of the products filling it is γ_c, then the mixture stay time in the chamber will evidently equal the ratio of the chamber charge $G_c = v_c \gamma_c$ (kg) to the weight discharge of the mixture per second G(kg/sec)

$$\tau_s = v_c \gamma_c / G = G_c / G \tag{2-1}$$

The quantity τ_s can also be expressed as the ratio of the average torch length l(m) (the chamber length in a first approximation) to the average velocity of the gases therein w_{av} (m/sec)

$$\tau_s = l / w_{av} \tag{2-2}$$

although both these quantities l and w_{av} do not always characterize the actual picture of the gas motion by a long shot. In conformance with the "zero-dimensional" model of the phenomenon (1-1), let us also assume that the average temperature and concentration of the mixture are, respectively, equal to the final values of T and c for the combustion products leaving the chamber. As was already mentioned, this assumption corresponds physically to the limiting case of complete mixing of the fresh mixture continuously entering

24

the chamber with combustion products which will be continuously eliminated from the chamber being formed therein. The reaction rate in the process under consideration will be defined as the ratio of the change in the concentration of the combustible mixture to the stay time

$$V = (c_0 - c)/\tau_S \qquad\qquad (2-3)$$

where V, as mentioned above, will be referred to 1 kg of mixture (V(kg/kg sec)).

We will consider the combustion process in the chamber steady and adiabatic, i.e., we will assume that all the heat being liberated because of the reaction within the chamber will transform completely, without losses, into the heat capacity of the combustion products (whose kinetic energy will be neglected for low velocities). The assumption of the adiabatic character of the process, i.e., of the possibility of neglecting the heat loss through the chamber walls, corresponds to a very intense thermal process typical for a forced, high-speed combustion chamber. Actually, the heat losses by cooling for these latter are usually so very small (of the order of one or several per cent) that it is superfluous to consider them in the total balance of heat in a qualitative investigation of the process. The assumption of an adiabatic process for medium and low intensity processes corresponds to the limiting case; its use is applicable not so much to the whole intensely cooled chamber as to its separate sections. The peculiarities of the process, related to heat exchange, will be considered later (Chapter 4).

The difference in the problem under consideration from the preceding (sections 1-3 and 1-4) is, at first glance, its approximation to the model of a steadily operating combustion chamber with a finite mixture stay time and consideration of the burning up of the mixture. In addition, the assumption of the continuous mixing of the fresh mixture with the combustion products permits extension beyond the limits of the "self-ignition" phenomenon, to which the problem of the thermal explosion referred. Actually, continuous ignition of the fresh mixture is guaranteed in the scheme under consideration, just as in the majority of actual chambers, by its being heated while being mixed with the incandescent combustion products filling the chamber. In other words, precisely this mixing of the initial and final reaction products[1] makes the continuous course of the process possible in a number of cases without an outside source of ignition for the combustion of the usual, non-self-reacting combustible mixtures.

---

[1]The question of heat supply, not related to the mixing with the combustion products (radiant, say), will be considered separately (4-1).

The substance of the problem under consideration reduces briefly to the following. In order to look for the steady-state levels of the process possible in this scheme, we will, as before, for simplicity of computation, start from the condition of the equality of the quantity of heat being liberated and eliminated referred to unit time in both cases and to 1 kg of combustible mixture. As before, the heat release rate will be determined by the course of the chemical reaction (however, burn-up of the mixture is taken into account). With respect to the heat loss rate, the heat loss in the adiabatic problem under consideration here corresponds to its being taken out of the chamber by the hot combustion products. The latter replace the heat emission to the ambient medium in the thermal explosion problem in the total heat balance. Let us also note that we actually speak of a nonstationary process in the latter, but consider it to be approximately quasi-stationary; the critical ignition condition separated out the region in which the existence of quasi-stationary states is possible from the region of nonstationary combustion ("thermal explosion"). In contrast to this, we speak in the problem under present consideration of possible steady states of a system whose length of existence is in principle never bounded.

In connection with the limits of the energy content in the original mixture and considering its partial combustion during the stay time in the chamber, investigation leads, as will be shown below, not to two but to three theoretically possible steady-state levels of the process and correspondingly, not to one but to two critical conditions of abrupt, jump-form changes in performance. This peculiarity of the actual performance of the process in the combustion chamber is explained by it being impossible to continue to consider the curve of the temperature dependence of the heat liberation rate as continuously (and hence sharply) increasing when taking the combustion process into account; as the combustible is consumed, this curve inevitably passes through the inflection point and will asymptotically approach a limit corresponding to the maximum combustion rate possible for a given (finite) stay time.

An explanation of the influence of separate parameters on the course of the process, in particular on the critical conditions, is also part of the problem of the investigation in addition to the search for stationary levels. Also to be analyzed here, in addition to the parameter T_0, the initial mixture temperature (analogous to the ambient medium temperature in the thermal explosion problem), is the influence of heating capacity of the mixture (or of one of its components) as well as the mixture stay time in the combustion chamber, i.e., the influence of the relative productivity (intensity) of the process (G/G_c) or the average chamber length (l) and the average velocity of the gas motion (w_{av}) therein, in conformance with formulas (2-1) and (2-2).

Taken all together this permits the results of the investigation to be interpreted more broadly and makes possible the drawing of certain conclusions of a technical nature.

Considering the large number of variables in the equations and also the desirability of obtaining results in the most general form possible, all the subsequent investigations will be made in nondimensional variables. However, each of the nondimensional variables to be introduced below will, mainly, characterize one of the physical variables fundamental to the process: Mixture temperature, its heat capacity, stay time, etc. Consequently, in order to conserve physical clarity, it is expedient to reserve the designation of the basic dimensional quantities, which define their physical meaning, to the nondimensional variables.

Hence, let us consider the fundamental equations of the process, and first, the heat-balance equation, as in the preceding problem. The quantity of heat being liberated per unit time is evidently equal to the product of the reaction rate (2-3) and the mixture heat content, i.e., the thermal effect of the reaction at constant pressure referred to 1 kg of mixture. Let us also take expression (1-7') from the previous chapter as the temperature and concentration dependence of V. Hence, we will have

$$Q_I = V \cdot q = (c_0 - c) q / \tau_s = k_0 e^{-E/RT} \cdot c \cdot q \qquad (2\text{-}4)$$

The coefficient k_0 has the dimensionality of inverse time for $n = 1$ in the form taken for the expression (1-7'). Consequently, it is natural to introduce the following reciprocal quantity instead of k_0:

$$\tau_K = 1/k_0 \qquad (2\text{-}5)$$

which has the meaning of a characteristic time scale for the course of the chemical reaction or, briefly, the "kinetic time." The quantity τ_K, as the primary reaction time scale, is independent of the temperature since the factor $\exp(-E/RT)$ which is in the expression for the reaction rate constant with k_0, is isolated in (1-7) and (2-4), separately.[2]

---

[2]A quantity similar to $\tau_K = 1/k_0$ for a first-order reaction can be introduced for the $n \neq 1$ case as follows: Let us write the expression for the reaction rate (1-6) as

$$V = W/\gamma = (k_0/\gamma) \, e^{-E/RT}(c')^2 = k_0' \, e^{-E/RT} (c/c_0)^{n-1} (\gamma/\gamma_0)^{n-1} c$$

and let us denote the following expression by the symbol τ_K

$$\tau_K = 1/k_0' = 1/k_0 (c_0')^{n-1} (\text{sec})$$

In this case, the kinetic time scale will evidently depend on the initial con-

In those cases when it is necessary to take the temperature dependence of the reaction time into account because of the nature of the problem, the following characteristic time will also be used in addition to the quantity $\tau_K = 1/k_0$

$$\tau_K' = 1/k = \frac{e^{E/RT}}{k_0} = \tau_K e^{1/\theta} \tag{2-5'}$$

where $\theta = RT/E$ (see below).

The quantity of heat carried away per unit time by the heated reaction products per kg of mixture, we will write as

$$Q_{II} = (c_p/\tau_s)(T - T_0) \tag{2-6}$$

where c_p is the average value of the specific heat of the mixture at constant pressure.

As before, we express the condition that the process is stationary by means of the equality

$$Q_I = Q_{II} \tag{2-7}$$

A graphical analytical investigation of this latter enables all the peculiarities of the phenomenon under investigation to be established. For brevity, let us first introduce nondimensional variables by grouping separate quantities in the heat-balance Eq. (2-7) so that each nondimensional variable would have explicit physical meaning.

We first introduce the relative (nondimensional) concentration of the combustible mixture

$$\bar{c} = c/c_0 \tag{2-8}$$

and the magnitude of the coefficient of the completeness of combustion related thereto

$$\varphi = 1 - \bar{c} = 1 - c/c_0 \tag{2-9}$$

Evidently, in the original mixture

$$\bar{c} = 1; \ \varphi = 0$$

while in the products of total combustion

$$\bar{c} = 0; \ \varphi = 1$$

The quantity φ can, equally, be called the coefficient of the completeness of heat liberation since

$$\varphi = 1 - c/c_0 = 1 - cq/c_0 q = 1 - h/h_0 \tag{2-9'}$$

centration of the combustibles in the mixture ($c_0' = \gamma_0 c_0$) also. As computations show, the qualitative character of the results explained below is conserved even for $n \neq 1$. Consequently, the whole investigation later is limited to the simplest case of $n = 1$.

that is, the value of φ is numerically equal to the fraction of the
heat liberated during the reaction process (if the initial value of
the chemical enthalpy per kg of mixture, h_0, is taken as the unit).

It is natural to take the quantity

$$\theta = RT/E \tag{2-10}$$

already encountered earlier, as the nondimensional temperature.
Use of this variable permits a single reaction procedure to be used
for mixtures differing in the values of the activation energy E. By
definition, the quantity θ can vary between the limits 0 and ∞;
however, apparently only the range of small values of θ (approximately to a θ of the order of 0.5) has any practical value in a wide
range of the quantity E.

The φ, θ coordinate system (completeness of combustion, temperature) is the most suitable for investigating the process; in
particular, its successive use differentiates the explanation used
here from other solutions of the adiabatic problem.[3]

It is convenient to take the ratio of the stay time τ_s to the characteristic reaction time $\tau_K = 1/k_0$ as the nondimensional time. Let
us denote this ratio by the same symbol with two subscripts[4]

$$\tau_{sK} = \tau_s / \tau_K \tag{2-11}$$

The large values of the quantity τ_{sK} (which, for brevity, we shall
call the nondimensional stay time or, briefly, simply the stay time
always keeping in mind that a change in the variable τ_K is the
rarer case) can evidently be obtained for high stay times of the
mixture in the chamber (large chamber dimensions, low values of
the motion velocity therein) or for low times and, therefore, high
chemical reaction rates. Conversely, low values of the nondimensional time τ_{sK} indicate an insignificant stay time (small size,
high-pressure chambers) or a low chemical reaction rate. Consequently, other conditions remaining equal, an increase in τ_{sK} during
the adiabatic process always (the effect of heat emission will be
considered separately in Chapter 4) leads to an increase in the completeness of combustion while a decrease in τ_{sK} leads to a drop in
φ. The use of the nondimensional time τ_{sK}, analogous to the measurement of the length in calibers (l/d) used in hydraulics and other
sciences, say, is of great convenience. Actually, an indication of

---

[3]For example, see Zel'dovich (15, 13a); an investigation is presented
in this work for different chemical kinetic schemes.

[4]Here and subsequently, the quantity τ with the two subscripts denotes
the ratio of two-dimensional times, where the first subscript refers to the
numerator and the second to the denominator, for example:

$$\tau_{1,2} = \tau_1 / \tau_2, \text{ etc.}$$

the absolute value of one of the dimensional quantities, mixture stay time in the chamber τ_s or characteristic reaction time τ_K is completely inadequate to estimate the degree of completeness of the combustion process; only their ratio (τ_{sK}) actually defines the course of the reaction.

We introduce the next nondimensional variable (for the adiabatic problem) as the group

$$\vartheta = Rqc_0/Ec_p \tag{2-12}$$

which it is natural to call the reduced heat production of the mixture. This characteristic is essential for a comparison of reactions with various thermal effects (at the very least, in connection with the narrower variations, for different values of the average specific heat), and also for an estimate of the influence of an excess of one of the components in the mixture. The maximum value of ϑ for certain mixtures, if the phenomenon of thermal dissociation is neglected, corresponds to the stoichiometric relation of the components. The deviation from this relation ($\alpha = 1$, where α is the coefficient of excess air or of oxidizer in the general case) toward poor ($\alpha > 1$) or rich ($\alpha < 1$) mixtures leads to a drop in the magnitude of ϑ because of the reduction in the heat production of 1 kg of mixture when diluting it with the excess component. (Taking dissociation into account, which is not considered herein, leads, as is known, to a displacement of the heat production maximum toward the rich mixture region for values of $\alpha \approx 0.85 - 0.9$.)

Now, let us transform (2-7) to nondimensional form. To do this, let us first write it as

$$(c_0 - c)q/\tau_s = c_p(T - T_0)/\tau_s = e^{-E/RT}c \cdot q/\tau_K$$

We obtain from the first equality

$$\varphi = 1 - c/c_0 = c_p(T - T_0)/qc_0$$

$$\varphi = \frac{1}{\vartheta}(\theta - \theta_0) \tag{2-13}$$

and from the equality of the first and third expressions, we obtain

$$\varphi = (\tau_s/\tau_K)e^{-E/RT}(c/c_0) = \tau_{sK}e^{-1/\theta}(1 - \varphi)$$

or finally

$$\varphi = \tau_{sK}/(\tau_{sK} + e^{1/\theta}) = 1/1 + e^{1/\theta}/\tau_{sK} \tag{2-14}$$

The expression (2-13) enables an additional physical interpretation to be given to the quantities φ and ϑ for the adiabatic process. Hence, let us turn to the total combustion case: $\varphi = 1$, for which there follows from (2-13)

$$\theta = \theta_{max} = \theta_0 + \vartheta \qquad (2\text{-}15)$$

or

$$\vartheta = \theta_{max} - \theta_0 \qquad (2\text{-}15')$$

Hence, the quantity ϑ in the adiabatic process corresponds to the maximum relative heating of the mixture during its total combustion. On the other hand, (2-13) for φ can be rewritten thus if (2-15) is taken into account:

$$\varphi = (\theta - \theta_0)/(\theta_{max} - \theta_0) = (T - T_0)/(T_{max} - T_0) \qquad (2\text{-}16)$$

The formula obtained indicates the similarity of the concentration and temperature in the adiabatic process; this similarity can also be expressed by the equality

$$\overline{c} = 1 - \varphi = (T_{max} - T)/(T_{max} - T_0) = (\theta_{max} - \theta)/\vartheta \qquad (2\text{-}17)$$

Both the last equalities (2-16) and (2-17) are valid in this form only for the adiabatic process. For the latter in particular, a change in φ is similar to a change in the temperature θ and, therefore, the graphs of φ and θ as a function of any variable at all (see below) differ only in scale.

Later (Chapters 3 and 6), more general similarity conditions will be analyzed for the concentration and temperature field during combustion.

Of the two expressions (2-13) and (2-14), obtained above for the coefficient of the completeness of combustion φ, one (2-14) has been derived by comparing two expressions for the reaction rate (rate of heat liberation); consequently we shall later call the corresponding curve $\varphi_I = \varphi(\theta)$ the "heat-liberation" curve, conditionally. The second formula (2-13) has been obtained from the equalization of the specific magnitude of the heat liberation and elimination, consequently, the curve $\varphi_{II} = \varphi(\theta)$, corresponding to (2-13), will be called, briefly, the "heat-elimination" curve (line for this problem).[5] Equating both values of φ, we obtain a heat balance equation for the stationary region of the course of the process ($Q_I = Q_{II}$; $\varphi_I(\theta) = \varphi_{II}(\theta)$) instead of (2-7) in the form of the transcendental equation

$$\tau_{sK}/(\tau_{sK} + e^{1/\theta}) = (\theta - \theta_0)/\vartheta \qquad (2\text{-}18)$$

which contains four nondimensional variables θ, θ_0, ϑ, and τ_{sK} instead of the ten dimensional quantities (T, T_0, R, E, c, c_0, τ_s, τ_K,

[5]The designations "heat-liberation" and "heat-elimination" curves are used only for brevity and reflect the physical meaning only indirectly; in substance, we speak only of a graphical solution of the heat balance equation.

q, and c_p) or, if a transformation is made to a φ, θ coordinate system for the graphical solution of (2-18) to be made more clear, five variables (including φ) related by the two equations

$$\varphi = \varphi_I(\theta) = \varphi_{II}(\theta)$$

Subsequently, taking the heat emission, mixing, etc., phenomena into account, the system of nondimensional variables will be supplemented by other quantities characteristic of these cases.

2-2. INVESTIGATION OF STATIONARY STATES

In order to look for the stationary levels of the process, let us resort to a graphical investigation of the heat-balance Eq. (2-18) in the φ, θ diagram (completeness of combustion, temperature). Let us first draw the curve $\varphi_I = \varphi(\theta)$ using (2-14). The family of these curves in the φ, θ coordinates is shown on Figure 2-2 for various values of the parameter τ_{sK}. The value of τ_{sK} on this graph increases as the transition is made toward the origin from one curve to the next. All the $\varphi_I(\theta)$ curves, as is seen from the graphs, issue from the origin ($\varphi_I(\theta) = 0$ for $\theta = 0$) and are of the characteristic S shape. As the temperature increases, the $\varphi_I(\theta)$ curves first increase sharply and then approach the limiting value:

$$\varphi_{I, \theta \to \infty} \to 1/1 + \tau_{Ks}; \quad (\tau_{Ks} = 1/\tau_{sK})$$

This limiting value $\varphi_{I, \theta \to \infty}$ will be smaller, the smaller the quantity τ_{sK}, that is, the smaller the stay time τ_s or the larger the time required for the course of the chemical reaction τ_K. Let us also note that the $\varphi_I(\theta)$ curves rise very steeply for large values of τ_{sK} and become shallower and shallower as the parameter τ_{sK} decreases.

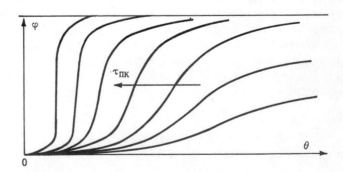

Fig. 2-2. Curves of completeness of combustion φ as a function of temperature θ. Generalized time τ_{sK} increases toward the origin.

Now, let us consider the expression $\varphi_{II} = \varphi(\theta)$ using (2-13). Straight lines intersecting the horizontal axis ($\varphi = 0$) at the point $\theta = \theta_0 (T = T_0)$ and the line $\varphi = 1$ at the point $\theta = \theta_{max} = \theta_0 + \vartheta$, or

$$T_{max} = T + qc_0/c_p \tag{2-19}$$

i.e., the maximum temperature of adiabatic combustion (which is usually called the theoretical flame temperature in heat engineering), evidently corresponds to it. The slope of the lines $\varphi_{II}(\theta)$ is $1/\vartheta$. This means that the lines corresponding to slightly exothermal reactions (low values of ϑ, i.e., qc_0/c_p; the influence of the quantity E, the activation energy in the expression $\vartheta = Rqc_0/Ec_p$, has already been taken into account in the abscissa scale; $\theta = RT/E$), have a very steep slope; the line $\varphi_{II}(\theta)$ is parallel to the ordinate axis in the limit for an isothermal reaction with $q = 0$; $1/\vartheta = \infty$. The lines $\varphi_{II}(\theta)$ have low slopes for high values of ϑ, i.e., for high-caloric mixtures; $\varphi_{II}(\theta) \to 0$ in the limit as $\vartheta \to \infty$.

These properties of the heat-liberation $\varphi_{I}(\theta)$ and heat-elimination $\varphi_{II}(\theta)$ curves are essential to the clarification of the physical meaning of the process in the subsequent investigation on the φ, θ diagram.

In particular should be recalled the very rapid change in the numerical value of the parameter τ_{sK} in the $\varphi = 0$ diagram (values of log τ_{sK} are superposed on the $\varphi_{I}(\theta)$ curves on Figure 2-7 (see below); as is seen from the graph, the change in the value of τ_{sK} attains several orders for an insignificant change in the temperature).

Now, let us turn to an investigation of the conditions for the curves $\varphi_{I}(\theta)$ and $\varphi_{II}(\theta)$ to intersect, just as for the curves $Q_{I}(T)$ and $Q_{II}(T)$ on Figure 1-4, i.e., to a graphical solution of the heat-balance equation.[6] As is seen from Figure 2-3a, the heat elimination line $\varphi_{II}(\theta)$ intersects an S-shaped $\varphi_{I}(\theta)$ curve in three points in the φ, θ diagram in the general case. In principle, a possible equilibrium stationary region corresponds to each of these points. The number of intersection points in particular cases can be one or, when tangency occurs at one of them, two.

A very simple investigation of the stability of the equilibrium states by the small deviations method[7] shows that only two, the

[6]The graphical solution of similar equations in the "reaction rate concentration" coordinates used by Zel'dovich (13a and 15) leads to the same conclusions; understandably, however, it is not as graphic.

[7]Exactly as this has been done for the thermal explosion problem. Shown by arrows near all the intersections of the $\varphi_I(\theta)$ curves are the directions, of the subsequent change in the state after a small deviation from equilibrium. The arrows approaching the equilibrium point correspond to stable and those going away to unstable equilibrium.

upper and lower, of the three possible stationary levels of the process are stable. Actually, any sign deviation from equilibrium (i.e., a rise or drop in temperature) leads to the return of the system to the initial equilibrium state since it causes a predominance of the heat elimination over the heat liberation ($\varphi_{II} > \varphi_I$ for $\delta\theta > 0$) and, therefore, cooling of the system as the temperature rises and an increase of the heat liberation over the heat elimination as the temperature drops ($\varphi_{II} < \varphi_I$ for $\delta\theta < 0$), i.e., heating of the system. In contrast to this, any deviations, as small as desired, from the intermediate equilibrium state (the middle point of intersection on Figure 2-3) lead to a further progressively increasing rise in the deviations from the equilibrium state: For $\delta\theta > 0$, near the middle intersection point, we will have $\varphi_I > \varphi_{II}$, i.e., further heating of the system occurs and it makes the transition to the upper stable stationary level, in the limit; for $\delta\theta < 0$, we will have $\varphi_I < \varphi_{II}$ and, therefore, nonstationary cooling occurs, down to the establishment of equilibrium in the lower stable stationary region. Hence only two, the upper and lower, stable levels of the stationary reaction progress are of real value and of practical interest; the middle level is never realized in practice because of the inevitability of random deviations in the whole process.

There is an essential difference between the upper and lower stationary levels of the progress of a reaction whose presence is typical for strongly exothermal processes (see below). The first, the lower, corresponds to negligibly small, almost zero, values of the completeness of combustion φ and to slight heating of the system. The latter is determined on the φ, θ diagram by the difference in the values of the stationary temperature θ_{stat} (at the point of intersection of the curves) and the initial mixture temperature θ_0 (at the point of intersection of the line $\varphi_I(\theta)$ with the horizontal axis for $\varphi = 0$). Physically, this region is slow oxidation; in practice, this region is the absence of combustion in the chamber.

The upper stable, stationary region is of considerably greater interest. Its characteristics are intense heat liberation, high (almost unity) value of the completeness of combustion and correspondingly, considerable heating of the system ($\theta_{stat} \gg \theta_0$). Precisely this region is the chamber operating region, the combustion region. In order to answer the question as to which of the two equilibrium states possible for the given values of the parameters θ_0, ϑ, τ_{sK} is actually realized, it is necessary to trace the "history" of the process. If the reaction originally occurred in the oxidation region, then the process will be retained in this (lower) stationary level down to the transition beyond the critical ignition point; conversely, if the combustion region were originally realized then the process would remain in the upper stationary level just as long as a

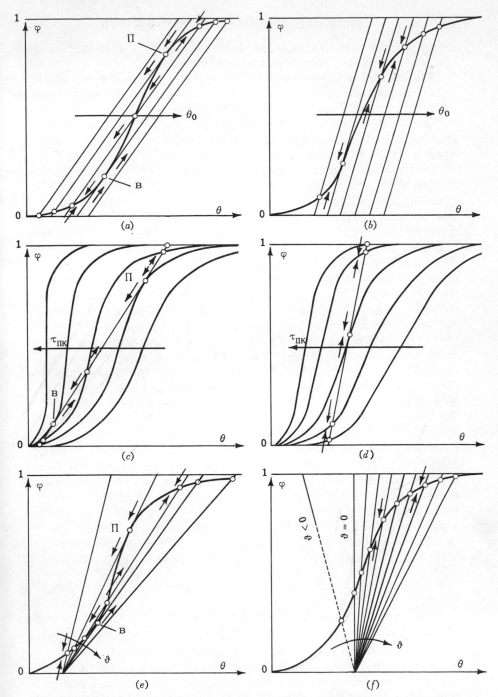

Fig. 2-3. Analysis of the stationary states. $B(i)$—Ignition; $\Pi(e)$—extinction; (a) and (b) Change of inlet temperature; (c) and (d) change of stay time; (e) and (f) change of heating value of mixture.

change in one of the parameters does not lead to a transition beyond the second critical, extinction, point.

The character of the intersection of the $\varphi_I(\theta)$ and $\varphi_{II}(\theta)$ curves analyzed in detail here is not, however, the only one possible. Shown on Figure 2-3b is such a mutual arrangement of the heat-liberation and-elimination curves to which only one intersection point corresponds in a wide range of values of the parameter θ_0, i.e., one, always stable and stationary equilibrium state.

Shown on the remaining graphs of Figure 2-3 are the conditions for the intersection of the $\varphi_I(\theta)$ and $\varphi_{II}(\theta)$ curves, obtained by changing the values of the other parameters: the nondimensional stay time τ_{sK} (Figure 2-3c and d) and the characteristic of the mixture heat production (Figure 2-3e and f). The arrows on Figure 2-3 indicate the direction of increasing values of the parameters. The three left-hand curves (Figure 2-3a, c, e) correspond to the presence of two stable stationary levels of the process and also, as will be shown below, to two critical conditions, ignition and extinction. The three right-hand curves (Figure 2-3b, d, f) correspond to a process with just one equilibrium state.

Let us note that all these cases of varying one of the parameters while keeping the other two constant have a completely clear physical meaning. In particular, they show that the heat production of the mixture or the stay time is accomplished by the lower, oxidation, region for low values of the initial mixture temperature while the upper, combustion, region is realized for high values of θ_0 and τ_{sK}. In other words, an increase in the initial mixture temperature, its heat productivity (approximation to the stoichiometric composition, say) and the stay time (i.e., the reduction of the mixture consumption, the decrease in the average velocity of the gas motion, or the increase in the volume for a series of chambers) leads to a shift of the process toward stable combustion; an inverse change in these quantities leads to a shift toward oxidation. The conditions of the transition of the process from one level to the other will be considered in more detail from quantitative aspects in the next section.

2-3. CRITICAL IGNITION AND EXTINCTION CONDITIONS

Let us investigate the character of the change in the stationary values of the temperature and the completeness of combustion, more carefully, for a variation of one of the process parameters, the initial temperature, the stay time, or the mixture heat productivity. Let us do this in detail first for one of them, the initial mixture temperature, and then briefly for the other two.

As is seen from Figure 2-3, just one intersection of the $\varphi_I(\theta)$

and $\varphi_{II}(\theta)$ curves corresponds to each value of θ_0 in the low-temperature range for given values of τ_{sK} and ϑ; namely, the lower stationary region (oxidation). Let us trace the variation in the values of φ_{st} and θ_{st}, corresponding to the stationary process (point of intersection of the curves), as the initial temperature θ_0 gradually rises (i.e., for the line $\varphi_{II}(\theta)$ moving parallel to the arrow direction on Figure 2-3a). As θ_0 increases, the point of intersection will first move along the curve $\varphi_I(\theta)$; the stationary values φ_{st} and θ_{st} will hence increase continuously. Such a law of the variation will be retained down to the point of tangency I of the curves $\varphi_I(\theta)$ and $\varphi_{II}(\theta)$ on Figures 2-3a and b. An infinitesimal rise in the initial temperature for the region corresponding to this critical point I, which is similar to ignition in the thermal explosion problem, will lead to a sharp, jump-shaped increase in the values of φ_{st} and θ_{st} and a transition to the upper, combustion, region. This transition related as before to an excess of heat liberation over heat elimination for a temperature rise, is called ignition, naturally.[8] A further increase in the value of the parameter θ_0 will be accompanied by a continuous increase in the stationary values φ_{st} and θ_{st}; the point of intersection of the curves will here slide over the upper branch of the $\varphi_I(\theta)$ curve.

Now, let us trace the change in the values of φ_{st} and θ_{st} at the point of intersection of the curves as θ_0 varies reciprocally (diminishes). At the beginning, the change in φ_{st} and θ_{st} will occur smoothly in the combustion region, where, and this is very essential, a continuous decrease in the stationary values of the temperature and the completeness of combustion is retained even during the passage through the value θ_{0I}, corresponding to ignition (as θ_0 increases, i.e., the tangents of the curves $\varphi_I(\theta)$ and $\varphi_{II}(\theta)$ below the curve for $(d^2\varphi I/d\theta^2) > 0$). Then an infinitesimal decrease in the value of θ_0 at the second critical point E (Figure 2-3a) again causes a sharp jump (a drop in this case) in the stationary values of φ_{st} and θ_{st} and the transition from the upper region (combustion) to the lower (oxidation). It is natural to call this second critical region of the process, which leads, in practice, to its collapse and to the cessation of combustion, extinction. A further decrease in the parameter θ_0 after extinction again leads to a continuous lowering of the stationary values of the temperature and the completeness of combustion.

---

[8]Ignition in the thermal explosion problem meant the transition to the nonstationary process of progressive mixture burn-up; in contrast, here (in connection with taking burn-up into account), we speak of the transition from one stationary level of the process (oxidation) to the other, also stationary, level (combustion).

Hence, both points, I and E, of tangency of the heat-liberation and -elimination curves are critical; the lower I corresponds to ignition, the upper E to extinction. The critical phenomena of ignition and extinction taking total burning up of the mixture into account, acquire the meaning of intermittent transition from one stable stationary level of the process to another. Shown on Figure 2-4 is a curve of the variation of the stationary values of the tem-

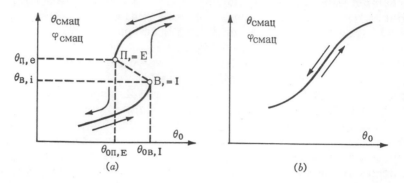

Fig. 2-4. Dependence of the stationary values of completeness and temperature of combustion on the initial mixture temperature. (*a*) Hysteresis process; (*b*) process without a crisis.

perature and the completeness of combustion as a function of the initial temperature.[9] (Let us recall that the curves $\varphi = \varphi_{st}(\theta_0)$ and $\theta = \theta_{st}(\theta_0)$ are similar, i.e., differ only in the ordinate scale.) It is seen from this curve and also from the reasoning presented above, that the critical ignition and extinction conditions do not coincide in the general case. Let us denote the critical values of φ and θ and also the parameter θ_0 corresponding to ignition and extinction by I and E subscripts. The following inequalities are characteristic for the relations between them:

$$\varphi_E > \varphi_I; \quad \theta_E > \theta_I$$

and

$$\theta_{oE} < \theta_{oI}$$

This means that the value of the initial mixture temperature (θ_{oI}), which leads to ignition in the warming-up process, is larger than its value (θ_{oE}) which corresponds to extinction (collapse) of combustion during cooling. In this connection, the curve of the stationary values of φ_{st} and θ_{st} on Figure 2-4*a* has a typical hysteresis character.

[9]The states corresponding to the average (instable), stationary level of the process are shown in Figure 2-4 by dashes connecting the points I and E.

A considerably simpler picture corresponds to the process for which the intersection of the curves $\varphi_I(\theta)$ and $\varphi_{II}(\theta)$ as the initial temperature θ_0 varies is shown on Figure 2-4b. In this case, the stationary values φ_{st} and θ_{st} always vary continuously as the values of θ_0 increase and then decrease and the point of intersection is displaced smoothly along the curve $\varphi_I(\theta)$. Here the critical ignition and extinction phenomena are lacking just as in the related hysteresis loop in the curve of the stationary values of the temperature and the completeness of combustion as a function of the initial mixture temperature (Figure 2-3b).

It is seen from a comparison of the graphs (Figure 2-3a and b) that the first corresponds to a comparatively steeper rise in the $\varphi_I(\theta)$ curve and a comparatively shallow $\varphi_{II}(\theta)$ line. Conversely, the second graph corresponds to a relatively steeper heat elimination line and a comparatively shallow heat liberation curve.

A similar character of the change in the stationary values of the temperature and completeness of combustion is retained also for two other cases of the change in one of the parameters: The stay time τ_{sK} for constant values of θ_0 and ϑ (Figure 2-3c and d) or the heating capacity of the mixture ϑ for constant values of τ_{sK} and θ_0 (Figure 2-3e and f). Here two types of process are also possible; with critical ignition and extinction conditions (Figure 2-3c and e) or without them (Figure 2-3d and f). Leaving the reader to trace the construction of the graphs as the parameter τ_{sK} changes by himself (just as before, by transforming from one S-shaped $\varphi_I\theta$ curve to the next, etc., in the direction of the arrows on Figure 2-3c and d as τ_{sK} increases and conversely as it decreases) or as the parameter ϑ changes (rotation of the line $\varphi_{II}(\theta)$ in the direction of the arrows on Figure 2-3e and f as ϑ increases and opposite[10] as it decreases), we shall explain the physical meaning of these constructions by examples.

For example, let us imagine a set of combustion chambers of different lengths, from a very small to a very large, or what perhaps is more graphic, an extensible (telescopic, say) experimental chamber. If an attempt is made to carry on a combustion process in a very short chamber, then it can happen that the combustible mixture will fly through it without being ignited successfully. Extending the chamber gradually, such a critical length can be reached at which the process of slow oxidation occurs comparatively remotely and leads to ignition and the establishment of a stationary combustion region. The latter will not be changed substantially as the chamber is lengthened further. If this imaginary experiment

[10]The graphs have shapes completely similar to the graphs of Figure 2-4 if the value of θ_0 on the horizontal axis is replaced by τ_{sK} and ϑ, respectively.

is repeated in the reverse order, i.e., if we begin with steady combustion in a sufficiently long chamber and gradually decrease the length then combustion will be disrupted, extinction will occur, at a certain new critical length, shorter than that at which ignition occurred.

This example, which graphically illustrates the influence of the time $\tau_{sK}(\tau_{sK} \approx 1/w_{av})$ requires explanation. The change in the chamber length of which we spoke above should be visualized as the successive shift of a set of steady regions close to each other and not as a continuous nonstationary process[11] [i.e., not a reactor in which there is a continuous change in composition as the mixture flows along its length. Ed.].

Similarly, the change in the τ_{sK} parameter can be visualized also as a successive reduction and then increase in the consumption of the combustible mixture (the average velocity of the gas motion). Here, the value of the velocity corresponding to ignition (for a reduction in the consumption) will be less than the value of the velocity occurring at the collapse in the process (extinction, for a velocity increase). Finally, a change in the parameter τ_{sK} can be conceived hypothetically as a successive reduction and then increase in the chemical reaction rate (a quantity inverse to the characteristic time τ_K), under the influence of external pressure, say, as the flight altitude of some apparatus varies or when the characteristics of the process for combustible mixtures of different reaction capacities are compared.

As regards the change in the characteristics of the heat productivity of the mixture, as has already been mentioned, the parameter ϑ is most simply visualized as the successive change in the mixture composition, rich, say, and then lean. This corresponds, for the combustion of any gas-air mixture, for example, to the transition from the limiting lean, incombustible mixture (too much air) to a rich mixture; the mixture ignites for a certain value of the excess coefficient α_I with the mixture being enriched and collapse of the process occurs at the values $\alpha_E > \alpha_I$.

Let us note that the difference between a lean $(\alpha > 1)$ and a rich $(\alpha < 1)$ mixture should be kept in mind when interpreting the change in the parameter as a variation in the mixture composition. If we start, as a first approximation, from purely thermal representations, then the heat production q of the working mixture, for a combustible mixture consisting of 1 kg fuel and $\chi = \alpha\chi_0$ kg oxidizer (here, as before, χ is the stoichiometric ratio of fuel to oxidizer)

---

[11]In this sense, the example with a set of chambers of different lengths and comparable steady-process characteristics in each of the chambers corresponds more to the stationary scheme.

with the heat production q_0 per unit stoichiometric mixture at $\alpha = 1$, equals the product $q_0 c_0$ at $\alpha \neq 1$, or

$$q/q_0 = c_0 = (1 + \chi_0)/(1 + \chi) = (1 + \chi_0)/(1 + \alpha' \chi_0) \qquad (2\text{-}20)$$

for the $\alpha = \alpha' > 1$ case, and

$$q/q_0 = c_0 = \alpha''(1 + \chi_0)/(1 + \chi) = \alpha''(1 + \chi_0)/(1 + \alpha'' \chi_0) \qquad (2\text{-}20')$$

for the $\alpha = \alpha'' < 1$ case (formulas (1-8) and (1-9) of section 1-1). Neglecting the change in the specific heat, we can assume

$$\theta/\theta_0 = q/q_0$$

where the value θ_0 corresponds to a stoichiometric mixture ($\alpha = 1$). A graph of the dependence of the ratio θ/θ_0 on α for three values

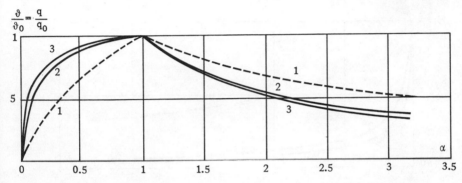

Fig. 2-5. Dependence of the relative heat production of a mixture on the coefficient of excess oxidizer. 1—for $\chi_0 = 1$; 2—for $\chi_0 = 10$; 3—for $\chi_0 = 15$.

of χ_0 is given on Figure 2-5. Equivalent rich and lean mixtures, in heat production respects, must evidently satisfy the equality

$$\theta_{\alpha' > 1} = \theta_{\alpha'' < 1}$$

where α' and α'' refer to lean and rich mixtures, respectively. It follows from the formulas cited above

$$1/(1 + \alpha' \chi_0) = \alpha''/(1 + \alpha'' \chi_0)$$

from which

$$[1 + (\chi_0 - 1) \alpha'']/\alpha'' \chi_0 \qquad (2\text{-}21)$$

or

$$\alpha'' = 1/[1 + \chi_0(\alpha' - 1)] \qquad (2\text{-}21')$$

Hence, the magnitudes of the excess coefficient $\alpha' > 1$ and $\alpha'' < 1$, which correspond to the same values of the heat production of lean and rich mixtures, depend on the stoichiometric relation of the fuel and the oxidizer; they are related by the simple formula $\alpha' \cdot \alpha'' = 1$ only in the hypothetical $\chi_0 = 1$ case.

Shown on Figure 2-6 are curves of the dependence of α' on α'' for various values of χ_0, from which it is seen that lean mixtures of the same heat production with $\alpha' = 1.07$; 1.03; 1.02, respectively, correspond to rich mixtures with $\alpha'' = 0.5$; 0.7; and 0.8 for the $\chi_0 \approx 15$ case (combustion of hydrocarbons in air). As was mentioned, these relations are approximate. Actually, taking thermal dissociation and the change in the specific heat into account leads to a certain displacement of the maximum curve $q = q(\alpha)$ on Figure 2-5 to the $\alpha < 1$ range.

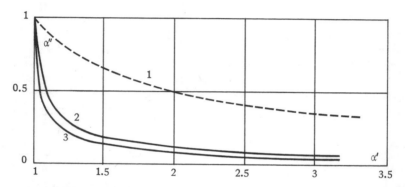

Fig. 2-6. Rich and lean mixtures equivalent in heat production. 1—for $\chi_0 = 1$; 2—for $\chi_0 = 10$; 3—for $\chi_0 = 15$.

It also follows from an analysis of the curves on Figures 2-5 and 2-6 that the following inequality

$$\alpha'_I < \alpha'_E$$

corresponds to the critical values of the heat production ϑ_I and ϑ_E (always in the relation $\vartheta_I > \vartheta_E$) in the lean mixture range and the following inequality

$$\alpha''_I > \alpha''_E$$

in the rich mixture range, where each pair of critical values α'_I, α''_I and α'_E, α''_E, respectively, is related by the above-mentioned approximate formula (2-21')

$$\alpha'' \approx 1/[1 + (\alpha' - 1)\chi_0]$$

These simple relations explain, to a known degree, the difference in the combustion of rich and lean mixtures usually observable in experiments.[12]

For example, a change in the content of the inert component in a combustible mixture, a change in the heat production of the mixture, etc., can correspond, in addition to a change in the mixture composition (a change in α), to a variation in the parameter ϑ.

All these examples, whose number can be multiplied, refer to the conditions of the course of the process shown on the left graphs of Figures 2-3 and 2-4, that is, to the presence of critical ignition and extinction phenomena and to a hysteresis form of the curves of the stationary values of φ_{st} and θ_{st}. Common to all these cases is the unusual "inertia" of the process expressed by the inequalities (Figure 2-4a)

$$\varphi_E > \varphi_I; \quad \theta_E > \theta_I$$

and

$$\theta_{oE} < \theta_{oI}; \quad \tau_{sKE} < \tau_{sKI}; \quad \vartheta_E < \vartheta_I$$

Considerably steeper $\varphi_{II}(\theta)$ lines and shallower $\varphi_I(\theta)$ curves correspond in all cases to the second type of process for which critical phenomena are absent; this very conditional demarcation receives a more rigorous quantitative expression in the sequel. As regards the illustration of such a process (without hysteresis), it can be reduced to the repetition of the same examples as above with the replacement of the critical transitions from one stationary level by another smooth, continuous change in the stationary state.

As is seen from the above, two sharply differing kinds of process progress are possible, with, or without, critical ignition and extinction phenomena. Stationary values of θ and φ included between the limits

$$\theta_0 \leq \theta_{st} < \theta_I; \quad 0 \leq \varphi_{st} < \varphi_I$$

and

$$\theta_E < \theta_{st} \leq \theta_{max}; \quad \varphi_E < \varphi_{st} \leq 1$$

are possible in the first process while the values

$$\theta_I \leq \theta_{st} \leq \theta_E; \quad \varphi_I \leq \varphi_{st} \leq \varphi_E$$

are impossible in the steady process; the stationary values of θ and φ run through all possible intervals of the quantities

$$\theta_0 \leq \theta_{st} \leq \theta_{max}; \quad 0 \leq \varphi_{st} \leq 1$$

[12]The influence of heat elimination by radiation, essentially close to the collapse of combustion, is also large in rich mixtures in connection with a sooty flame.

in the second. The first type of process, whose realization is probable in the range of high values of ϑ (high-caloric mixtures), small θ_0 and large τ_{sK}, is called [one with, Ed.] "hysteresis," or "conditionally exothermal."

The second, probable for small ϑ, large θ_0, and small τ_{sK}, is called "uncritical," or "conditionally isothermal."[13] Let us note that this division is not absolute; in general, it is not difficult to create conditions corresponding both to a hysteresis and to a non-critical character of the thermal process for the same combustible mixture (ϑ = const) by choosing the values of the other parameters (θ_0 and τ_{sK}). It is also necessary to take into account that the non-critical process, probable, in particular, in the high-temperature region and also in the region of low values of the activation energy, can occur very violently on the outside [i.e., without being mixed with reacting material, Ed.] and can resemble active combustion itself in a number of ways (flame brightness, etc.). The recombination reaction of atomic hydrogen, whose activation energy is zero (13 a), can serve as an example of an exceptionally rapid, highly exothermal noncritical process.

Although the hysteresis process is apparently more widespread for the usual very caloric combustible mixtures and the normal furnace conditions, the probability of realizing a noncritical process is also large for the high temperature and low concentration region (burnout zone). Moreover, as will be shown below, the presence of heat emission, in particular radiation, as well as of the mixing of the mixture components during the reaction markedly extends the range of the noncritical process.

2-4. QUANTITATIVE RELATIONS

The critical ignition and extinction conditions corresponding to the tangency of the liberation and elimination curves in the φ, θ diagram are expressed by the following system of equations:

$$\varphi_I(\theta) = \varphi_{II}(\theta); \quad \varphi = \tau_{sK}/(\tau_{sK} + e^{1/\theta}) = (\theta - \theta_0)/\vartheta \qquad (2\text{-}22)$$

$$\frac{d\varphi_I}{d\theta} = \frac{d\varphi_{II}}{d\theta}; \quad \frac{e^{1/\theta} \cdot \tau_{sK}}{\theta^2(\tau_{sK} + e^{1/\theta})^2} = 1/\vartheta$$

There are three equations for the five variables (φ, θ, θ_0, ϑ, and τ_{sK}). Consequently, in principle, an expression can be obtained for

[13]The vertical line $\varphi_{II}(\theta)$ corresponds to a real isothermal process; finally, a line with the negative slope ($q < 0$; $\vartheta < 0$, dashed on Figure 2-3f) corresponds to an endothermal reaction whose stationary flow is possible with heat delivered from outside. Critical values of ignition and extinction are absent in both cases.

the critical value of any of the variables as a function of any two others if the remaining two are eliminated. The formulas thus obtained, however, should not be considered as independent equalities since the realization of the corresponding conditions is related to the satisfaction of the remaining equations between the variables.[14] However, an investigation of such particular dependences between the separate variables under critical region conditions permits the physical peculiarities of ignition and extinction to be interpreted considerably more deeply and, in particular, permits the boundary between the hysteresis and the noncritical processes to be traced.

Let us first consider the dependence of the critical value of the completeness of combustion φ_{cr} on the critical temperature θ_{cr} and the critical value of the initial temperature $\theta_{0\ cr}$:

$$\varphi_{cr} = \varphi(\theta_{cr}, \theta_{0\ cr})$$

In order to simplify the writing, let us later retain the subscript cr, indicating that the values of the variable refer to the critical conditions, only in the final formulas for the quantities for which the equation is solved, for example:

$$\varphi_{cr} = \varphi(\theta;\theta_0), \text{ etc.}$$

From the first two equations of the system (2-22), let us express the values

$$1/\vartheta - \varphi/(\theta - \theta_0); \quad \exp(1/\theta)/\tau_{sK} = (1 - \varphi)/\varphi$$

Taking these into account, let us rewrite the third equation (the equality of the derivatives) as

$$\varphi_{cr} = 1 - \theta^2/(\theta - \theta_0) \tag{2-23}$$

The curves of the critical values of the completeness of combustion and of the temperature, constructed using (2-23) with the parameter $\theta_{0\ cr}$ = const, are superposed on the φ, θ diagram of Figure 2-7 by dashes. Complementation of the φ, θ diagram by these curves affords the possibility of determining all the characteristic (critical) values of the variables.

---

[14] For example, having obtained the dependence of the ignition temperature on the mixture initial temperature and heat production: $\theta_I = \theta(\theta_0, \vartheta)$, it should be recalled that the values of the arguments θ_0 and ϑ selected are related to the remaining variables of Eq. (2-22); this means that completely specific values of not only the ignition temperature $\theta_{I1} = \theta(\theta_{01}; \vartheta_1)$ but of the completeness of combustion $\varphi_1 = (\theta_{I1} - \theta_{01})/\vartheta_1$ and of stay time $\tau_{sK_1} = \varphi_1 \exp(1/\theta)/(1- \varphi_1)$ etc., correspond to certain arbitrarily selected values of θ_{01} and ϑ_1.

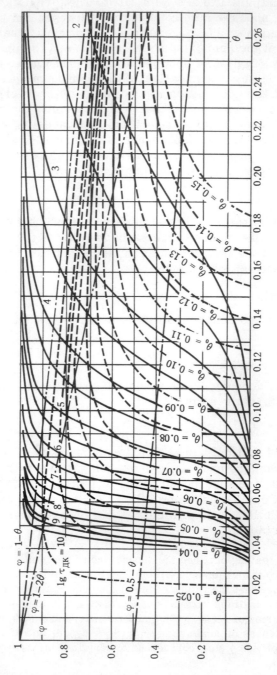

Fig. 2-7. Curves of the critical values in the φ, θ diagram. Solid line $\varphi_1(\theta)$, parameter τ_{sK}; dashed line $\varphi_{cr}(\theta)$, parameter θ_0.

For example, if one of the $\varphi_{cr}(\theta)$ curves (θ_0 parameter) inter- sects a heat-liberation curve $\varphi_I(\theta)$ (τ_{SK} parameter) at two points, then one of them, low in the diagram, i.e., corresponding to a low value of φ and θ, corresponds to ignition I and the second, high (large values of φ and θ), to extinction E. Evidently, this case corresponds to a hysteresis process (Figure 2-8a). Joining the point $\theta = \theta_0$, $\varphi = 0$ to I or E by the line $\varphi_{II}(\theta)$, we determine the appropriate critical values of the heat productivity ϑ_I and ϑ_E in terms of its slope.

The boundary case of coincidence of the critical ignition and ex- tinction conditions (Figure 2-8b) occurs when the $\varphi_{cr}(\theta)$ and the $\varphi_I(\theta)$ curves are tangent at the point of inflection of the latter $(d^2\varphi_I/d\theta^2 = 0)$. Finally, the case when the $\varphi_{cr}(\theta)$ and $\varphi_I(\theta)$ curves have no common points (Figure 2-8c) corresponds to the uncritical process.

Three lines, characteristic to the investigation of the thermal region, are also drawn (dashed) for a clearer quantitative delimita- tion of these cases on the φ, θ diagram (Figure 2-7).

The first of these, with the equation

$$\varphi_{cr} = 1 - \theta \qquad (2\text{-}24)$$

corresponds to the limiting extinction conditions as $\theta_0 \to 0$. This line is the asymptote of all the right branches of the curves of the critical values of $\varphi_{cr}(\theta)$; critical phenomena to its right on the φ, θ diagram are impossible.

The second line, with the equation

$$\varphi_{max} = 1 - 2\theta \qquad (2\text{-}25)$$

passes through the maximum values of critical completeness of combustion (in the extinction region (see below)). Actually, we have from (2-23)

$$\frac{d\varphi_{cr}}{d\theta} = \frac{2(\theta - \theta_0) - \theta^2}{(\theta - \theta_0)^2} = 0$$

or

$$\theta = 2\theta_0; \quad \theta_0 = \theta/2$$

from which[15]

$$\varphi_{cr,\,max} = 1 - 2\theta = 1 - 4\theta_0 \qquad (2\text{-}25')$$

[15]This equation can be obtained from (2-23) if it is solved for $\theta:\vartheta$

$$\theta^2 - (1 - \varphi)\theta + (1 - \varphi)\theta_0 = 0$$

from which

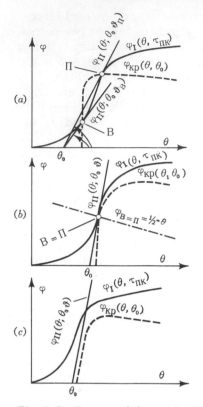

Fig. 2-8. Curves of the critical values in the φ, θ diagram (τ_{sK} and θ_0 parameters). (a) Hysteresis process; (b) boundary case of ignition and extinction coincidence; (c) uncritical process.

Finally, the third, most interesting line with the equation

$$\varphi_{I=E} = 1/2 - \theta \qquad (2\text{-}26)$$

passes through points of the curves $\varphi_{cr}(\theta)$ in which the critical ignition and extinction conditions coincide. Formula (2-26) is obtained most simply from the condition for an inflection of the $\varphi_I(\theta)$ curves, i.e., the limiting condition for the coincidence of the points of tangency in the lower and upper branches of these curves. We have from Eq. (2-14)

$$\varphi_I \theta = 1/(1 + e^{1/\theta}/\tau_{sK})$$

$$\frac{d\varphi_I}{d\theta} = \frac{e^{1/\theta}/\tau_{sK}}{\theta^2(1 + e^{1/\theta}/\tau_{sK})^2}$$

$$= (1 - \varphi)\varphi/\theta^2$$

$$\frac{d^2\varphi}{d\theta^2}$$

$$= \frac{(1-2\varphi)\theta\,\dfrac{d\varphi}{d\theta} - 2(1-\varphi)\theta\varphi}{\theta^2}$$

Substituting the value of $d\varphi_I/d\theta$ in the last expression and equating to zero, we obtain (2-26) after simple manipulation.

Equating Eqs. (2-23) and (2-26)

$$1 - \frac{\theta^2}{\theta - \theta_0} = \frac{1}{2} - \theta$$

we obtain an expression relating the values θ and θ_0 when ignition and extinction coincide:

$$\theta_{cr} = (1 - \varphi)/2 \pm 1/2\sqrt{(1 - \varphi)^2 - 4(1 - \varphi)\theta_0}$$

Evidently, the unique value $\theta_{cr} = (1 - \varphi)/2$; $\varphi_{cr\,max} = 1-2\theta$; corresponds to the maximum of the $\varphi_{cr}(\theta)$ curve; equating the radicand to zero taking (2-25) into account, we also obtain the equalities: $\theta = 2\theta_0$; $\varphi_{cr\,max} = 1-4\theta_0$ (2-25′).

$$\theta_{I=E} = \theta_0/(1 - 2\theta_0); \quad \theta_{0,\, I=E} = \theta/(1 + 2\theta) \qquad (2\text{-}27)$$

The line (2-26) of coincidence of the ignition and extinction conditions and the limiting line (2-24) divide the φ, θ diagram (Figure 2-9) into three regions: the ignition region 1, extinction region 2, jointly composing the hysteresis region and the region of absence of critical conditions (region of the uncritical process) 3. The numerical values characterizing the boundaries of these regions are easily obtained from the formulas cited. Thus, for example, the ignition region is bounded by the values of the temperature $0 \leqslant \theta_I \leqslant 0.5$, completeness of combustion $0 \leqslant \varphi_I \leqslant 0.5$, and the initial temperature from (2-27) $0 \leqslant \theta_{0I} \leqslant 0.25$. Correspondingly, we have for the extinction region: $0 \leqslant \theta_E \leqslant 1$, $0 \leqslant \varphi_E \leqslant 1$, and, as for ignition, $0 \leqslant \theta_{0I} \leqslant 0.25$. Although the upper (limiting) values of the temperature lie above the practical region encountered in furnace processes, the demarcation of the $\theta\varphi$ diagram itself is of undoubted interest, in principle, for the adiabatic case; the influence of heat loss thereon will be shown later (Chapter 4), which considerably diminishes the region for the existence of a hysteresis process (in particular, for strong radiation).

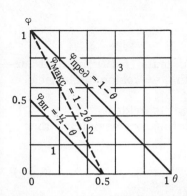

Fig. 2-9. Characteristic regions of the combustion process in the φ, θ diagram. 1—Ignition; 2—extinction (hysteresis) process; 3—uncritical process.

The line (2-26) divides each of the curves of the critical values $\varphi_{cr}(\theta)$, given by (2-23), into two branches; ignition and extinction. As is seen from Figure 2-7, the ignition temperature varies very slightly (for $\theta_0 = $ const) in each case in the range of low values of the initial temperature and remains comparatively close to the value θ_0. On the contrary, the extinction temperature (under the same condition, $\theta_0 = $ const) varies within comparatively broad limits (Figure 2-7).

It follows from (2-23) in the limiting case of $\varphi_{cr} = 0$, i.e., burnout being neglected

$$1 - \theta^2/(\theta - \theta_0) = 0; \quad \theta^2 - \theta + \theta_0 = 0$$

from which

$$\theta_{cr,\, \varphi = 0} = \frac{1 \pm \sqrt{1 - 4\theta_0}}{2} \qquad (2\text{-}28)$$

The minus sign corresponds to ignition, the plus to extinction. In the first case, (2-28) yields

$$\theta_{I,\,\varphi=0} = \frac{1 - \sqrt{1 - 4\theta_0}}{2} \tag{2-29}$$

or in dimensional form

$$T_{I,\,\varphi=0} = \frac{E}{2R}(1 - \sqrt{1 - 4RT_0/E}) \tag{2-29'}$$

that is, in agreement with the Semenov formula (1-19) obtained during the solution of the problem of a thermal explosion neglecting burning up of the combustible mixture.

The physical meaning of this agreement is evident.

The second root of (2-28) yields a limiting expression for the extinction temperature

$$\theta_{E,\,\varphi=0} = \frac{1 + \sqrt{1 - 4\theta_0}}{2} \tag{2-30}$$

which again agrees with the second root of the Semenov formula, discarded previously from physical considerations. This value has the meaning of a theoretical limit corresponding to neglecting burnout, or an unlimited increase in the heat production of the mixture. Its meaning, as that of (2-29), becomes clearer later when a transformation is made to the $\theta_{cr} = \theta(\theta_0; \vartheta)$ coordinate system.

Now let us turn to a derivation of the relations between the critical values of the other variables. Let us first add curves of the constant critical values of the mixture heat production ($\vartheta_{cr} = $ const) to the φ, θ diagram. Replacing

$$\theta - \theta_0 = \varphi\vartheta$$

from (2-13) in the equality

$$1 - \theta^2/(\theta - \theta_0) = (\theta - \theta_0)/\vartheta$$

we obtain

$$\vartheta_{cr} = \theta^2/\varphi(1 - \varphi) \tag{2-31}$$

The curves $\vartheta_{cr} = $ const constructed by using this formula are shown in the φ, θ diagram on Figure 2-10. They are parabolas, symmetrical about the line $\varphi = 0.5$ and convex toward the increasing temperature side. Different cases of the intersection of the $\vartheta_{cr} = $ const curves (2-31) with the $\tau_{sK} = $ const curves (2-14) are shown on Figure 2-10, just as on Figure 2-8. The vertical axis ($\theta_{cr} = 0$) and the lines $\varphi_{cr} = 0$ (horizontal axis[16]) and $\varphi_{cr} = 1$ correspond to the limiting cases $\vartheta_{cr} = 0$ and $\vartheta_{cr} = \infty$, respectively.

[16]Here again there is agreement with the Semenov formula (1-19).

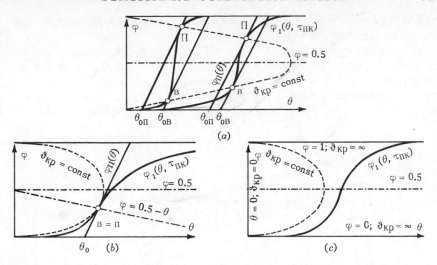

Fig. 2-10. Curves of the critical values in the φ, θ diagram (τ_{sK} and ϑ are parameters). (a) Hysteresis process; (b) boundary case of coincidence of ignition and extinction; (c) uncritical process.

Let us also derive the expression $\theta_{cr} = \theta(\theta_0; \vartheta)$ which relates the critical value of the temperature to the parameters θ_0 and ϑ. To do this, let us again use the equality of the expressions (2-14) and (2-23):

$$1 - \theta^2/(\theta - \theta_0) = (\theta - \theta_0)/\vartheta$$

which, after manipulation transforms into a quadratic equation in θ_{cr}:

$$(1 + \vartheta)\theta^2 - (\vartheta + 2\theta_0)\theta + (\vartheta + \theta_0)\theta_0 = 0$$

There follows from the latter that

$$\theta_{cr} = \frac{1 + \dfrac{2\theta_0}{\vartheta} \pm \sqrt{1 - 4\theta_0 - 4\theta_0{}^2/\vartheta}}{2(1 + 1/\vartheta)} \tag{2-32}$$

As before, the minus sign before the radical corresponds to ignition and the plus to extinction. Equation (2-32) again transforms into the formula of Semenov (1-19) as

$$\theta_{cr,\vartheta \to \infty} = \frac{1}{2} \pm \frac{\sqrt{1 - 4\theta_0}}{2}$$

Actually, neglecting the burnout is physically equivalent to the assumption of infinitely large mixture heat production since only infinitely large heat production of the mixture (or its specific heat equal to zero) in combination with zero completeness of combustion can yield finite heat liberation during the reaction and a finite temperature increase, respectively (7).

A detailed diagram of the critical ignition and extinction conditions constructed in the θ, θ_0 coordinates by using (2-32) is given on Figure 2-11. The values ϑ_{cr} = const, $\tau_{sK_{cr}}$ = const, and φ_{cr} = const are the parameters for the different curves. The last two families of curves are plotted on Figure 2-11 for greater clarity.

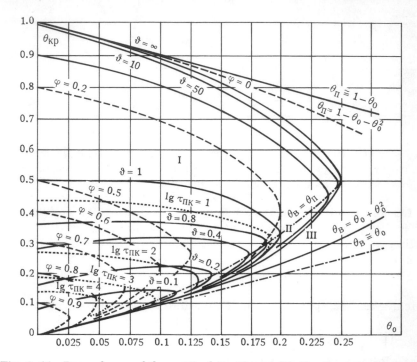

Fig. 2-11. Dependence of the critical ignition and extinction temperature on the initial mixture temperature. I—Extinction; II—ignition (region of the hysteresis process); III—region of the uncritical process; solid line ϑ_{cr} = const; dashed line φ_{cr} = const; dotted line $\tau_{sK\ cr}$ = const; dashed and dotted line, curve of ignition and extinction coincidence.

It is seen from this diagram that the region of the hysteresis process ("ignition and extinction peninsulas") is bounded by the curve (2-28), i.e., by the values $\varphi_{cr} = 0$; $\vartheta_{cr} = \infty$. The lower branch of this curve corresponds to the Semenov formula (1-19). The curve, drawn by using the formula $\theta_{I=E} = \theta_0/(1 - 2\theta_0)$ divides the region of the critical phenomena into two unequal sections, ignition and extinction, the first of which (lower on Figure 2-11) is always bounded and the second (upper) is considerably more broad. The diagram on Figure 2-11 includes the whole range of critical values of the variables possible in principle; in practice, only its lower section is of interest, approximately up to $\theta_{cr} = 0.5$. It is essential that the boundary of the region of the hysteresis process, curve (2-28), be independent of the kind of dependence of the reaction rate on the concentration.

Beyond the region bounded by the curve (2-28), the critical values of the ignition and extinction are absent. Curves of the approximate values obtained by expanding (2-28) into series are also plotted on Figure 2-11 for comparison. For ignition these are lines corresponding to (1-20) $\theta_{I\,min} = \theta_0$ and (1-21) $\theta_{I\,min} = \theta_0 + \theta_0^2$ (section 1-4[17]); for extinction, similar approximations yield: $\theta_{E\,max} \approx 1 - \theta_0$ (first) and $\theta_{E\,max} \approx 1 - \theta_0 - \theta_0^2$ (second).

The relations and graphs considered up to now did not contain the critical stay time τ_{sK} in explicit form; however, an investigation of the influence of this quantity on the critical ignition and extinction conditions is of considerable interest. We obtain from equations (2-14) and (2-23)

$$\tau_{sK}/(\tau_{sK} + e^{1/\theta}) = 1 - \theta^2/(\theta - \theta_0)$$

from which

$$\tau_{sK\,cr} = \frac{\theta - \theta_0 - \theta^2}{\theta^2} \cdot e^{1/\theta} \tag{2-33}$$

Similarly, the condition of coincidence of ignition and extinction from the equality of expressions (2-13) and (2-16)

$$\tau_{sK}/(\tau_{sK} + e^{1/\theta}) = 1/2 - \theta$$

is

$$\tau_{sK,\,I\,=\,E} = \frac{1 - 2\theta}{1 + 2\theta} e^{1/\theta} \tag{2-34}$$

Finally, from the equality of expressions (2-13) and (2-24)

$$\tau_{sK}/(\tau_{sK} + e^{1/\theta}) = 1 - \theta$$

we obtain the equation of the limiting curve which divides the regions of the hysteresis and uncritical processes in the diagram, $\theta_{cr} = \tau_{sK\,cr}$, as

[17]Let us note that the second approximation for the minimum ignition temperature agrees with the Frank-Kamenetskii formula, obtained by expanding the exponential in the expression for the reaction rate in a power series in the difference $(T - T_0)$ (44). A more detailed comparison and also approximate formulas to compute the extinction temperature, which are suitable for the range of temperature values of practical interest will be given below (section 3-3).

$$\tau_{sK \; \text{lim}} = \frac{1 - \theta}{\theta} e^{1/\theta} \tag{2-35}$$

The dependence $\theta_{\text{cr}} = \theta(\theta_0; \tau_{sK})$, according to (2-33), is given on Figure 2-12 for three values of the parameter θ_0. In conformance with the results presented earlier, this graph shows that the ignition temperature varies slightly in a wide range of τ_{sK} values in practice, while the extinction temperature rises sharply as the stay time diminishes. Physically, this means that collapse of the combustion process occurs at a higher temperature in shorter or more heavily loaded chambers (smaller τ_{sK} values) than in a longer (lower output) chamber.

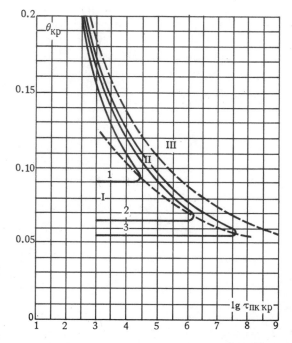

Fig. 2-12. Dependence of ignition and extinction temperatures on the stay time. I—Ignition; II—extinction (hysteresis process region); III—uncritical process region; solid line $\theta_{\text{cr}} = \theta(\tau_{sK}; \theta_0)$; dashed line, critical boundary; dashed and dotted line, ignition and extinction coincidence; 1—for $\theta_0 = 0.08$; 2—for $\theta_0 = 0.06$; 3—for $\theta_0 = 0.05$.

Given on Figure 2-13 is the dependence of the critical values of the ignition and extinction times on the other two parameters of the process, the initial mixture temperature and its heat productivity.[18] This graph, therefore, does not contain the quantities θ_{cr} and φ_{cr} which are the result of relations combined in the process but it relates the critical values of all three "external" parameters τ_{sK}, θ_0, and ϑ.

[18]The curves $\tau_{sK \; \text{cr}} = \tau(\theta_0; \vartheta)$ are constructed by using the parametric equations $\tau_{sK \; \text{cr}} = \tau(\theta; \theta_0)$ of formula (2-23) and $\theta_{\text{cr}} = \theta(\theta_0; \vartheta)$ of formula (2-32) and by eliminating the value θ_{cr}.

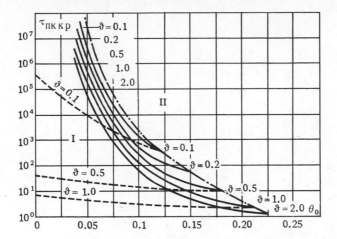

Fig. 2-13. Dependence of the critical ignition and extinction time on the initial mixture temperature and heat productivity. I—region of hysteresis process; II—region of uncritical process; solid line, ignition; dashed line, extinction; dashed and dotted line, coincidence of ignition and extinction.

Let us note that the quantity $\tau_{sK,\,I}$ has the meaning of the so-called ignition lag (or "induction period") in the stationary ignition theory for the ignition phenomenon. As is seen from Figure 2-13, the magnitude of $\tau_{sK,\,I}$ drops very sharply as the initial temperature θ_0 or the mixture heat productivity (the parameter on Figure 2-13) increases. The critical extinction time $\tau_{sK,\,E}$ depends considerably more weakly on the magnitude of θ_0 (it should be kept in mind that Figure 2-13 is constructed in semilogarithmic coordinates: $\log \tau_{sK,\,E} = \tau(\theta_0, \vartheta)$).

In conclusion, all the formulas for the critical values of the variables are presented in Table 2-1 for convenience of later use.

Similarly, expressions of all the variables corresponding to the limits of the regions of the hysteresis and uncritical processes, i.e., ignition and extinction coincidence, are presented in Table 2-2.

The expressions presented in Tables 2-1 and 2-2 (the latter are supplemented by the formula (2-34): $\tau_{sK,\,I\,=\,E} = (1 - 2\theta)/(1 + 2\theta)$ $\exp(1/\theta)$ for the transition to the parameter τ_{sK}) refer to the adiabatic combustion of a well-mixed mixture. They will be used later for a comparison with similar formulas for other more complex cases. In one of them, in the heterogeneous process (coal combustion), in the simplest case of heat emission by convection alone, all the formulas and relations obtained in this paragraph are retained without variation. In other cases, although there will not be exact agreement, the critical conditions will always correspond to the

Table 2-1. Critical Values of the Variables for Ignition and Extinction

	$\theta;\ \theta_0$	$\theta,\ \tau_{sK}$	$\theta;\ \vartheta$	$\theta;\ \varphi$
φ_{cr}	$1 - \dfrac{\theta^2}{\theta - \theta_0}$	$\dfrac{\tau_{sK}}{\tau_{sK} + e^{1/\theta}}$	$\dfrac{1}{2}\left(1 \pm \sqrt{1 - \dfrac{4\theta^2}{\vartheta}}\right)$	
$\theta_{0,\,cr}$		$\theta - \theta^2\left(1 + \dfrac{\tau_{sK}}{e^{1/\theta}}\right)$	$\theta - \dfrac{\vartheta}{2}\left(1 \pm \sqrt{1 - \dfrac{4\theta^2}{\vartheta}}\right)$	$\theta - \dfrac{\theta^2}{1 - \varphi}$
$\tau_{sK,\,cr}$	$\dfrac{\theta - \theta_0 - \theta^2}{\theta^2}\,e^{1/\theta}$		$e^{1/\theta}\left[\dfrac{\vartheta}{2\theta^2}\left(1 \pm \sqrt{1 - \dfrac{4\theta^2}{\vartheta}}\right) - 1\right]$	
ϑ_{cr}	$\dfrac{(\theta - \theta_0)^2}{\theta - \theta_0 - \theta^2}$	$\theta^2\,\dfrac{(e^{1/\theta} + \tau_{sK})^2}{\tau_{sK}\,e^{1/\theta}}$		$\dfrac{\theta^2}{\varphi(1 - \varphi)}$
θ_{cr}	$\varphi;\ \theta_0$ $\dfrac{1 - \varphi}{2}\left(1 \pm \sqrt{1 - \dfrac{4\theta_0}{1 - \varphi}}\right)$	$\varphi;\ \tau_{sK}$ $\dfrac{1}{\ln\left(\dfrac{1 - \varphi}{\varphi}\,\tau_{sK}\right)}$	$\varphi;\ \vartheta$ $\sqrt{\vartheta\,\varphi(1 - \varphi)}$	$\theta_0;\ \vartheta$ $\dfrac{1 + \dfrac{2\theta_0}{\vartheta} \pm \sqrt{1 - 4\theta_0 - \dfrac{4\theta_0^2}{\vartheta}}}{2\left(1 + \dfrac{1}{\vartheta}\right)}$

Table 2-2. Values of Variables for Coincidence of Ignition and Extinction

	φ	θ	θ_0	ϑ
$\varphi_{I=E}$		$\dfrac{1}{2} - \theta$	$\dfrac{1 - 4\theta_0}{2(1 - 2\theta_0)}$	$\dfrac{1}{2}\left(1 - \sqrt{\dfrac{\vartheta}{1 + \vartheta}}\right)$
$\theta_{I=E}$	$\dfrac{1}{2} - \varphi$		$\dfrac{\theta_0}{1 - 2\theta_0}$	$\dfrac{1}{2}\sqrt{\dfrac{\vartheta}{1 + \vartheta}}$
$\theta_{0,\,I=E}$	$\dfrac{1 - 2\varphi}{\varphi(1 - \varphi)}$	$\dfrac{\theta}{1 + 2\theta}$		$\dfrac{\vartheta}{2}\left(\sqrt{\dfrac{1 + \vartheta}{\vartheta}} - 1\right)$
$I = E$	$\dfrac{(1 - 2\varphi)^2}{4\varphi(1 - \varphi)}$	$\dfrac{4\theta^2}{1 - 4\theta^2}$	$\dfrac{4\theta_0^2}{1 - 4\theta_0}$	

formulas of Table 2-1 in order of magnitude. The question of the change in reaction rate will be considered below in section 3-3.

Chapter 3

Heterogeneous and Diffusional Combustion Concepts

3-1. BASIC REPRESENTATIONS OF THE HETEROGENEOUS PROCESS

The stationary theory of the adiabatic combustion of a well-mixed mixture analyzed in detail in the preceding chapter does not take into account two important aspects of the phenomenon. We mention, first, the influence of heat exchange and, second, that of those phenomena related to practical methods of supply of combustible mixture components; the fuel and air (oxidizer, in the general case) are usually unmixed at first. Leaving the first of these questions for a later chapter, let us consider the peculiarities induced in the thermal region of adiabatic combustion by the second, by partial or complete combination of the fuel distribution with the combustion process proper in the chamber. This problem is referred to as the so-called "diffusion theory" of combustion developed in the research of Soviet scientists in the last decade.

The diffusion theory achieved its greatest clarity in research on heterogeneous combustion, in particular, on the combustion of carbon (7, 13b, 25, 32, 40, 42, 50, etc.). Consequently, it is natural to consider precisely this most simple case of the combustion of unmixed components first, all the more so, since the most explicit scheme of the process results from this with a number of additional assumptions. As in the previous explanations, let us be limited to the very general properties of the phenomenon without analyzing the details of the heterogeneous reaction mechanism which are explained for example, for carbon combustion in the research of A. S. Predvoditelev and his colleagues (34) and in other work (25, 42, 50, etc.).

In particular, let us assume that only one combustion reaction occurs between the carbon and oxygen, that it occurs on the surface of the solid phase, and that it is of first order with respect to the concentration of oxygen. Let us also consider that the process is not accompanied by secondary reactions in the gaseous phase (combustion of carbon monoxide) or on the carbon surface (reduction of carbon dioxide). Hence, many questions essential to the theory of carbon combustion are evidently not taken into account (penetration of the reaction deep into the solid phase in the range of comparatively low temperatures, which was considered for porous bodies by Zel'dovich (20) in general form and by Khitrin (34) for coal combustion, the influence of the ashing of coal (8), the assumption, expressed by Frank-Kamenetskii, of the fractional order of the reaction of coal with oxygen (50, etc.).

Let us first recall the general elementary concepts of the diffusion theory of heterogeneous combustion (7, 34, 42, 50).

Outlining the combustion process in conformance with the above, let us isolate two basic component phenomena therefrom: delivery of the reacting gas to the surface of the solid phase and occurrence of the chemical reaction thereon.

The observed rate of the total combustion process will depend in the general case on the rates with which each of these phenomena can occur individually.

The rate of oxygen diffusion to the coal surface in the steady process naturally equals the rate of its reaction at the reacting surface, i.e., equals the total (observed) combustion rate calculated in terms of the gas. However, the possible ("potential") diffusion and reaction rates can differ radically. When one of the possible rates is considerably less than the other, the actual rate of the process (and also the actual rates of both component phenomena) practically agrees with the lesser of the possible rates of the individual phenomena, that which plays a decisive part in the whole combustion procedure.

Following the terminology successfully proposed by D. A. Frank-Kamenetskii (52) and used universally at the present time, let us call the combustion process "diffusion" [-controlled," Ed.] if the diffusion rate of the reacting gas is substantially less possible under these conditions and, therefore, the chemical reaction rate on the surface is not realized. We designate as "kinetic" [-controlled," Ed.] combustion the opposite limiting case of the process in which the slowest link determining the total rate is the course of the reaction and the high diffusion rate possible under these conditions is not realized.

Finally, we designate as an "intermediate" type of process the general case of combustion, with commensurable values of the diffusion and reaction rates (possible in the given arrangement of the progress of the process).

These representations of the limiting (diffusion and kinetic) regions of combustion and the general case (intermediate combustion region) have not only methodological but also practical value when applied to actual processes. In reality, the combustion progress, the character of the influence of the individual parameters, the methods of increasing the completeness of combustion or the intensification of the process, differ sharply for diffusion and kinetic combustion regions; they also differ in the intermediate region for a noticeable, although not predominant, surmounting of the role of one of the factors, diffusion rate or chemical reaction rate. Consequently the effectiveness of any kind of technological measures to improve the combustion process will always be related to a determination of the slowest phenomena retarding the total process.

The difference between diffusion and kinetic combustion is traced most easily by the example of the reaction of carbon with oxygen, although the basic considerations are applicable to other cases of the heterogeneous process (reactions on solid catalysts (5, 6, 49, 50)).

The progress of the steady process in the diffusion combustion region is defined principally by the hydrodynamic properties of the system. In particular, according to the convective diffusion law which practically agrees with the convective heat emission laws (33), two factors play a basic role: The relative velocity of the air flow and the size of the coal particles. An increase in the relative velocity of the air motion, or a decrease in the particle size, will lead to intensification of the oxygen diffusion to the coal surface.

Since the total process is limited in the diffusion region by the rate of oxygen supply to the surface, and the possible reaction rate on the latter is much higher than is realized in actuality (because of the oxygen insufficiency), the oxygen concentration on the surface is practically zero in diffusion combustion.

Naturally, the hydrodynamic factors do not influence the combustion rate in the kinetic combustion region, since there is always an oxygen surplus at the coal surface; any noticeable drop in the oxygen concentration at the coal surface is absent in this case. In contrast to the rate of diffusion combustion,[1] the rate of kinetic combustion depends highly exponentially on the temperature; the kinetic properties of the coal (the so-called "reaction capacity") can also affect the rate substantially in this case.

All the factors, hydrodynamic and kinetic, influence the total process in the general, intermediate combustion case; an increase in the velocity of the air or [fineness of, Ed.] grinding the coal increases the diffusion rate, raises its actual (realizable under given conditions) value near the possible maximum, and thus leads to a shift of the total process toward the kinetic region. In contrast, an increase in the temperature leads to a sharp increase in the chemical reaction rate and to a displacement of the total process toward diffusion combustion. It is natural that the general, intermediate

[1]The temperature influences only the value of the physical properties in diffusion combustion; consequently its role is small in comparison to [that for, Ed.] kinetic combustion.

combustion case is most prevalent. However, it can be assumed in a general way that diffusion combustion prevails at high temperatures, low air velocities, and large particle sizes; conversely, the role of kinetic combustion is particularly great in regions of low temperatures, high values of the relative air velocities, and very small particle sizes. It is clear that none of these factors, taken individually, can determine the character of the total process; only by analyzing all of them jointly while also taking into account the kinetic properties of the fuel (high "reaction capacity," predominance of diffusion; low, i.e., inert fuel, kinetic combustion region) can a correct conclusion be made on the actual character of the combustion progress.

The concepts of the diffusion theory of the heterogeneous combustion have received explicit confirmation in theoretical and experimental research of Soviet scientists, in particular, in investigations made under the simplest geometric and hydrodynamic arrangement (combustion of a carbon channel, particles, etc. (See 3, 4, 7, 8, 9, 24, 34, 36, 40, 42, and others.)). As a result, diffusion and kinetic phenomena could be successfully separated quantitatively in a number of cases and kinetic characteristics of the coal combustion reaction determined successfully (3, 8, 40, 42, 50).

However, the majority of these works and also the development of the above general considerations refer to the progress of the combustion reaction in a given or arbitrarily regulated arrangement.[2] Another formulation of the question, the explanation of the characteristic, stationary thermal levels of combustion inherent in the process itself and the transition conditions from one equilibrium state to another, is the major objective of this book. Similarly, the question of the influence of a change of any of the parameters (the air-blast velocity, say) on combustion in investigations of the thermal region of the process acquires another, deeper meaning than in the usual "static" investigation which assumes, say, that the combustion temperature is constant as the air-blast velocity varies, etc. We speak first of the precise explanation of the influence of various parameters, say the air-blast velocity, on the combustion temperature when investigating the thermal region. Despite this difference in the formulation of the problem, the use of the concepts and terminology borrowed from the diffusion theory of combustion to investigate the thermal region appears to be very fruitful. Let us illustrate this by the example of coal combustion.

[2]That is, with the possibility of an independent change of not only the process parameters but also of the combustion temperature which is a function of the rest of the variables in the general case.

The thermal region of carbon combustion was first investigated in 1939 by V. I. Blinov (4) and D. A. Frank-Kamenetskii (50, 51) and in more detail in later works developing the results of these authors. In particular, Frank-Kamenetskii (51) first indicated the relation between the critical coal ignition and extinction phenomena and the transition from the kinetic to the diffusion combustion region and conversely.

Let us consider the problem under the following assumptions which simplify the investigation.

First, let us be limited to an investigation of the thermal region of an isolated element of the coal surface without considering the distribution of the concentration, temperature, etc., in the furnace space at the beginning (for example, according to the layer depth or the volume of the coal-dust jet). Second, let us assume that the elimination of heat from the coal surface is performed solely by convection; in other words, let us consider that all the heat being liberated during combustion is absorbed by the combustion products and is eliminated thereto from the coal surface. Third, as already indicated, let us assume that there is only one reaction occurring between carbon and oxygen, that it occurs on the reagent surface, which is practically coincident with the coal surface, and that it is first order in the oxygen concentration.

The introduction of these assumptions substantially facilitates the investigation and permits writing for an appropriate choice of the variables, a system of relations identical to the system of relations in the problem of the adiabatic combustion of a well-mixed mixture (Chapter 2). The qualitative analogy between the critical phenomena in the combustion of a well-mixed mixture (in the jet or the chamber) and in heterogeneous combustion was mentioned repeatedly in the literature (13a, 13b, 50). However, these remarks[3] were mainly of a general nature while the mathematical apparatus for both problems and the final results of the solution remained uncorrelated. However, it is not difficult to establish a very simple physical analogy between the phenomena under consideration.

A reaction which progressed in a well-mixed mixture was considered in the previous chapter. A fresh mixture is presented to the chamber and, completely receiving all the heat liberated during combustion in the latter and being converted into a final mixture of

[3]For example, it was remarked that two critical regions are observed in both cases: ignition and extinction, that the critical values of firing during ignition and cooling during extinction were approximately the same during the combustion of a well-mixed mixture and in the heterogeneous process, etc.

combustion products and [some, Ed.] unburned initial components, its heat productivity and the relative stay time in the chamber were essential for [evaluating, Ed.] the progress of the process. The stationary values of the temperature and of the completeness of combustion as well as the critical ignition and extinction conditions were determined as a result of computation.

Exactly the same diagram of the process can be obtained if the usual reference of the combustion process to the solid phase (carbon) is rejected and all the reasoning applicable to a reacting gas (oxygen) is introduced. Actually, a reacting gas of a certain initial concentration arrives (diffuses) at the coal surface at which the gas combustion occurs. The mixture of combustion products and unburned gas being formed as a result of the reaction completely absorbs all the heat being liberated at the surface and eliminates it from the latter. As before, essential to [determination of, Ed.] the progress of the process are the initial values of the temperature and concentration of the reacting gas far from the surface, the gas heat productivity, and the relative diffusion time to the surface (i.e., the ratio of the diffusion time to the characteristic chemical reaction time). The assumption of purely convective heat elimination from the surface in this scheme is identical to the assumption of the adiabatic character of the process since all the heat being liberated, in the absence of other kinds of heat emission, transforms into the heat content of the reaction products. As before, the magnitude of the completeness of total combustion of the reacting gas, related to the gas concentration at the surface of the solid phase, is determined in addition to the combustion temperature in the computation. Since the order of the reaction in both cases is assumed to be identical ($n = 1$; this assumption is apparently reasonable for coal combustion (34, 42, 50)), the complete agreement of all the computational results becomes perfectly natural. As for the coal combustion characteristics, its surface temperature agrees with the final temperature of the reacting gas and the combustion rate is easily determined by a recalculation if the stoichiometric reaction equation is known. Let us also note that the scheme used of reducing the heterogeneous process to complete gas burn-up is also directly applicable to the investigation of the progress of gas reactions on a solid catalyst (for example, for the catalytic oxidation of hydrogen on platinum (5, 6, 50)). These introductory remarks permit all the results, formulas, and graphs obtained in the preceding chapter to be used in the problem of the thermal region of coal combustion with convective heat emission and all the attention to be concentrated on an analysis of the physical peculiarities of the heterogeneous process.

Let us visualize (Figure 3-1) a certain section of the reacting coal surface. Let the concentration of the reacting gas far from the surface be c_0 and the concentration on the surface itself, c, where $c_0 > c$.

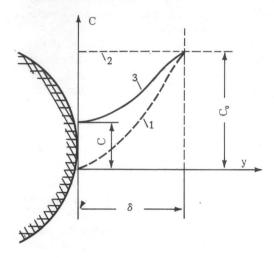

Fig. 3-1. Heterogeneous combustion scheme. Distribution of the reacting gas concentration in the boundary layer. 1—Diffusion combustion; 2—kinetic combustion; 3—intermediate case.

For simplicity of calculation, let us refer the equation of stationary heat balance to unit reaction surface. To do this, let us first write the expression for the quantity of heat being liberated per unit time per unit surface separately:

$$Q_{\rm I} = \alpha_D (c_0 - c)\, q = k_0\, e^{-E/RT} c \cdot q \qquad (3\text{-}1)$$

where α_D is a quantity similar to the convective heat transfer coefficient and which we shall designate as the diffusion-exchange coefficient or, briefly, coefficient of gas transport;[4] k_0 is the heterogeneous reaction constant whose dimensionality for a first-order reaction (just as the coefficient α_D) agrees with the dimensionality of a linear velocity (m/sec); q is the heat effect of the reaction, referred to unit volume of reacting gas; the remaining quantities have the same meanings as before.

Let us note that for the heterogeneous process, in particular for coal combustion, the quantities k_0 and E in the Arrhenius equation $(k = k_0 \exp(-E/RT))$ have the meaning of reduced, total kinetic reaction characteristics. As before, let us consider them as certain constants subject to experimental determination which do not reflect the actual reaction mechanism but are sometimes very com-

[4]The designation "diffusion-rate constant" encountered in the literature (50) corresponds less to the physical sense of the coefficient α_D since the latter, just as the heat transfer coefficient α, is introduced for convenience of computation and depends on a large number of factors.

plex (32). Results of a considerable number of experimental investigations (34, 40, 42) are known for the carbon combustion reaction, in which the quantities k_0 and E have been determined to the same degree of accuracy for different kinds of coal; there are also attempts to extend these results (8, 42, and 50).

The experimental values of the constants k_0 and E obtained in these investigations, in particular the detailed characteristics cited in the monograph of A. S. Predvoditelev (34) can be used for the approximate engineering computations of coal combustion (coke). Consequently the relations cited earlier for heterogeneous combustion have quantitative as well as qualitative value.

The quantity of heat eliminated per unit coal surface per unit time we shall write as

$$Q_{II} = \alpha(T - T_0) \tag{3-2}$$

where α (kcal/m² sec deg) is the convection heat transfer coefficient; T and T_0 are the respective gas temperatures directly at the coal surface and far removed.

The first of these values (T) naturally agrees with the temperature of the coal surface.

Equating (3-1) and (3-2), we obtain the stationary heat-balance equation

$$\alpha_D(c_0 - c)q = k_0 e^{-E/RT} cq = \alpha(T - T_0) \tag{3-3}$$

As before, let us introduce the coefficient of completeness of the burn-up of the reacting gas:

$$\varphi = 1 - \bar{c} = 1 - c/c_0 \tag{3-4}$$

where $\bar{c} = c/c_0$ is the nondimensional concentration of the reacting gas.

Let us note that the quantity φ can be given an additional physical interpretation (7) in the heterogeneous process. By definition, the concentration of the reacting gas at the coal surface equals zero in the diffusion combustion region

$$\bar{c} = 0; \quad \varphi = 1.0 \tag{3-5}$$

In this case, the rate of gas diffusion to the coal surface (proportional to the rate of coal burn-up from unit surface) will evidently equal the product $\alpha_D c_0$. Correspondingly, the value

$$\varphi = 1 - c/c_0 = (\alpha_D(c_0 - c)/\alpha_D c_0) \tag{3-6}$$

characterizes the degree of approximation of the process to the diffusion combustion region ("measure of diffusivity"). [A measure of relative diffusional resistance, Ed.]

The expression (3-6) can be given still another form convenient for practical computations. Noting that its numerator $\alpha_D(c_0 - c)$ is the rate of combustion referred to unit reacting surface, let us introduce an additional equality to determine the quantity of heat being liberated per unit surface per unit time:

$$Q_I = \alpha_D(c_0 - c)q = kcq = k_{eff} \cdot c_0 q \qquad (3\text{-}1')$$

where

$$k_{eff} = \cfrac{1}{\cfrac{1}{\alpha_D} + \cfrac{1}{k}} = \cfrac{1}{\cfrac{1}{\alpha_D} + \cfrac{e^{-E/RT}}{k_0}} \qquad (3\text{-}7)$$

is the reduced (effective) first-order reaction-rate constant (9, 50) [and q is the heat of reaction per unit concentration of oxygen, Ed.]. Hence, it follows from (3-6)

$$\varphi = k_{eff}/\alpha_D \qquad (3\text{-}6')$$

that is, the coefficient of completeness of combustion equals the ratio of the reduced reaction-rate constant k_{eff} to the gas transport coefficient α_D. The expression (3-7) will be used in a computational example in section 5-2. In its physical meaning, such a method of computation is analogous to the addition of "resistances" in a series circuit; the quantity $1/\alpha_D$ corresponds to the diffusion resistance, $1/k$ to the kinetic, and the total resistance is $1/k_{eff} = (1/\alpha_D) + (1/k)$. From the first equality in the system (3-3), which expresses the heat-liberation rate during the reaction in two ways,

$$\varphi_I = \cfrac{1}{1 + \cfrac{e^{1/\theta}}{k_0/\alpha_D}} \qquad (3\text{-}8)$$

The nondimensional ratio of the quantities characterizing the reaction and diffusion rates k_0/α_D can be replaced by the reciprocal ratio characteristic of the times for these processes, i.e., we can put

$$\tau_{DK} = \tau_D/\tau_K = k_0/\alpha_D \qquad (3\text{-}9)$$

where τ_D and τ_K are, respectively, quantities characterizing the time required for gas diffusion to the reacting surface and the time for the chemical reaction to progress on the latter.[5] Hence, (3-8) rewritten taking (3-9) into account as

$$\varphi_I = \frac{1}{1 + \dfrac{e^{1/\theta}}{\tau_{DK}}} = \frac{\tau_{DK}}{\tau_{DK} + e^{1/\theta}} \tag{3-10}$$

agrees with (2-14) for $\varphi_I(\theta)$ in the preceding chapter, when the nondimensional time τ_{SK} is replaced by the nondimensional time τ_{DK} (i.e., when the stay time is replaced by the diffusion time τ_D).

Now let us turn to the equality of the first and third expressions in the system (3-3), i.e., to the derivation of an expression for $\varphi_{II}(\theta)$ for the heat elimination. Taking (3-4) into account, we have from (3-3)

$$\varphi_{II} = \frac{\alpha}{\alpha_D \cdot q c_0}(T - T_0) = \frac{E\alpha}{Rq c_0 \alpha_D}(\theta - \theta_0) \tag{3-11}$$

Hence, the expression $\varphi_{II}(\theta)$ here corresponds to a line in the $\varphi - \theta$ diagram, which is completely in accord with the convective heat transfer law used (i.e., the adiabatic region of the progress of the process for the reacting gas).

Let us consider the ratio of the coefficients α/α_D in the right side of (3-11) in more detail.

Let us write the empirical relation between the similarity criteria for forced convection which is usual in heat transmission (33) for the heat transfer coefficient α

$$\frac{\alpha d}{\lambda} = C\left(\frac{wd}{\nu}\right)^n \left(\frac{\nu}{a}\right)^m \tag{3-12}$$

where d is the characteristic dimension; λ, ν, and a are, respectively, the heat conductivity, kinematic viscosity, and the thermal diffusivity of the gas; w is the relative gas flow velocity.

Similarly we can take for the gas transfer coefficient α_D:

$$\frac{\alpha_D d}{D} = C\left(\frac{wd}{\nu}\right)^n \left(\frac{\nu}{D}\right)^m \tag{3-12'}$$

where, in addition to the above, D is the [molecular, Ed.] diffusion coefficient.

[5]The time $\tau \approx l/w$. The same length scale l, the boundary-layer thickness or the characteristic particle size, say, is introduced for both characteristic process rates (k_0 and α_D) upon transformation to the characteristic time. In this connection, (3-7) can be given another form if the total effective time is introduced

$$\tau_{eff} = l/k_{eff}; \; \tau_{eff} \neq \tau_D + \tau'_K = \tau_D + \tau_K e^{1/\theta} \tag{3-7'}$$

The characteristic times of the phenomenon components are summed in a "series connection" (exactly as are individual "resistances" (50)).

Since both phenomena, heat exchange and gas exchange during combustion, occur under the conditions of the very same process and the forced heat transfer and forced diffusion phenomena are analogous (50), the values of the empirical constants C, n, and m in (3-12) and (3-12') can be taken as practically identical. In this case, we obtain

$$\frac{\alpha}{\alpha_D} = \frac{\lambda}{D}\left(\frac{D}{a}\right)^m \approx c_p\left(\frac{a}{D}\right)^{1-m} \tag{3-13}$$

where c_p is the average specific heat per m³ of gas. As is known from heat transmission (33), the value of the exponent m in (3-12) is small for forced convection ($m = 0.3 - 0.4$); consequently, taking into account the equality $a \approx D$ for gases,[6] it can be assumed approximately that $(a/D)^{1-m} \approx 1$.

Hence, approximately

$$(\alpha/\alpha_D) \approx c_p \tag{3-14}$$

this expression allows (3-11) for $\varphi_{II}(\theta)$ to be rewritten in a form identical to (2-13)

$$\varphi_{II} = (\theta - \theta_0)/\vartheta \tag{3-15}$$

where, as before, $\vartheta = Rqc_0/Ec_p$ is the characteristic heat productivity of the reaction (or the oxygen content in the reacting gas, say).

As in the adiabatic combustion of a well-mixed mixture (Chapter 2), (3-15) can be rewritten as

$$\varphi_0 = \frac{\theta - \theta_0}{\theta_m - \theta_0} ; \quad \theta_m = \theta_0 + \vartheta \tag{3-15'}$$

It is essential that the similarity of the temperature and concentration fields, Eq. (3-15') should here be a consequence not only of the adiabaticity of the process but also of the equality of the transport coefficients: $a = D$. The case $a \neq D$ will be considered below (see section 6-4). Let us review briefly. Both expressions for the curves in the $\varphi - \theta$ diagram, namely, the heat-liberation curve $\varphi_I(\theta)$, Eq. (3-10), and the heat-elimination curve $\varphi_{II}(\theta)$, Eq. (3-15), agree with the analogous expressions used in the preceding chapter. The difference between (3-10), for the heterogeneous process, and (2-14) for the combustion of a well-mixed mixture, reduces to the quantity τ_D, the characteristic diffusion time, being

_____

[6]For an ideal gas, $a = D$; for real gases with similar properties, say diatomic gases excepting hydrogen, the values of a and D are very close. The relation $a = D$ for gases is violated if, and only if, a gas which is radically different from all the others is in the mixture (for example considerably lighter, as hydrogen). For details, see (13a, 28, 50).

introduced into the first, and τ_s, the mixture stay time in the chamber, into the second as a ratio to the characteristic reaction time τ_K in both cases. It will be shown later that this difference leads to different physical interpretations of the critical ignition and extinction phenomena depending on the nondimensional time.

In order to look for the stationary regions of the process, as in the preceding chapter, we start from the equality

$$\varphi_I(\theta) = \varphi_{II}(\theta) \tag{3-16}$$

and determine the critical ignition and extinction conditions from the system of equations

$$\varphi_I(\theta) = \varphi_{II}(\theta)$$

$$\frac{d\varphi_I}{d\theta} = \frac{d\varphi_{II}}{d\theta} \tag{3-17}$$

Now let us turn directly to an interpretation of the results obtained in Chapter 2 as applied to the heterogeneous process.

3-2. THERMAL REGION OF COAL COMBUSTION

Let us apply, briefly, the fundamental results of the investigation of the thermal region of the adiabatic combustion of a well-mixed mixture to the problem of the coal combustion region. As was shown in the previous chapter, the graphical solution of the heat-balance equation, in conformance with the different conditions of the $\varphi_I(\theta)$ and $\varphi_{II}(\theta)$ curves intersecting in the $\varphi - \theta$ diagram, leads to the possibility of the existence of two kinds of processes, hysteresis and uncritical. Three stationary reaction states are typical for the first, of which two, the lowest and the highest, are stable and the middle is unstable and not realized in practice. The lowest stationary region corresponds to slight heating of the coal surface and very slow reaction; this region is slow oxidation substantially. The highest region is characterized by high completeness of combustion of the reacting gas whose concentration, c, at the coal surface is very small, and rapid combustion of the coal; in substance, this is the combustion region.

The temperature of the coal surface during combustion (upper region) is almost a maximum[7]

$$T_{\max} = T_0 + qc_0/c_p; \quad \theta_n = \theta_0 + \vartheta$$

[7]The coal temperature for $a \neq D$ can be greater or less than the quantity $T_{\max} = T_0 + (qc_0/c_p)$. See (5, 6) for details on the temperature of the solid phase surface, taking the inequality $a \neq D$, the influence of the change in the number of moles during the reaction, thermal diffusion, etc., into account.

The circumstance that the concentration gradient in the reacting gas is practically zero (its concentration on the surface is almost the value far removed from the surface) permits this region to be identified with kinetic combustion. Intense diffusion is lacking here and the process as a whole is determined by the temperature and kinetic characteristics of the fuel.

In contrast, the upper region, the combustion region, is close to diffusion combustion (gas concentration zero on the surface) or to intermediate combustion in the range of low values of the parameter τ_{DK}. The finiteness of the value of the nondimensional time τ_{DK} also limits the growth of the heat-liberation curve $\varphi_I(\theta)$ here as the temperature increases without limit

$$\varphi_{I(\theta \to \infty)} \to \frac{1}{1+\tau_{KD}}; \quad \tau_{KD} = \frac{1}{\tau_{DK}} = \frac{\tau_K}{\tau_D}$$

Here again, the progress of the process does not depend on one of the nondimensional quantities τ_D or τ_K (i.e., on α_D and k_0) but on their ratio $\tau_{DK} = k_0/\alpha_D$. The completeness of gas burn-up $\varphi \to 1$ as $\tau_{DK} \to \infty$ (i.e., $\alpha_D \to 0$; $\tau_D \to \infty$ or $k_0 \to \infty$; $\tau_K \to 0$); $\varphi \to 0$ for $\tau_{DK} \to 0$ (i.e., as $\alpha_D \to \infty$; $\tau_D \to 0$ or $k_0 \to 0$; $\tau_K \to \infty$).

These relations permit the critical coal ignition and extinction phenomena to be explained otherwise, in the light of the diffusion combustion theory.[8] The first, ignition, represents the transition from the kinetic into the diffusion region (into the intermediate, in the general case). The second, extinction, corresponds to the transition to the kinetic process (oxidation). It is extremely important that ignition always occurs, in practice, in the kinetic region in which the role of diffusion is negligibly small. In its turn, extinction always is realized in the intermediate (sometimes close to the kinetic) region. The critical phenomena of ignition and extinction are missing in the diffusion region (limiting case $\bar{c} = 0$; $\varphi = 1$). Hence the ignition and extinction phenomena are always continuously related to the kinetic process, to the real chemical reaction rate; the first occurs in the kinetic region, the second in the intermediate region for commensurable values of the diffusion and chemical reaction rates (or times). Consequently, the elimination of the reaction rate from the considerations used in many works (by assuming it to be infinite $\tau_K' \to 0$) permits the peculiarities of stationary combustion to be investigated approximately, which is especially convenient in solving spatial (two- or three-dimensional) problems.

[8] As was mentioned already, the relation between the critical phenomena and the limiting regions of the process was first indicated by Frank-Kamenetskii (51) in connection with a discussion of the Chukhanov, Grodzovskii (40) experiments on the high-speed gasification of coal.

However, in principle, the results obtained under the assumption $\tau'_K = 0$ cannot contain any information on the critical combustion regions, in particular on the collapse conditions (extinction). This important conclusion has a very general character and is not limited to questions of coal combustion. Later it will be encountered many times.

Now, let us trace the variation in the stationary values of φ and θ in particular, beyond the critical ignition and extinction conditions as the parameters θ_0, ϑ, and τ_{DK} vary. The influence of the variation in the first two parameters, the reacting gas temperature far from the surface and the heat productivity characteristic (or gas composition), on the process is in no way different from the influence of θ_0 and ϑ considered earlier on the combustion process of a well-mixed mixture (Figures 2-3, 2-4); an increase in the value of the temperature θ_0 and the heat productivity ϑ leads to ignition, and a decrease to extinction, where the characteristic hysteresis combustion inertia occurs under the conditions of an "exothermal" process, which is reflected by the inequalities

$$\theta_I < \theta_E; \quad \varphi_I < \varphi_E$$

$$\theta_{0I} > \theta_{0E}; \quad \vartheta_{0I} > \vartheta_{0E}$$

An uncritical process is also possible in addition to the hysteresis process, as was shown on the same graphs. As regards the physical nature of the variation of the parameters θ_0 and ϑ, everything that referred to the θ_0 parameter in the problem of the combustion of a well-mixed mixture remains valid for the first, the gas temperature [θ_0, Ed.] far from the solid phase surface. It is not at all the same situation in the case of the second, the characteristic heat productivity ϑ. In the case under consideration, of a heterogeneous combustion process progressing on an isolated element of the coal surface, the value of ϑ is not related to the general coefficient of excess air in the chamber. In this process, a change in the heat productivity corresponds to a change in the oxygen content in the reacting gas (because of a change in the content of inert impurities), say, or to a change in the heat-producing capacity of the coal itself.

The influence of the magnitude of the nondimensional time $\tau_{DK} = k_0/\alpha_D$ (3-9) merits more detailed discussion. Without analyzing the case of the variation of the kinetic constant k_0, which is of slight interest in the total plan (for example, the comparison of the process for coals of different activity or different catalysts for heterogeneous catalysis), let us dwell on the change in the gas transfer coefficient α_D.

We have from (3-13)

$$\alpha_D = \left(\frac{\alpha_D d}{D}\right) \cdot \frac{D}{d} = C\left(\frac{wd}{\nu}\right)^n \left(\frac{\nu}{D}\right)^m \frac{D}{d}$$

or, in a first approximation, without taking the change in the physical constants into account

$$\alpha_D = \text{const } w^n/d^{1-n} \tag{3-18}$$

from which (for $k_0 = \text{const}$)

$$\tau_{DK} = \text{const } d^{1-n}/w^n \tag{3-18'}$$

Hence a change in the parameter τ_{DK} reflects first the influence of the two basic characteristics of diffusion exchange: The relative gas flow velocity and the particle size. As is known from heat transmission (33), the value of the exponent n in (3-18) is always less than one. For the so-called "internal problem" (motion in a channel or over plates) $n \approx 0.75\text{-}0.8$; for the "external problem" (flow around individual particles such as a sphere, etc.) the value of n lies within the limits $0 < n < 0.5\text{-}0.6$.

The value of n is small for low values of $R = wd/\nu$; thus, $n = 0$ for $R < 1$; $n \approx 0.5$ for $R \approx 10^2$. A. P. Sokol'skii (42) obtained the following empirical formula for very fine particles of a size similar to coal dust by correlating his experimental data on the evaporation of fluid droplets

$$\frac{\alpha_D d}{D} = 2(1 + 0.08\,R)^{2/3} \tag{3-19}$$

which is in good agreement with experimental results in the R number range from $1 - {\sim}100$; the following formula, proposed by D. N. Vyrubov (12), can be used for larger values of R, say

$$\frac{\alpha_D d}{D} = 0.54\sqrt{R} \tag{3-20}$$

Finally, B. D. Katsnel'son and F. A. Timofeeva (22) took into account the effect of various values of the ratio ν/D.

It is seen from formula (3-18) that an increase in the gas transport coefficient α_D occurs, basically, for an increase in the relative velocity (the $n > 0$ case) and a decrease in the particle size (or the channel diameter, say). The role of the latter factor increases as R decreases; in the region of very small values of $R < 1$, in particular for fine coal dust, it can be assumed approximately (from (3-19) and also from a simple computation of the molecular diffusion to a sphere)[9]

$$\alpha_D \approx 2\frac{D}{d} = \text{const} \cdot \frac{1}{d}, \quad \tau_{_{JK}} \approx \text{const} \cdot d$$

[9]From the equation of molecular gas diffusion to the surface of a sphere of radius r_0 from a fixed, ambient medium

Both factors, the increase in w or the decrease in d, lead to intensification of the diffusion, displacement of the total process to the kinetic region, and, in the long run, to extinction. Conversely, a decrease in w and an increase in d, therefore the growth of τ_{DK}, leads to the process approaching the intermediate and diffusion regions and, if we speak of oxidation, to ignition in the long run. Hence, replacing the parameter τ_{sK} on the horizontal axis of Figure 2-4 by τ_{DK} for the heterogeneous process, it should be kept in mind that its growth is physically equivalent to a decrease in the relative velocity of the air blast or to a size increase.

The conclusion obtained that an increase in the velocity (a size decrease, analogously) leads to collapse of combustion in the limit (extinction) and a decrease in w (an increase in d) to ignition, contradicts the usual observations on the combustion process at first glance. For example, it is well known, and not only from furnace technique but also from a simple live experiment, that glowing coals are "inflated," burn up in air blast; an increase in the air-blast velocity in this example and in many similar examples leads to ignition and not to extinction, as was shown above. It is not difficult to cite as well numerous examples of a reduction in the air-blast velocity causing extinction and not ignition, as would follow from Figure 2-4. A similar contradiction between the results obtained above and observations in practice also refers to the influence of the particle size; a reduction in the particle size (coal dust, say) often facilitates ignition and a consolidation (coarsening of coal-dust pulverization, say) leads to the collapse of combustion, extinction.

$$\frac{d^2c}{dr^2} + \frac{2}{r}\frac{dc}{dr} = 0$$

taking into account the boundary conditions ($c = c_{r0}$ for $r = r_0$; $c = c_0$ for $r = \infty$) there follows

$$\frac{dc}{dr} = -\frac{A}{r^2}; \quad c = B + \frac{A}{r}; \quad B = c_0; \quad A = (c_{r0} - c_0)\,r_0$$

or

$$\frac{dc}{dr} = -(c_{r0} - c)\frac{r_0}{r^2}; \quad c - c_0 = (c_{r0} - c_0)\frac{r_0}{r}$$

Let us write the flux of substance per unit surface on the surface of the sphere as

$$\lambda = -D\frac{dc}{dr} = \alpha_D(c_{r0} - c_0)$$

from which at $r = r_0$

$$\frac{D}{r_0} = \alpha_D; \quad \frac{\alpha_D r_0}{D} = 1; \quad \frac{\alpha_D d}{D} = 2$$

This apparent contradiction receives its complete explanation in the next chapter with the investigation of the coal combustion process with additional (besides convective) heat transfer. However, it is expedient to explain the substance of the question briefly here. Let us note first that the law considered above concerning the approach to the critical phenomena, ignition for a reduction in the air-blast velocity or increase in the particle size, and extinction for an increase in the velocity or a reduction in the particle size, and the opposite character of the influence of these factors (w and d), is very widespread in the actual coal combustion process.

Apropos of this, for example, it is possible to refer to the following simple experiment, which is easily reproducible under laboratory conditions, and has been frequently carried out by the author.[10] A rod of electrode carbon was first heated in the experiment by an electric current to a dark-red incandescence after which an air jet was directed thereon. An intensive combustion process, which continued even after the electric heating was disconnected, started on the coal surface for a certain air-blast velocity. As the air-blast velocity increased, the carbon rod burned all the more, and its temperature grew and approached the theoretical (estimated by optical measurements) at a significant air velocity. However, a sharp, practically instantaneous, extinction occurred as still higher velocities were reached (of the order of 220 to 250 m/sec); a section of the carbon surface being blasted directly by the air jet, darkened instantly and became dark from a dazzling white; the temperature on this section of coal dropped approximately from 2000 to 500 to 700°K. Conversely, as the air-jet velocity was subsequently reduced, the combustion of the carbon rod, being continued at a certain distance from the place being blasted directly by the high-speed air jet, again spread to the dimmed section and a sharp, clearly observable ignition occurred. These phenomena, the ignition of carbon for a reduction of the air velocity and extinction with a significant increase, evidently correspond to the critical phenomena considered above for combustion with purely convective heat transfer.

A second extinction was observed simultaneously in the same experiment as the air velocity was diminished further (in the range of very small values of the jet velocity); conversely, an initial increase in the air velocity (when lightly glowing carbon heated by a current was blown upon) caused ignition; i.e., a sharp increase in the temperature and the formation of a stationary combustion region which was conserved when the electric heater was disconnected.

[10]In the thermal physics laboratory of the Leningrad Polytech. Inst. in 1940-1941.

Hence, the two critical conditions of ignition and extinction were successfully observed in the experiments described for both an increase and a decrease in the air velocity.

It is evident that the critical regions obtained in an investigation of the process in the $\varphi - \theta$ diagram (Figure 2-3c) correspond to the case of purely convective heat transfer to which the process at comparatively high values of the air velocity can be approximated in the experiments described (these ignition and extinction regions will later be called "adiabatic" conditionally); the second, conditionally "heat exchange", pair of critical phenomena in the range of low values of the velocity is related to intense radiant heat loss. A similar picture can apparently also be observed when the particle size changes over a sufficiently wide range. This whole complex of questions, one of the most interesting in the theory of the thermal region of combustion, will be analyzed in detail later during investigations of complex heat exchange and, partially, at the end of this chapter in connection with the general case of the combustion of unmixed components in a chamber.

Intrinsically, the nature of extinction for a decrease in the τ_{sK} parameter in the well-mixed mixture combustion problem and that for a decrease in the τ_{DK} parameter in the heterogeneous combustion problem are rather different. In the first case (well-mixed mixture), we speak of the intensity of heat liberation becoming inadequate to sustain the combustion process for a small stay time in the chamber τ_s; in the second (heterogeneous process), for a low value of the time τ_D, i.e., very intense diffusion of the reacting gas to the surface of the solid phase, as if the possible chemical reaction rate is "exhausted"; a further increase in the gas supply leads to part of it not participating in the reaction and only cooling the surface and a resulting collapse of combustion (extinction) occurs. This difference becomes especially evident in the transition from an analysis of the phenomenon on an isolated surface element of coal to an investigation of the thermal process in the chamber when the critical ignition and extinction phenomena appear to be possible under the conditions of an adiabatic process for both an increase in the time τ_D (a reduction in the air velocity, say) or for a decreased τ_D (an increase in the air velocity, say).

A reduction of the air velocity in the adiabatic heterogeneous process considered here, neglecting the effect on the gas stay time in the chamber, leads to ignition and an increase, to extinction, exactly the same as a change in the average velocity during the combustion of a well-mixed mixture

$$(\tau_D \approx 1/\alpha_D \approx 1/w^n; \quad \tau_s \approx 1/w_{av})$$

An increase in w denotes a drop in τ_{sK} or τ_{DK} on Figure 2-3c.

Allowing for a finite stay time in the chamber in the heterogeneous process or on the other hand, for the component mixing in the chamber for different supplies, leads to ignition under an increase in the air velocity and extinction under a decrease. Hence, the region of stable combustion in both cases appears to be bounded both by very low values of the air velocity and by very high values.

In conclusion, let us note that the following inequalities are retained, as in the rest of the cases, for the hysteresis process with a change in the parameter τ_{DK}

$$\theta_B < \theta_S; \quad \varphi_B < \varphi_S \text{ but } \tau_{DKB} > \tau_{DKS}$$

or

$$\alpha_{DB} < \alpha_{DS}; \quad w_B < w_S; \quad d_B > d_S$$

For example, ignition occurs at a lower value of the velocity than that for which the collapse of combustion, extinction, occurs. Finally, all the above mentioned on the uncritical process also refers to the influence of a change in the parameter τ_{DK} and, very probably, also to coal combustion in the high-temperature region in a furnace, in general.

As regards the quantitative relations, as already mentioned, all the results, the relations, graphs, etc., cited in Chapter 2, are retained for heterogeneous combustion, but with the replacement of τ_{SK} by τ_{DK} and the introduction of the appropriate corrections in the physical interpretation of the process.

The discussions cited were limited to the case $a = D$ (3-14), i.e., to $\alpha/\alpha_D = c_p$. In the absence of the equality (3-14), i.e., for $a \neq 0$; $\alpha \neq \alpha_D c_p$, it should be assumed instead of (3-15)

$$\varphi = \frac{\theta - \theta_0}{\mu\theta} \qquad\qquad (3\text{-}15')$$

where

$$\mu = \frac{\alpha_D c_p}{a} = \left(\frac{D}{a}\right)^{1-m}$$

In this case, the similarity of the temperature and concentration fields is violated

$$\varphi = 1 - c/c_0 = \frac{\theta - \theta_0}{\theta_m - \theta_0}$$

where

$$\theta_m = \theta_0 + \vartheta$$

In particular, this latter means that the stationary surface temperature will be larger for $D > a$ and less for $D < a$ than the quantity

$$T_m = T_0 + qc_0/c_p$$

(See details in section 6-4.)

The inequality $a \neq D$ and (3-15') also mean that the reduced (effective) value of the mixture heat productivity in (3-15'), $\varphi_{II} = (\theta - \theta_0)/\vartheta_{eff}$ can also be represented for $a \neq D$ as

$$\vartheta_{eff} = \frac{\alpha_D c_p}{a} = \left(\frac{D}{a}\right)^{1-m} = \mu$$

Evidently, $\vartheta_{eff} > \vartheta$ for $D > a$; conversely, $\vartheta_{eff} < \vartheta$ for $D < a$. Consequently, combustion will progress more stably when the diffusion coefficient of the active gas is greater than the temperature production coefficient and, conversely, less stably for $D < a$.

The influence of the difference in the values of the coefficients D and a (in the values of $\alpha_D c_p$ and α, respectively) on the intersection of the $\varphi_I(\theta)$ and $\varphi_{II}(\theta)$ curves should be felt most noticeably at the critical ignition and extinction conditions. This conclusion is qualitatively in agreement with the Zel'dovich observations, in an investigation of the concentration limits of flame propagation in lean mixtures (13a).

3-3. CERTAIN ADDITIONAL RELATIONS

The relations presented in sections 2-4 and 3-2 permit establishment of the influence of any of the parameters on the progress of the process and, in particular, on the critical ignition and extinction phenomena. In order to complete the picture, certain questions related to the nature of the phenomena under consideration should be discussed, before turning to more complex problems of the thermal region of the process in a combustion chamber for different supplies of mutually unmixed components (sections 3-4 and 3-5) and the nonadiabatic process (Chapter 4).

In this connection, let us dwell on two questions; the use of approximate formulas to compute the critical values of the parameters in the thermal region theory first, and the dependence of the actual reaction rate on the combustion temperature and the nondimensional time (τ_{sK} or τ_{DK}) second.

The necessity for a comparatively detailed analysis of the first of these questions is dictated by approximate methods of representing the temperature dependence of the reaction rate, by replacing $\exp(-E/RT)$ to some degree of accuracy, being widely used in work on the thermal theory of combustion. As will be shown below, in order to produce a uniform picture of the process, it is preferable to use the exact exponential formula and to rely on approximate relations only in the final results for quantitative estimates.

With respect to the second of the above mentioned questions, the derivation of relations defining a stable, steady reaction rate, these latter are necessary in connection with the estimate of one of the most important technical characteristics, the specific intensity of the combustion process. In connection with the generality established above of the relations for the combustion of a well-mixed mixture and the heterogeneous process, the reasoning and relations presented in this paragraph refer to both cases.

As already remarked, the approximate method of representing the reaction-rate constant in the following form is widely used:

$$k(T) = k_0 e^{-E/RT} = k_0 e^{E/RT_0} e^{E(T-T_0)/RT_0^2} \qquad (3\text{-}21)$$

This method is based on an expansion of $\exp(-E/RT)$ in a power series of the difference $T - T_0$, as proposed by D. A. Frank-Kamenetskii (50).

In order to derive (3-21), let us first represent the function $\exp(-E/RT)$ thus:

$$\exp(-E/RT) = \exp\left(\frac{E}{R} \frac{1}{T_0 - T - T_0}\right) = \exp\left(\frac{E}{RT_0} \cdot \frac{1}{1 - (T - T_0)/T_0}\right)$$

Expanding the fraction in the exponent in the series

$$\frac{1}{(T - T_0)/T_0} = 1 + \frac{T - T_0}{T_0} + \left(\frac{T - T_0}{T_0}\right)^2 + \dots\dots$$

and being limited to the first two terms of the series, we obtain

$$\exp(-E/RT) = \exp\left(\frac{E}{RT_0} + \frac{E(T - T_0)}{RT_0^2}\right)$$

i.e., the expression in the approximate formula (3-21). Evidently, this expansion is admissible under compliance with the inequality

$$\frac{T - T_0}{T_0} \ll 1; \quad \frac{T}{T_0} \approx 1$$

The latter corresponds to very slight heating because of the reaction (negligible in comparison with the magnitude of the initial temperature).

Using (3-21) leads to replacement of a function such as $\exp(-1/x)$ by the function e^{ax} which is simpler and more suitable for computations.[11]

[11] The expression $\exp(E/RT)$ in (3-21) can be represented, in the notation used in this book, as

$$e^{-1/\theta} \approx e^{1/\theta_0} \cdot e^{(\theta/\theta_0^2) - (1/\theta_0)} = e^{\theta/\theta_0^2} = e^{a\theta}$$

where

$$a = \frac{1}{\theta_0^2}$$

In addition, the number of variables is successfully diminished by choosing $E(T - T_0)/RT_0^2$ as a nondimensional temperature in certain cases (for example, considering in the problem of a thermal explosion the temperature distribution in the vessel, etc.). Use of (3-21) would appear to be very expedient and fruitful in a number of cases, in particular, when the phenomena near a certain temperature, T_0, say, were to be investigated. (It is clear that such an expansion is possible even near any other characteristic value of the temperature, say, the maximum combustion temperature, T_M.)

In particular, as did both Frank-Kamenetskii himself and Zel'-dovich, et al. (13a, 16, 19, 50, 51, etc.), many new results were obtained in investigation of the thermal combustion region, flame propagation, its propagation limits, etc., by using (3-21). Finally, this approximate formula is very convenient for numerical computations and estimates.

In those cases when the problem of the investigation is an explanation of the laws in a comparatively broad temperature range, it is more expedient to rely on the exact formula of the temperature dependence of the reaction rate to derive general relations in order to avoid not only quantitative but even possible qualitative distortion of the result.

In particular, this situation refers to the construction of the different regions of the progress of the process (hysteresis, uncritical, boundary curve of ignition and extinction coincidence, etc.) in the $\varphi - \theta$ diagram in the whole theoretically meaningful temperature range. As an illustration, let us compare certain final formulas obtained by both methods of computation.

Let us represent the basic equations of heat liberation and elimination based on (3-21) as

$$Q_I \approx A_1 e^{E(T-T_0)/RT_0^2} \tag{3-22}$$

and as before

$$Q_{II} = B(T - T_0) \tag{3-23}$$

The ignition conditions written as the equalities

$$Q_I = Q_{II}; \quad \frac{dQ_I}{dT} = \frac{dQ_{II}}{dT}$$

yield

$$\frac{A_1}{RT_0^2} e^{E(T-T_0)/RT_0^2} = B = \frac{A_1 e^{E(T-T_0)/RT_0^2}}{T - T_0}$$

from which, after manipulation, we obtain the expression for the ignition temperature

$$T_B = T_0 + \frac{RT_0^2}{E} \tag{3-24}$$

or, in nondimensional form, after substituting $\theta = RT/E$; $\theta_0 = RT_0/E$

$$\theta_B \approx \theta_0 + \theta_0^2 \tag{3-24'}$$

The formula obtained is in agreement with the second approximation of the N. N Semenov formula (1-19):

$$\theta_B = \frac{1 - \sqrt{1 - 4\theta_0}}{2} \approx \theta_0 + \theta_0^2 \tag{1-21}$$

Hence, the second approximations (just as the first: $\theta_B \approx \theta_0$), obtained by a series expansion in the original or final expressions, are in agreement in this problem.

The approximate formula (3-21) was used by Frank-Kamenetskii also for the theory of the thermal region of the heterogeneous process. It is consequently expedient to compare briefly the final results obtained by approximate means with the above.

Let us start with the condition of the coincidence of the critical ignition and extinction phenomena, which is expressed in the approximate theory by a formula for the nondimensional parameter ξ (50, 51)

$$\xi_{i-e} = q c_0 / R T_0^2 \cdot {}^{\alpha}D/\alpha = 4 \tag{}$$

Introducing the nondimensional variables $\vartheta = R q c_0 / E c_p$ and $\theta_0 = RT_0/E$ for the case $a \approx D$; $\alpha_D c_p$ (3-14), let us rewrite (3-25) as

$$\xi_{i-e} = \frac{\vartheta}{\theta_0^2} = 4 \tag{3-25'}$$

or

$$\vartheta_{i-e} = 4\theta_0^2 \tag{3-26}$$

This expression should be compared with the exact formula cited in Table 2-1:

$$\vartheta_{i-e} = \frac{4\theta_0^2}{1 - 4\theta_0}$$

Evidently both expressions yield close numerical results for small values of θ_0 ($\theta_0 \ll 0.25$) and diverge noticeably as the initial temperature increases. Thus, the approximate formula yields $\vartheta_{i-e} \approx 0.0004$ and the exact 0.00042 for $\theta_0 = 0.01$ and 0.04 and 0.067, respectively, for $\theta_0 = 0.1$, etc. It is more essential that the exact formula afford the possibility of determining the limiting value of the initial temperature at which the region of critical phenomena existence is terminated: $\theta_{0\,cr\,max} = 0.25$ (Figure 2-14), while it is generally impossible to establish the boundary of the hysteresis process from the approximate formula (3-26).

The Frank-Kamenetskii critical ignition and extinction condition (50, 51) leads, for the region of high values of the criterion $\xi = \vartheta/\theta_0^2$, namely:

$$\xi \gg 1; \; \vartheta \gg \theta_0^2$$

to the following symmetric form:

$$k_0 e^{-E/RT} = \frac{\alpha_D}{\xi} \tag{3-27}$$

for ignition and

$$k_0 e^{-E/RT} = \alpha_D \xi \tag{3-28}$$

for extinction.

These relations have been obtained by using the approximate relation (3-21); however, the exact value of the exponential $k_0 \times \exp(-E/RT)$ has been substituted in the final result in order to diminish the error of computation. In the notations used herein (3-27) and (3-28) can be rewritten as

$$\tau_{DKi} = \frac{Q_0^2}{\vartheta} e^{1/\theta} \tag{3-27'}$$

for ignition and

$$\tau_{DKe} = \frac{\vartheta}{\theta_0^2} e^{1/\theta} \tag{3-28'}$$

for extinction. The nondimensional time τ_{sK} should be substituted for τ_{DK} in these formulas for the combustion of a well-mixed mixture.

For convenience of comparison, let us transform these expressions to the variables $\theta_{cr} = \theta(\theta_0, \vartheta)$ by eliminating the critical value of the nondimensional time by using the equality encountered earlier:

$$\frac{e^{1/\theta}}{\tau_{DK}} \equiv \frac{1 - \varphi}{\varphi} = \frac{1 - (\theta - \theta_0)/\vartheta}{(\theta - \theta_0)/\vartheta} = \frac{\vartheta - \theta - \theta_0}{\theta - \theta_0}$$

Hence, replacing $e^{1/\theta}/\tau_{DK}$ in (3-27') for ignition, we obtain

$$\theta_i = \theta_0 + \frac{\theta_0^2}{1 + \theta_0^2/\vartheta} \tag{3-29}$$

and, correspondingly, for extinction we obtain

$$\theta_e = \theta_0 + \frac{\vartheta}{1 + \theta_0^2/\vartheta} \tag{3-30}$$

instead of the exact formula

$$\theta_{cr} = \frac{\vartheta + 2\theta_0 \pm \vartheta_0\sqrt{1 - 4\theta_0 - 4\theta_0^2/\vartheta}}{2(1 + \vartheta)} \tag{2-32}$$

(the minus sign is for ignition, the plus is for extinction).

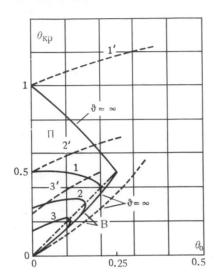

Neglecting burn-up, as was already remarked, (3-29) yields for high values of ϑ

$$\theta_{i,\,\vartheta \to \infty} = \theta_0 + \theta_0^2 \tag{1-21}$$

while (2-32) transforms into the Semenov formula as $\vartheta \to \infty$:

$$\theta_{cr,\,\vartheta \to \infty} = \theta_0 + \theta_0^2 \tag{1-19}$$

Expanding (1-19) in series, we obtain (1-21) for ignition and the following symmetric formula for extinction

$$\theta_{e,\,\vartheta \to \infty} = 1 - \theta_0 - \theta_0^2 \tag{1-21'}$$

Fig. 3-2. Comparison of exact and approximate computations of the critical temperature. $B(i)$—Ignition temperature curve; $\Pi(e)$—extinction temperature curve; solid line, exact computations; dashed line, approximate computations; 1 and $1'$—$\vartheta=1.0$; 2 and $2'$—$\vartheta = 0.5$; 3 and $3'$—$\vartheta = 0.2$.

Both equations (1-19) for the computation of the extinction temperature and (1-21') are qualitatively the same; in both cases the limiting value $\theta_{e,\,\vartheta \to \infty}$ decreases as θ_0 increases. Meanwhile (3-30) transforms into the equality of the extinction temperature and the maximum combustion temperature[12] for a sufficient increase in ξ:

$$\theta_{e\,II} \to \theta_0 + \vartheta = \theta_{max}$$

from which follows the monotonic rise in the extinction temperature as ϑ increases. As is seen from Figure 3-2, there is not only a significant quantitative but also a qualitative divergence in the determination of the extinction temperature here; for example, the

[12]The tendency of the extinction temperature to the maximum combustion temperature means that extinction occurs practically in the diffusion region ($\theta \approx \theta_{max}$, $\varphi \approx 1$) as ϑ grows, which contradicts the nature of the phenomenon. Actually, the critical value φ_{II} drops as ϑ increases but the difference $\theta_m - \theta_e$ increases (Table 3-1).

values of the extinction temperature determined using (3-30) for $\vartheta \gg 1$ and any values of θ_0 lie outside the region of the hysteresis process.

Table 3-1. Comparison of Exact and Approximate Computations of the Critical Temperature

Computed value	θ_0	ϑ = 0.2 computation 1*	2†	0.5 / 1	2	1.0 / 1	2
Ignition temperature	0.05	0.0525	0.0525	0.0525	0.0525	0.0525	0.0525
	0.10	0.116	0.110	0.115	0.110	0.114	0.110
Extinction temperature	0.05	0.197	0.248	0.384	0.55	0.50	1.05
	0.10	0.239	0.29	0.354	0.59	0.485	1.09
Maximum temperature	0.05	0.25		0.55		1.05	
	0.10	0.30		0.60		1.10	
Completeness of combustion with extinction $\varphi_e = \dfrac{\theta_e - \theta_0}{\theta_M - \theta_0}$	0.05	0.745	0.99	0.60	1	0.45	1
	0.10	0.60	0.95	0.51	0.98	0.385	0.99
Temperature difference $\theta_M - \theta_e$	0.05	0.053	0.002	0.202	0	0.55	0
	0.10	0.081	0.01	0.246	0.01	0.615	0.01

*Computation using Eq. (2-32).
†Computation using the approximate formulas (3-29) and (3-30).

A number of numerical results is also presented in Table 3-1 for comparison and the completely satisfactory agreement between the results of the approximate and the exact computations of the ignition temperature, and the substantial divergence in the determination of the critical values of the temperature and completeness of combustion for extinction and, mainly, the character of their dependence on the parameter are seen therefrom.

Let us note that the quantities presented in Table 3-1 refer to the interval of values of the criterion $\xi = \vartheta/\theta_0^2$ from 20 to 400 in correspondence with the condition of the applicability of Eqs. (3-29) and (3-30), $\xi \gg 1$ (50).

Hence, use of the approximate formula (3-21) in the whole critical condition range leads to a noticeable distortion in the determination of the extinction temperature and does not permit the regions of the existence of hysteresis and noncritical processes to be delimited correctly.

The comparison carried out shows the expediency of the computation used in this book (and in other research also[13]) which enables an investigation of the whole range of critical phenomena to be included by using in the simple final formulas derived from the approximate computation the exact formula of the temperature dependence of the reaction rate and enables a clear delimitation of the hysteresis and noncritical process regions to be given.

These conclusions certainly do not contradict the expediency remarked above of using the approximate formulas based on the expansion of the power of the exponential in series (3-21), all the more so since use of this method would permit its author and other investigators to obtain many valuable results in computations for the temperature range close to the initial temperature or correspondingly close to the maximum.

With respect to the approximate relations for the computation of ignition and extinction which are suitable for the region of violently exothermal reactions with low values of the initial temperature, the formula presented above can be mentioned for ignition

$$\theta_i \approx \theta_0 + \theta_0^2 \qquad (1\text{-}21)$$

or

$$\theta_i - \theta_0 = \theta_0^2; \quad \theta_i/\theta_0 = 1 + \theta_0; \quad T_i/T_0 \approx 1 + RT_0/E$$

corresponding to the limiting value of $\vartheta \to \infty$.

The analogous formula (1-21') $\theta_e \approx 1 - \theta_0 - \theta_0^2$ (for $\vartheta \to \infty$) is of no interest in practice for the approximate computation of the extinction temperature. We obtain a convenient approximate relation for $\theta \ll 1$ if we expand the radical in the exact equation

$$\theta_e = \frac{1 + \dfrac{2\theta_0}{\vartheta} + \sqrt{1 - 4\theta_0 - 4\theta/\vartheta}}{2(1 + 1/\vartheta)} \qquad (2\text{-}32)$$

in series and limit ourselves to the first term

$$\sqrt{1 - 4\theta_0 - 4\frac{\theta_0^2}{\vartheta}} \approx 1 - 2\theta_0\left(1 + \frac{\theta_0}{\vartheta}\right)$$

We obtain from (2-32) after simple manipulations

$$\theta_e \approx \frac{(1 - \theta_0)(\theta_0 + \vartheta)}{1 + \vartheta} \qquad (3\text{-}31)$$

[13] For example, see the Bubnev (5, 6) investigation in which the influence of the difference in the thermal diffusivity and the molecular diffusion coefficients $(a \neq D)$, the influence of thermal diffusion, the change in the number of moles during the reaction, and the convective flow to the surface caused thereby, etc., are studied along with the exact exponential formula for an nth-order chemical reaction.

or, replacing $\theta_0 + \vartheta$ by θ_m

$$\theta_e \approx (1 - \theta_0)\frac{\theta_m}{1 + \theta_m - \theta_0} \tag{3-32}$$

The difference between the maximum temperature θ_m and the extinction temperature equals, correspondingly

$$\theta_m - \theta_e \approx \frac{\theta_m(\theta_m - \theta_0)}{1 + \theta_m - \theta_0} \approx \frac{\theta_m^2}{1 + \theta_m}; \quad (\theta_0 \ll \theta_m) \tag{3-33}$$

or in relative units

$$\frac{\theta_e}{\theta_m} \approx \frac{1}{1 + \theta_m}; \quad \frac{T_e}{T_m} \approx \frac{1}{1 + RT_m/E} \tag{3-33'}$$

Hence, the heating during ignition is proportional, in order of magnitude, to the initial temperature squared

$$\theta_i - \theta_0 \approx \theta_0^2; \quad T_i - T_0 \approx RT_0^2/E \tag{3-34}$$

and the reduction in the temperature during extinction is correspondingly proportional to the maximum combustion temperature squared

$$\theta_m - \theta_e \approx \theta_m^2; \quad T_m - T_e \approx \frac{RT_m^2}{E} \tag{3-35}$$

A result, analogous to the last relation (for extinction) was obtained by Zel'dovich for the limit of flame propagation in a well-mixed mixture in tubes (13 a) and for the collapse of the laminar combustion of unmixed gases (19) by expanding the exponential in series according to formula (3-21) near the maximum temperature T_m. Apparently (3-34) and (3-35) are the most suitable to estimate the critical ignition and extinction temperature values under very different conditions of the progress of the process.

Let us now turn to the question of the reaction rate. Until now all the reasoning on the effectiveness of the process was made from the viewpoint of explaining the conditions which would correspond to the maximum values of the completeness and the temperature of combustion. In addition, it is essential to establish a law for the change of the stationary value of the reaction rate, referred to unit chamber volume or to unit surface of the solid phase in the heterogeneous process

Hence, let us introduce the additional variable[14]

$$\chi = \frac{k_{eff}}{k_0} = \frac{1}{e^{1/\theta} + \tau_{DK}} = \left(\frac{1}{e^{1/\theta} + \tau_{sK}}\right) \tag{3-36}$$

[14] The nondimensional time τ_{DK} for the combustion of a well-mixed mixture should be replaced by the quantity τ_{sK}, the stay time, in all the formulas.

where according to (3-7) and (3-7′)

$$k_{eff} = V/c_0 = \frac{k_0}{e^{1/\theta} + \tau_{sK}}$$

(k_{eff} is the reduced effective first-order reaction-rate constant).

The quantity χ, the nondimensional reduced reaction-rate constant, characterizes the effective rate of the process; the transition to the dimensional reaction rate is not difficult:

$$V = \chi k_0 c_0 = k_{eff} c_0$$

Using (3-10) and (3-15) for a stationary process

$$\varphi = \frac{\tau_{DK}}{e^{1/\theta} + \tau_{DK}} = \frac{\theta - \theta_0}{\vartheta}$$

as well as the formula $\theta_m = \theta_0 + \vartheta$ for the maximum combustion temperature (for $\varphi = 1$ and $\alpha \approx D$), it is not difficult to relate χ to the remaining variables. As a result of simple manipulations similar to those often made earlier, we obtain

$$\chi = \varphi/\tau_{DK} = (1 - \varphi)e^{-1/\theta} = \frac{\theta_m - \theta}{\theta_m - \theta_0} e^{-1/\theta} \qquad (3\text{-}37)$$

Let us use the latter formula to determine the maximum value of the reaction rate χ_m and the corresponding values of the variables.

From the equality

$$\frac{d\chi}{d\theta} = 0$$

we obtain

$$\frac{d\chi}{d\theta} = -\frac{e^{-1/\theta}}{\theta_m - \theta_0} + \frac{(\theta_m - \theta)e^{-1/\theta}}{(\theta_m - \theta_0)\theta^2} = 0$$

or after combining

$$\theta^2 + \theta - \theta_m = 0 \qquad (3\text{-}38)$$

From (3-38), we find the value of the temperature corresponding to the maximum reaction rate

$$\theta\chi_m = \frac{(\sqrt{1 + 4\theta_m}) - 1}{2} \qquad (3\text{-}39)$$

The appropriate dependence $\theta\chi_m = \theta(\theta_m)$ is given on Figure 3-3, on which is also imposed the curve of the ratio

$$\frac{\theta\chi_m}{\theta_m} = \frac{T\chi_m}{T_m}$$

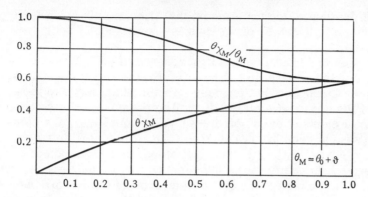

Fig. 3-3. Temperature corresponding to the maximum reaction rate as a function of the maximum combustion temperature.

as a function of the maximum combustion temperature. It follows from (3-39) and Figure 3-3 that the maximum value of the reaction rate corresponds to combustion conditions which are comparatively close to total burn-up. For example, the following value of the completeness of combustion

$$\varphi \chi_m = \frac{\theta \chi_m - \theta_0}{\theta_m - \theta_0}$$

equal to ~0.77 and 0.64, respectively, corresponds to the initial temperature $\theta_0 = 0.05$ for $\vartheta = 0.2$ and 0.7. The maximum value itself, χ_m, can be determined from (3-36) and (3-37) by substituting the values of $\theta \chi_m$ therein, as

$$\chi_m = \frac{\theta_m - \theta \chi_m}{\theta_m - \theta_0} \cdot e^{1/\theta} \chi_m \qquad (3-40)$$

It is obvious that the region in which the reaction rate is almost the maximum must be relatively small. It should be noted that a considerable part of the $\chi = \chi(\theta)$ curve drops into the unstable stationary states for the hysteresis process and, therefore, is not realized in practice. This circumstance is seen clearly on Figure 3-4a, on which are shown two examples of the reaction rate as a function of the completeness of combustion (for $\theta_0 = 0.05$ and $\vartheta = 0.7$ and 0.2). Sections of the unstable regions are superposed on Figure 3-4 by dashes and the stable regions by solid lines; the latter are bounded in practice by the combustion region between the extinction point φ_e and completion of combustion, $\varphi = 1$.

Of considerable interest also is the dependence of the quantity χ on the nondimensional time. The stationary curves $\tau_{DK} = \tau(\varphi)$ are also plotted on Figure 3-4a for illustration and the reaction

rate as a function of the nondimensional time for the hysteresis
(1) and the noncritical (2) processes is shown schematically on
Figure 3-4*b*.

As is seen from the graph, an increase in the nondimensional
stay (τ_{sK} for the combustion of a well-mixed mixture) or diffusion
(τ_{DK} for the heterogeneous process) times, which leads to the
growth of the stationary values of the temperature and the completeness of combustion (Figure 3-4), is accompanied by a comparatively rapid drop in the reaction rate after a certain time,
equal to $\tau_{DK\chi_m} = \varphi\chi_m/\chi_m$, and, therefore, to a reduction in the
heat-liberation intensity of the process $Q = V\gamma q$ (kcal/m³ sec) for
combustion in a chamber or $Q = Vq$ (kcal/m² sec) for a process per
unit solid phase surface. For high values of the mixture stay time

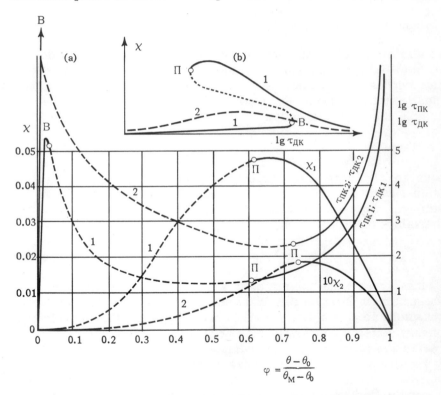

$$\varphi = \frac{\theta - \theta_0}{\theta_M - \theta_0}$$

Fig. 3-4. Stationary reaction rate as a function of completeness of combustion and nondimensional time. (*a*) Example of a computation of the de-
pendence $\chi = \chi(\theta)$: $1 - \theta_0 = 0.05$; $\vartheta = 0.2$; $\theta_M = 0.25$; $2 - \theta_0 = 0.05$; $\vartheta = 0.7$;
$\theta_M = 0.75$. *Remark*: The $\chi_2 = \chi(\theta)$ curve for the second example is plotted
to a cartesian scale, solid line, stable states; dashed line, unstable states;
(*b*) schematic dependence of reaction rate on nondimensional time; 1—hysteresis process; 2—noncritical process.

in the chamber τ_s or for high values of the gas diffusion time to the coal surface τ_D, the combustion process progresses as if for a high temperature level and for high completeness of combustion; however, it is characterized by low intensity. The reaction rate drops to zero in the limit as $\varphi = 1$, i.e., $\tau_D \rightarrow \infty$. It is natural that the optimum relations for practice (furnace size, thermal stress, etc.) are selected taking engineering considerations into account, which indicate the reasonable limits, for example, an increase in the stay time which will be accompanied after a certain value by a very small rise in the completeness of combustion and, simultaneously, by a sharp drop in the load. The latter, in its turn, is related to an increase in the thermal losses and, as will be shown later, can be a second cause for extinction (Chapter 4).

3-4. GENERAL CASE OF ADIABATIC COMBUSTION

Before turning to an investigation of complex heat exchange, let us try to analyze in general form the thermal process in a combustion chamber under conditions of interaction of the diffusion (mixing) and chemical reaction phenomena, in a first approximation.

Let us begin with certain general remarks. Generally, practical furnaces are designed to deliver the combustible mixture components separately and unmixed into the furnace. Such designs are primarily characteristic of coal and pulverized-coal furnaces, but are also typical of many combustion chambers using liquid or gas fuel. Even with fuel atomized and comparatively uniformly distributed in air, such a mixture differs substantially from a completely well-mixed combustible mixture.

The final mixing of the fuel and air (in the general case, oxidizer) occurs in the chamber at the same time as the combustion. It would be wrong to assume that the fuel-oxidizer mixing is completed in all cases prior to the ignition of the well-mixed combustible mixture being formed in the individual chamber locations. As in every other process, the fuel-air mixing requires a specific time for its accomplishment. The time required will depend first on the preliminary (primary) atomization and mixing of the components and, then, on factors of a hydrodynamic nature (the relative velocities of the motion of the mixture components and their distribution over the furnace volume; the character and degree of stream turbulence, etc.).

Leaving aside specific mixing conditions, in particular conditions of the evaporation of liquid fuel (whose combustion peculiarities are not considered in this book), the mixing process can be characterized by a certain conditional total mixing time τ_D in order to appraise the phenomenon generally.

The "diffusion time" τ_D in the coal combustion process had a completely different meaning, since we spoke of the diffusion of a reacting gas to the isolated surface of solid phase. The inhomogeneity of the burning mixture in this case (coal combustion) is conserved up to the very end of the process; for this very reason, heterogeneous combustion is a typical case in which diffusion is a major part.

In the general case, for example, in the combustion of unmixed gases, liquid fuel, etc., it is extremely difficult, and in the majority of cases impossible, to indicate (exactly as in the solid fuel case) a clearly defined surface in the furnace space on which the reaction would occur (or even an intense process would begin), the ignition surface. However, such a surface always exists even if it be complex, developed in the furnace space, and multiform. This surface ("flame front") serves as the "meeting place" of the reacting molecules. Consequently, making a limiting diagram of the phenomenon, the order of magnitude of the characteristic time τ_D can be determined approximately from dimensionality considerations as a ratio of the characteristic linear dimension d (initial scale of mixture atomization related to the structural dimensions and peculiarities of the furnace burner, etc.) and the diffusion rate. The same gas transport coefficient α_D can be taken as a defining quantity for this latter; for example, in this case, it is reasonable to take the following definition for τ_D

$$\tau_D \approx d/\alpha_D$$

The magnitude of τ_D can be determined from the same dimensionality considerations by means of the so-called turbulent diffusion coefficient[15] D_T; in this case

$$\tau_D \approx d^2/D_T$$

As was mentioned, the quantity d, the characteristic dimension, plays the part of the geometric characteristic of the primary mixing here (for example, the average size of the individual gas volumes of pure fuel and air, etc.).

Both these expressions indicate a decrease in the mixing time as the relative velocity increases and as the average size, characterizing the individual regions subject to further mixing, decreases.

Actually, as already indicated, the quantity α_D can be represented approximately as the relation

$$\alpha_D \approx \text{const } w^n d^{1-n} \tag{3-18}$$

[15]The turbulent exchange mechanism and its characteristic quantities are discussed briefly in section 7-2.

In its turn, the turbulent diffusion coefficient can be written as (13b, 28, 29, 50)

$$D_T \approx lu'$$

where l and u' are the scale of turbulence and the mean-square value of the pulsating velocity, respectively (see section 7-2).

If it is assumed in addition that $l/d \approx$ const as well as that $u'/w_{av} \approx$ const for the average pulsation intensity, then the second of the relations presented above for τ_D can be altered by assuming

$$\tau_D \approx \frac{d^2}{D_T} \approx \frac{d}{w}$$

Certainly, neither form of the expression for τ_D $(d/\alpha_D$ and $d^2/D_T \approx d/w)$ is quantitative and each serves only as a qualitative explanation of the influence of the individual parameters on the character of the process.

Consequently, to prefer one of these expressions over the other, generally, has no substantial value although the former (d/α_D) is probably closer to the real relations in the mixing process since the latter (diffusion) has much in common with heat exchange processes (temperature equalization, etc.). Extensive experimental justification for the latter is conveyed well by the empirical dependence (3-18) which is also in agreement with theoretical solutions. The exponent n in (3-18) is less than unity in all the cases known.

Let us note that the magnitude of the time defining the mixing process τ_D has been selected above by starting from the turbulent mixing rate. However, turbulent mixing is evidently inadequate for total burn-up to occur since finer, molecular mixing is required for this. Only the latter, accomplished by molecular diffusion, leads the reacting substance to molecular contact at which the progress of the reaction is possible. Therefore, in addition to the quantity $\tau_{D\,turb}$, an analogous characteristic for molecular mixing $\tau_{D\,mol} \approx d^2/D$ must be introduced, where D is the molecular diffusion coefficient.

The quantity $\tau_{D\,mol} \gg \tau_{D\,turb}$ since $\tau_{turb}/\tau_{mol} \approx D/D_T \ll 1$.

It can be shown that this inequality $(\tau_{D\,mol} \gg \tau_{D\,turb})$ indicates that the selection of the characteristic time made above is incorrect since a smaller time was discarded in the limiting cases of the heterogeneous process when comparing the times $\tau_D \approx 1/\alpha_D$ and $\tau_K' \approx e^{-1/\theta}/k_0$ and the total process was characterized by a larger time (the quantity τ_D or the gas transport coefficient α_D, "diffusion" combustion for $\tau_D \gg \tau_K'$; the quantity τ_K' or the reaction-rate constant k, "kinetic" combustion, for $\tau_D \ll \tau_K'$).

On the contrary, the larger of the two quantities $\tau_{D\,turb}$ and $\tau_{D\,mol}$, related thus $\tau_{D\,turb} \ll \tau_{D\,mol}$, is discarded for the mixing process and the lesser, $\tau_{D\,\mathrm{turb}}$, is retained for the characteristic of the mixing process as a whole

This contradiction is explained thus. The mixing and reaction processes are in sequence; therefore, the total time of the progress of the individual phenomena: $\tau = \tau'_K + \tau_D$ or the "resistance," i.e., the quantities reciprocal to the specific velocities: $1/k_{\mathrm{eff}} = (1/k) + (1/\alpha_D)$, Eq. (3-7). In contrast, turbulent and molecular mixing occur basically in parallel, consequently the total mixing time equals approximately

$$\tau_D \approx \frac{1}{\dfrac{1}{\tau_{D\,\mathrm{turb}}} + \dfrac{1}{\tau_{D\,\mathrm{mol}}}}$$

and $\tau_D \ll \tau_{D\,\mathrm{turb}}$ for $\tau_D \approx \tau_{D\,\mathrm{mol}}$. In its turn, the total mixing rate is characterized by the sum of the values $D + D_{\mathrm{turb}} \approx D_{\mathrm{turb}}$. Naturally these approximate reasonings are valid only for sufficiently small values of the scale of turbulence. It should also be taken into account that the combustible mixture breaks up continuously in the turbulent mixing process and, therefore, the value of the scale for molecular mixing diminishes.

The influence of the molecular mixing becomes perceptible at comparatively low values of $R = wd/\nu$ (more exactly, for small values of the ratio R/R_{cr} (28); the ratio D_T/D is of the order of 10^2-10^3 for $R \approx 10^5$-10^6).

Introducing the quantity τ_D, the characteristic mixing time, it is not difficult to arrive at an extension of the concept of the diffusion theory of combustion to the case of the combustion of any combustible mixture at first unmixed, by comparing it with the characteristic chemical reaction time τ_K.

In particular, it is possible to speak of "diffusion" combustion (high temperature, low relative velocities, and large primary volumes of the individual components) for the combustion of unmixed gases, vapors of liquid fuels, etc., when the rate of the total combustion process is determined by the mixing path. Schematically, this can be conceived thus: At individual places in the chamber where ignition of almost stoichiometric compositions would occur, a combustion front built up by developing a burning surface distributed in the chamber in a complex manner toward diffusion of air or of fuel will occur from volumes rich in either. The combustible mixture being formed burns continuously; the combustion rate equals the mixing rate in the steady-state process. The influence of the primary mixing caused by the burner, here reduces to a fuel and oxidizer distribution in the furnace volume in the form of separate concentration bands of very rich ($\alpha \approx \infty$ in the limit) and very lean ($\alpha \approx 0$ in the limit) mixtures. Later, mixing regions, within which a flame front is built up in its turn after ignition, form at the places where these primary zones make contact. If we were to speak of two parallel fuel and air streams, then one mutual diffusion boundary layer would be formed. Such a case will be analyzed for molecular diffusion in section 6-5. Since the furnace burners create a large number of individual fuel and air streams and therefore there are all concentrations between the limits $0 < \alpha < \infty$ in the chamber, the probability of diffusion combustion at high temperatures in the chambers is very large. Let us note that such a case of turbulent combustion with preliminary mixture atomization was designated "microdiffusion" (13b, 31, 50) by D. A. Frank-Kamenetskii, contrasting it to simple diffusion combustion in the presence of specific "macroscopic" fuel and air interfaces.

The second limiting case, "kinetic" combustion, corresponds to such conditions in the chamber (comparatively low values of the temperature, high mixing rates, very fine primary mixing, etc.), at which the final mixing is terminated completely prior to ignition; significant local differences in concentration do not exist here.

In this case, the rate of the complete process is determined by the rate at which the chemical reaction progresses. Apparently such a kind of combustion predominates in those chamber sections where ignition occurs.

Finally, in the most general case of the "intermediate" process, the mixing and reaction rates (times) are commensurable; combustion progresses according to a certain average between the limiting cases of the mechanism; the concentration of the combustible is lower than the initial concentration but not zero at the ignition surface; and the total combustion rate depends in a complex manner on both hydrodynamic and kinetic factors.

All three combustion cases can most often be realized simultaneously in a real combustion chamber; kinetic combustion predominates for some sections of the chamber (comparatively low-temperature region) and diffusion combustion for others (raised-temperature region).

An approximate, quantitative estimate of this complex process within the limits used here of the zero-dimensional model is possible if it is assumed that the mixing τ_D and reaction τ_K times are combined in the expression for the reaction rate, since these processes (mixing and reaction) proceed successively.

It is possible to arrive at such a very simple law of combining the mixing and reaction times if we start from the following scheme:

Let us assume that regions of unmixed components and regions in which combustion occurs exist separately in the combustion chamber. A solid phase surface is an example of a combustion region for the simplest case, that of the heterogeneous process, combustion bands are the combustion regions for the combustion of non-premixed gases, and a flame front, in the limit, for diffusion combustion. In conformance with this assumption, let us differentiate the combustible mixture concentration c in the combustion region, and the average combustible mixture concentration in the whole chamber volume c_k (calculated under the assumption of total mixing of the components) which equals the concentration of the initial substances in the reaction products. In both cases (c_k and c), we speak of stoichiometric mixtures corresponding to the reaction equation. The initial value of the combustible mixture concentration under the assumption of total mixing of the components will be denoted by c_0, as before.

Let us write the expression for the completeness of combustion φ as

$$\varphi \approx 1 - \frac{c_k}{c_0} \tag{3-41}$$

The average reaction rate V can evidently be represented as

$$V = \frac{c_0 - c_k}{\tau_s} \tag{3-42}$$

or as the equality

$$V = \frac{c\, e^{-1/\theta}}{\tau_k} \tag{3-42'}$$

where c is the concentration in the combustion zone (for example, on the coal surface).

It follows from the steady-state condition of the process that the quantity of stoichiometric combustible mixture being formed in the combustion zone must be equal to its quantity consumed per unit time. Assuming that the mixing process occurs under the influence of a difference in concentration $c_k - c$ and is characterized by the mixing time τ_D, the expression for the reaction rate can be written also as

$$V = \frac{c_K - c}{\tau_D} \tag{3-42''}$$

Let us now equate all three expressions for V

$$\frac{\varphi}{\tau_s} = \frac{c}{c_0} \cdot \frac{e^{-1/\theta}}{\tau_K} = \frac{1 - \varphi - \dfrac{c}{c_0}}{\tau_D} \tag{3-43}$$

and let us eliminate the ratio c/c_0 which evidently equals

$$\frac{c}{c_0} = \frac{\varphi e^{1/\theta}}{\tau_{sK}} = \frac{1 - \varphi}{1 + \tau_{DK}\, e^{-1/\theta}} \tag{3-44}$$

We find from the equation obtained an expression for $\varphi_I = \varphi(\theta \tau_{sk}, \tau_{DK})$ in the form

$$\varphi_I = \frac{1}{1 + \dfrac{1}{\tau_{sD}} + \dfrac{e^{1/\theta}}{\tau_{sK}}} \tag{3-45}$$

Let us note that if we put the value $c = c_0(1 - \varphi)/(1 + \tau_{DK} e^{1/\theta})$, say, in (3-42), then we would obtain

$$V = c_0 \frac{1 - \varphi}{\tau_D + \tau_K'} = \frac{c_K}{\tau_D + \tau_K'} = \frac{c_K}{\tau_D + \tau_K e^{1/\theta}} \tag{3-46}$$

Hence, Eq. (3-45) for $\varphi_I(\theta)$ corresponds to the assumption of the combination of the characteristic times $\tau_D + \tau_K'$ or what is substantially the same, to the transformation to an effective reaction rate-constant (for the heterogeneous process) $k_{eff} = 1/(1/k + 1/\alpha_D)$ by using (3-7)

$$V = \frac{c_K}{\tau_D + \tau_K'} = k_{eff} \cdot c_K \tag{3-47}$$

where c_K is the concentration of the reacting gas far from the combustion surface (different from c at the surface and from the initial mixture concentration c_0, entering the chamber).

As earlier, the quantity τ_D in (3-45) should be considered as a certain structural and regional constant whose order of magnitude is given by the estimates presented above ($\tau_D \sim a/\alpha_D \sim d^2/D_T$).

The expression (3-45) obtained for $\varphi_I(\theta)$ in the limiting case of $\tau_{sD} \to \infty$ (i.e., $\tau_D \to 0$ is instantaneous mixing) transforms into (2-14) for kinetic combustion

$$\varphi_I = \frac{\tau_{sK}}{\tau_{sK} + e^{1/\theta}}$$

In the other limiting case, for very high reaction rates ($\tau_K \to 0$; $\tau_{sK} \to \infty$) we obtain the following simple formula from (3-45):

$$\varphi_I = \frac{1}{1 + \tau_{Ds}} \tag{3-48}$$

for purely diffusion combustion with a finite mixture retention time in the chamber τ_s.

The quantity φ, the coefficient of completeness of combustion, acquires an additional simple interpretation for diffusion combustion here:

$$\varphi = \frac{\tau_s}{\tau_s + \tau_D} \tag{3-48'}$$

the completeness of combustion equals the ratio of the retention time and the mixing ($\varphi \to 1$ for $\tau_D \to 0$ or $\tau_s \to \infty$; conversely, $\varphi \to 0$ for $\tau_D \to \infty$ or $\tau_s \to 0$).

Let us consider initially the limiting case of diffusion combustion which is mainly of interest for the high temperature range ($k_0 \exp(-E/RT) \gg 1/\tau_D$).

The curve of the completeness of combustion $\varphi_I(\theta)$ as a function of the nondimensional time τ_{sD} constructed by using (3-48) is shown on Figure 3-5.

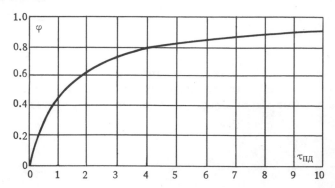

Fig. 3-5. Dependence of completeness of combustion on the nondimensional time for diffusion combustion.

The completeness of combustion is also small for small values of the time τ_{sD}, i.e., for low stay times or for low diffusion rates; however, the completeness of combustion increases, approaching unity asymptotically, as τ_{sD} increases (i.e., as τ_s increases or τ_D diminishes).

In practice, it is important that the rise of φ is significant in the range of low values of τ_{sD} and very slow for large τ_{sD} (and, correspondingly, large φ, of the order of 0.85 and higher). This means that an increase in the chamber length, say, becomes hardly logical, starting with a certain value of τ_{sD} and an appropriate value of φ, since a significant increase in τ_{sD} in this range only slightly increases the completeness of combustion (Figure 3-5).

In order to look for the steady-state combustion region, it is possible to return, as before, to the intersection of the $\varphi_I(\theta)$ curve from (3-48) with the heat-elimination lines $\varphi_{II}(\theta)$

$$\varphi_{IID} = \frac{1}{\vartheta}(\theta - \theta_0) \tag{3-10}$$

It is expedient to reduce the last formula to a more simple form, in connection with the kinetic characteristics dropping out of the problem

$$\varphi_{II} = \frac{c_p T_0}{q c_0}\left(\frac{T}{T_0} - 1\right) = \frac{1}{\vartheta_D}(\theta_D - 1) \tag{3-49}$$

where, for brevity, the following notation has been used: $\theta_D = T/T_0$ is the nondimensional temperature (for diffusion combustion); $\vartheta_D = q c_0/c_p T_0$ is the heat production characteristic of the mixture (for diffusion combustion).

As is seen from Figure 3-6, the intersection of the lines $\varphi_I(\theta_D)$ and the lines $\varphi_{II}(\theta_D)$ in the $\varphi - \theta_D$ diagram always occurs at just one point. This means that there is just one stationary and stable (Figure 3-6) region in the limiting case of purely diffusion combustion, which is characterized by very high values of completeness of combustion and heating of the mixture.

According to (3-48) and (3-49), the intersection of the lines $\varphi_I(\theta_D)$ and $\varphi_{II}(\theta_D)$ permits stationary values of the temperature and the completeness of combustion to be found.

However, it is simpler to find them directly from (3-49) for φ_D and an analogous expression

$$\theta_D = 1 + \varphi \vartheta_D \left(T_D = T_0 + \frac{\tau_s}{\tau_s + \tau_D} \cdot \frac{q c_0}{c_p}\right) \tag{3-50}$$

for the combustion temperature. Neither of these formulas is quantitative since the values of τ_D in (3-49) and (3-50) are unknown in the general case and even a rough estimate (in the absence of experimental results) is very complex.

Now, let us return to the general case. The heat-liberation curves $\varphi_I(\theta)$ according to (3-45) are shown schematically in the $\varphi - \theta$ diagram on Figure 3-7. Each group of curves corresponds to one value of the τ_{sK} parameter here; the nondimensional time τ_{sD} (or the time τ_{DK} for $\tau_K = $ const for each pencil of curves with

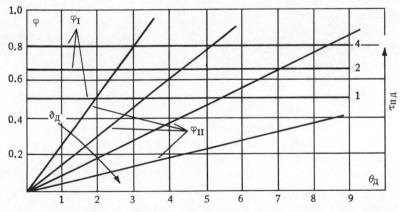

Fig. 3-6. Stationary diffusion combustion region in the $\varphi - \theta_D$ plane.

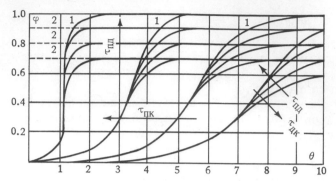

Fig. 3-7. $\varphi - \theta$ Diagram (completeness of combustion-temperature) for the general case of an intermediate combustion range. $1-\tau_{sD} = \infty$; kinetic curves $\varphi_I(\theta)$; $2-\tau_{sK} = \infty$; diffusion curves $\varphi_I(\theta)$.

one value of τ_{sK}) is the second parameter for the curves within the pencil. The curves $\varphi_I(\theta)$ are constructed according to the kinetic relationship (2-14): $\varphi_I = \tau_{sK}/(\tau_{sK} + e^{1/\theta})$, for $\tau_{sD} = \infty$ ($\tau_D = 0$ is the upper curve 1 in all the pencils). The $\varphi_I(\theta)$ curves in the other limiting case $\tau_{Ds} \to 0$ ($\tau_D \to \infty$ is the line 2 on Figure 3-7) depend on the temperature and agree with the lines parallel to the horizontal axis drawn for diffusion combustion according to (3-48): $\varphi_I = 1/(1 + \tau_{Ds})$.

As is seen from Figure 3-7, the curves of heat liberation $\varphi_I(\theta)$ practically coincide with the kinetic curves in the beginning on the section of low φ and θ values, in the general case when $\tau_{sK} \neq 0$ and $\tau_{sD} \neq 0$. As the temperature increases, the curves $\varphi_I(\theta)$, drawn according to (3-45) for the intermediate combustion range, deviate all the more from the kinetic curves; the deviation starts earlier here and is greater the smaller the value of τ_{sD}, i.e., the larger the mixing time τ_D for given values of τ_s and τ_K. As the temperature increases further, the $\varphi_I(\theta)$ curves for the general case approximate the diffusion lines for the appropriate τ_{sD} values more and more and then practically coincide.

Hence, a kinetic (1), intermediate (2), and diffusion (3) combustion range (Figure 3-8) can be isolated approximately for each of the curves for given τ_{sD} and τ_{sK}.

As follows from the derivation of (3-45), the latter refers, in the same degree, both to unmixed and to heterogeneous combustion in a chamber with finite stay time.

As regards the second equation for $\varphi_{II}(\theta)$, it can be retained for the process in an adiabatic chamber as (2-13) or (3-15)

$$\varphi_{II} = \frac{\theta - \theta_0}{\vartheta} \tag{3-51}$$

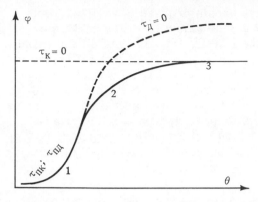

Fig. 3-8. Heat-libera-
tion curve, general
case. 1—Kinetic; 2—
intermediate; 3—dif-
fusion combustion.

Let us note that this expression corresponds not only to the assumption of the adiabatic character of the whole process but also to the
assumption of the identity of the mixing and heat-transmission
mechanisms within the chamber, since only thus does similarity in
the temperature and concentration distributions occur:

$$\varphi = \frac{\theta - \theta_0}{\theta_m - \theta_0}$$

This latter means that equalization of the concentration and temperature occurs in identical degree in the mixing process and,
therefore, $a \approx D$; $a_{\text{turb}} \approx D_{\text{turb}}$ or finally $\alpha = \alpha_D c_p$. In other words,
the characteristic mixing and heat exchange times used in (3-51)
are identical. This question will be considered more rigorously in
section 6-2.

For greater clarity, let us analyze briefly the influence of the
separate parameters on the stationary level of the process and the
critical ignition and extinction conditions.

To do this, it is simplest to resort again to a construction of the
curves of the stationary values of the temperature and the completeness of combustion for different cases of the variation of just
one of the process parameters. Let us do this, for example, for a
variation in the initial mixture temperature θ_0 for constant values
of τ_{sK} and ϑ for several values of the parameter τ_{DK}, i.e., values
of the mixing time τ_D for $\tau_K = \text{const}$.

Shown diagramatically on Figure 3-9 is a pencil of heat-liberation curves, constructed using (3-45) for one value of τ_{sK} and several values of τ_{DK} or in dimensional units, for identical stay τ_s
and reaction τ_K times for all the curves but for different values of
the mixing time τ_D. The direction of the increase in the τ_{DK} parameter is shown by arrows on Figure 3-9.

As results from the condition of the intersection of the heat-lib-
eration curves $\varphi_I(\theta)$ (3-45) with the heat-elimination lines $\varphi_{II}(\theta)$

(3-51) on Figure 3-9 a, the hysteresis process is realized for the four upper curves (3-6) over a wide variation of the parameter θ_0; the curve 2 corresponds to the limiting case of ignition and extinction coincidence (tangent to the inflection point); curve 1 refers to the uncritical process range. The appropriate curves of the stationary values of the temperature are shown on Figure 3-9 b. It is clearly seen from the latter that increased mixing time τ_D causes a contraction of the hysteresis loop, an approach in the critical values of φ and θ for the ignition and extinction regions (i and e) and a transition to the uncritical process for sufficiently large values of τ_D (small enough τ_{sD}—curves 2 and 1).

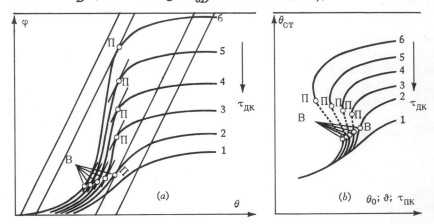

Fig. 3-9. Stationary levels of the process and critical ignition and extinction phenomena for a finite mixing time. (a) Intersection of the heat–liberation and –supply curves in a $\varphi - \theta$ diagram (θ_0 and τ_{sD} parameters); (b) curves of stationary values of the combustion temperature; 3, 4, 5, 6—hysteresis process; 2—limiting case of ignition and extinction coincidence; 1—uncritical process; $B(i)$—ignition; $\Pi(e)$—extinction.

It would not be difficult to perform a similar construction for the variation of the other two process parameters, the nondimensional stay time τ_{sK} for fixed θ_0 and ϑ (and separately τ_K) or the characteristic heat productivity ϑ for fixed values of θ_0 and τ_{sK} (i.e., τ_s and τ_K). Since, as is not difficult to establish, the influence of the mixing time τ_D in all these cases is qualitatively uniform, let us be limited to just indicating the direction of the increase in the values of τ_{sK} and ϑ (along the abscissa of Figure 3-9 b).

The curves of the stationary values can also be obtained for a variation in the τ_{DK} parameter (as before, for a change in τ_D and $\tau_K = $ const) and for constant θ_0, τ_{sK}, and ϑ. Such a case is shown on Figure 3-10 constructed, for illustration, in a rather distorted form (the divergence between the $\varphi_I(\theta)$ curves for different

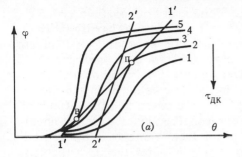

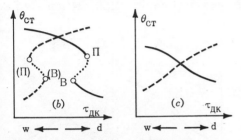

values of τ_{DK} in the range of low φ and θ values is exaggerated). A characteristic hysteresis curve of the stationary temperature (Figure 3-10b) is obtained for the heat-elimination line 1'-1' on Figure 3-10a, and the corresponding continuous stationary temperature curve (Figure 3-10c) for the line 2'-2'.

Just as before in the case of the hysteresis process, an increase in the parameter τ_{DK} leads to a shift in the stationary level to the region of lower values of the completeness and temperature of combustion and to extinction; a decrease in τ_{DK} leads to an increase in the stationary values of φ and θ and to ignition. The critical values of the variables for ignition and extinction are related by the following inequalities in this case

$$\theta_e > \theta_i; \quad \varphi_e > \varphi_i$$

and

$$\tau_{DKi} < \tau_{DKe}$$

Fig. 3-10. Influence of mixing time on the critical temperature and completeness of combustion. (a) Intersection of heat-liberation and-elimination curves in the $\varphi - \theta$ diagram ($\tau_{DK_1} > \tau_{DK_2} >$ ..... τ_{DK_3}); (b) and (c) curves of the stationary values of temperature for the hysteresis and uncritical processes; solid line, thermal region of the chamber; dashed line, thermal region of the combustion zone.

which, as before, reflect the "inertia" of the process.

Let us recall that the reasoning developed above on the influence of the mixing time on the thermal region of the process refers to the solid curves mapped on Figures 3-10b and c. The probable character of the curves of the stationary values of the combustion temperature in the region of low mixing-time values is shown by dashes on the same Figures 3-10b and c. Such a curve corresponds to the assumption that the value of the stationary temperature and the total completeness of combustion of the mixture ($\varphi = 1 - c_k/c_0$) is limited, in principle, by both small and large values of τ_{DK} or by the velocity w and dimension d. As regards the character of the curve, it can have, for example, two hysteresis loops on both sides of the stable combustion section (Figure 3-11a), or it can drop smoothly on both sides (Figure 3-11c) or, finally, it can have a

hysteresis loop on one side and a continuous temperature reduction on the other.[16] (Figure 3-11*b* and *c*.) It would hardly be expedient to express quantitative relations corresponding to Figures
3-10 and 3-11 in general form without analysis of experimental
material. They could be of practical interest only in connection
with the consideration of changes in the flow velocity and in the
residual parameters. Apparently, very different local relations between the individual parameters are possible under specific conditions; in particular, an increase in the local velocity in the region
close to diffusion combustion can lead to intensification of the process and an increase in the completeness of combustion, within limits.

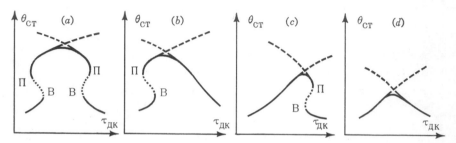

Fig. 3-11. Examples of curves of the dependence of the stationary combustion temperature on mixing time.

Let us also note that these derivations are complicated still
more by allowance for heat loss, an essential allowance for low
values of the velocity and high values of τ_D, respectively.

Consequently, let us turn to more general results. Let us first
note that in practice the combustion of non-premixed combustible
mixture components is determined by purely diffusion combustion,
when the mixing time and the reaction [time, Ed.] of the upper stationary level of the process (combustion far from the extinction
region) are commensurable. This level is characterized by the
stationary values of mixture heating and completeness of combustion, mentioned above for the diffusion combustion case, Eqs. (3-49)
and (3-50).

In contradistinction to this, the lower stationary level (oxidation)
and approximately the ignition conditions lie in the kinetic combustion region and therefore agree with the analogous relations for the
combustion of a well-mixed mixture. Finally, the extinction conditions for appreciable values of τ_D (i.e., comparatively low values
of τ_{SD}) correspond to a considerably lower completeness of com-

[16]Analogous curves with two pairs of critical conditions, etc., will be
considered in more detail in the next chapter under the investigation of a
process with heat loss.

bustion than in the kinetic combustion of a well-mixed mixture and to almost the same values of the temperature; extinction in the combustion of inhomogeneous mixtures is always accomplished in the intermediate region.

On the whole, an increase in the mixing time τ_D lowers the stationary values of φ and θ, other conditions being equal, facilitates extinction and makes ignition difficult and, finally, narrows the region where critical phenomena exist (the region of the hysteresis process). The process makes the transition into the uncritical region for sufficiently large values of τ_D (although a clearly marked hysteresis process corresponds to the same values of the quantity τ_{sK} and all the rest of the parameters in purely kinetic combustion).

The last conclusions can also be verified by a quantitative estimate of the influence of mixing on the critical ignition and extinction conditions. Let us derive certain expressions for the critical values of the variables φ_{cr} and θ_{cr} for this purpose. From the general ignition and extinction equations

$$\varphi_I(\theta) = \varphi_{II}(\theta); \quad \frac{d\varphi_I}{d\theta} = \frac{d\varphi_{II}}{d\theta}$$

where

$$\varphi_I = \frac{1}{1 + \dfrac{1}{\tau_{SD}} + \dfrac{e^{1/\theta}}{\tau_{sK}}} \tag{3-45}$$

and

$$\varphi_{II} = \frac{\theta - \theta_0}{\vartheta} \tag{3-51}$$

and, respectively:

$$\frac{d\varphi_I}{d\theta} = \frac{e^{1/\theta}/\tau_{sK}}{\theta^2 \left(1 + \dfrac{1}{\tau_{SD}} + \dfrac{e^{1/\theta}}{\tau_{sK}}\right)^2} = \frac{1 - \varphi(1 + \tau_{DS})}{\theta^2}\varphi$$

$$\frac{d\varphi_{II}}{d\theta} = \frac{1}{\vartheta}$$

It is not difficult to obtain an expression for the critical completeness of combustion $\varphi_{cr} = \varphi(\theta; \theta_0; \tau_{SD})$ in the form

$$\varphi_{cr} = \frac{1 - \dfrac{\theta^2}{\theta - \theta_0}}{1 + \tau_{DS}} = \frac{\varphi_{cr,kin}}{1 + \tau_{DS}} \tag{3-52}$$

$$\varphi_{cr,kin} = 1 - \frac{\theta^2}{\theta - \theta_0} \tag{2-23}$$

As in kinetic combustion, the maximum values of $\varphi_{cr,\,max}$ correspond to the lines[17]

$$\varphi_{cr,\,max} = 1 - 2\theta = 1 - 4\theta_0 \tag{2-25}$$

while the limiting values for $\theta_0 \ll \theta$ correspond to the family

$$\varphi_{cr,\,lim} = \frac{1 - \theta}{1 + \tau_{DS}} \tag{3-53}$$

This formula transforms into (2-24) for kinetic combustion as $\tau_{SD} \to \infty$ ($\tau_D \to 0$). As τ_D increases, the region where the hysteresis process exists in the $\varphi - \theta$ diagram diminishes more and more in ordinate while remaining invariant along the abscissa.

Similarly, the ignition region is also displaced toward lesser values of the completeness of combustion. Its boundary, the line where ignition and extinction coincide, from the inflection conditions of the $\varphi_I(\theta)$ curve, according to Eq. (3-45)

$$\frac{d^2\varphi_I}{d\theta^2} = 0 = -\frac{e^{1/\theta}}{\theta^2}\left(1 + \frac{1}{\tau_{SD}} + \frac{e^{1/\theta}}{\tau_{sK}}\right)^2 \theta^2 - 2\theta\, e^{1/\theta}\left(1 + \frac{1}{\tau_{SD}} + \frac{e^{1/\theta}}{\tau_{sK}}\right)^2 +$$

$$2\theta^2 e^{1/\theta}\left(1 + \frac{1}{\tau_{SD}} + \frac{e^{1/\theta}}{\tau_{sK}}\right)\frac{e^{1/\theta}}{\tau_{sK}\theta^2}$$

is expressed by

$$\varphi_{i-e} = \frac{\dfrac{1}{2} - \theta}{1 + \tau_{DS}} = \frac{\varphi_{i-e,\,kin}}{1 + \tau_{DS}} \tag{3-54}$$

where $\varphi_{i-e,\,kin}$ is defined by (2-26). This reduction in the region of the hysteresis regime for an increase in τ_D, and all the other parameters constant, is illustrated in Figure 3-12 and in Figure 3-13a also (see below).

Now, let us equate the values of $\varphi_{cr}(\theta)$ from (3-52) and $\varphi_{II}(\theta)$

$$\frac{1 - \dfrac{\theta^2}{\theta - \theta_0}}{1 + \tau_{DS}} = \frac{\theta - \theta_0}{\vartheta} \quad \text{or} \quad 1 - \frac{\theta^2}{\theta - \theta_0} = (1 + \tau_{DS})\frac{\theta - \theta_0}{\vartheta}$$

The expression obtained differs from the analogous expression for the kinetic combustion case (section 2-4) in that the value of the

---

[17] From (3-52)

$$\frac{d\varphi_{cr}}{d\theta} = \frac{1}{1 + \tau_{DS}}\frac{d\varphi_{cr,\,max}}{d\theta} = 0$$

and therefore

$$\varphi_{cr,\,max} = \varphi_{cr,\,kin,\,max} = 1 - 2\theta \tag{2-25}$$

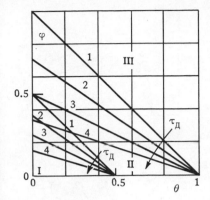

Fig. 3-12. Influence of mixing time on the distribution of characteristic regions in the diagram. I—Ignition; II—extinction (region of the hysteresis process); III—region of the hysteresis process; $1-\tau_{SD} = \infty$; $2-\tau_{SD} = 2.5$; $3-\tau_{SD} = 1$; $4-\tau_{SD} = 0.5$.

heat productivity characteristic ϑ is as though reduced by the ratio $1/(1 + \tau_{SD})$. Consequently, the expression $\theta_{cr} = \theta(\theta_0, \vartheta, \tau_{SD})$ can be written without derivation to replace (2-32) for kinetic combustion, as

$$\theta_{cr} = \frac{1 + \dfrac{2\theta_0}{\vartheta}(1 + \tau_{DS}) \pm \sqrt{1 - 4\theta_0 - 4\theta_0^2 \dfrac{1 + \tau_{DS}}{\vartheta}}}{2\left(1 + \dfrac{1 + \tau_{DS}}{\vartheta}\right)} \qquad (3\text{-}55)$$

The minus sign corresponds to ignition, the plus to extinction. We again arrive at the Semenov formula (for ignition) as $\vartheta \to \infty$ (neglecting complete burn-up; the value of φ_{cr} in (3-52) is zero)

$$\theta_{i,\,\vartheta \to \infty} = \frac{1 - \sqrt{1 - 4\theta_0}}{2} \qquad (1\text{-}19)$$

The character of the dependence (3-55) is shown on Figure 3-13c below. Using as a basis the same effect of an apparent reduction in the heat productivity of the mixture because of a finite mixing time, we also write the expression for $\theta_{cr} = \theta(\varphi, \vartheta, \tau_{SD})$, without derivation, as

$$\theta_{cr} = \sqrt{\varphi(1 - \varphi)\frac{\vartheta}{1 + \tau_{DS}}} = \frac{\theta_{cr,\,kin}}{\sqrt{1 + \tau_{DS}}} \qquad (3\text{-}56)$$

where

$$\theta_{cr,\,kin} = \sqrt{\varphi(1 - \varphi)\vartheta} \qquad (2\text{-}31)$$

The influence of a finite mixing time τ_D on the critical ignition and extinction conditions which result from (3-52) to (3-56) is illustrated diagramatically on Figure 3-13. The first graph (Figure 3-13a) is similar to Figure 2-10c in the preceding chapter and is a supplement to Figure 3-12. The second graph (Figure 3-13b) is

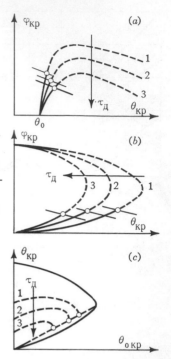

Fig. 3-13. Influence of mixing time on the
curves of the critical temperature and completeness of combustion values. *Remarks:*
1—Parameters on the graphs: (*a*) θ_0 = const;
(*b*) *e* = const. 2—The arrows show the direction of increasing mixing time τ_D. Solid
line, ignition; dashed line, extinction; dotted
and dashed line, coincidence of extinction
and ignition.

analogous to Figure 2-13; finally, the third (Figure 3-13*c*) is similar to Figure 2-14. They all show that an increase in the mixing
time leads to an increase in the region of the uncritical process,
difficult ignition, easy extinction, etc., for the total process in the
chamber.

Chapter 4

Complex Heat Exchange

4-1. PROCESS WITH HEAT SUPPLY

In the preceding chapters, the combustion process was assumed to be adiabatic; it was assumed that all the heat liberated during combustion transforms into the heat content of the combustion products. Both the simplest problems considered above correspond to this assumption: the thermal region of an adiabatic chamber when a well-mixed or unmixed mixture is burned or the thermal region of the surface of a solid phase during heterogeneous combustion. In the latter case, the concept of the adiabatic character of the process was referred to the reacting gas whose combustion products completely absorb and eliminate from the surface all the heat being liberated in the case of purely convective heat emission.

In contrast, elementary cases of the thermal region of the combustion processes will be analyzed in this chapter, which proceed nonadiabatically, i.e., with a supply of heat to the reacting mixture or its elimination. In this case, particularly in the process with heat supply, we shall speak not of the whole combustion chamber but about a certain isolated part of it. In actual processes, heat supply from a developed flame tongue or incandescent walls of the chamber to the fresh mixture in the initial zone of the chamber plays a very large part in the reliability and stability of ignition. Precisely this heat supply, more exactly the continuous recycle of part of the heat from the region of the developed combustion process to the ignition zone of the fresh mixture, guarantees the accomplishment of a steady-state process in the chambers in which components usually not self-igniting burn.

One of the most widespread methods of returning a part of the heat to the fresh mixture is to mix the latter with hot combustion products. Consequently, let us start with precisely this very simple problem. For simplicity let us be limited to the case of the burning of a well-mixed mixture (kinetic combustion); let us also assume that the mixing process of the fresh mixture and the combustion products proceeds very rapidly, and let us compare the stationary levels corresponding to the initial (fresh mixture) and the final (well-mixed mixture of the initial components and the reaction products) states. In such a formulation of the problem, the part of the mixing is reduced, first, to a decrease in the heat productivity of the final mixture in comparison with the fresh initial mixture because of dilution and second, to an increase in the initial temperature (θ_0) of the final mixture in comparison with that of the fresh mixture. As before, we neglect the change in specific heat.

To be more graphic, let us consider the following simple example. Let us assume that the intersection of the heat-liberation curve $\varphi_I(\theta)$ and the heat-elimination line $\varphi_{II}(\theta)$ (solid line 1) shown on Figure 4-1, corresponds to the stationary course of the reaction in the fresh mixture. Let us use the subscript 1 for the fresh mixture quantities entering in the heat-elimination expression $\varphi_{II}(\theta)$ and the subscript 2 for the final mixture (i.e., the mixture of the initial components and the combustion products).

Therefore, let be for the fresh mixture

$$\varphi_{II,1} = \frac{1}{\vartheta_1}(\theta - \theta_{0,1}) \tag{4-1}$$

where this equation refers to a certain initial section of the chamber. Denoting the mixture stay time in this section by τ_{s1} and selecting the appropriate curve on the $\varphi - \theta$ diagram, we obtain, for example (Figure 4-1), that the point of intersection I lies on the lower level (oxidation). If it is assumed for simplicity that the mixing with the combustion products occurs in equal ratio (1:1), then the parameters of the new mixture in this same part of the chamber will be

$$\vartheta_2 = \vartheta_1/2 \text{ heat productivity and}$$

$$\theta_{02} = \frac{\theta_{01} + \theta_{02}}{2} = \theta_{01} + \frac{\vartheta_1}{2} \text{ initial temperature}$$

It is assumed here that the fresh mixture is mixed with the total combustion products returning from the end zone of the chamber. For the latter $\varphi = 1$; $\theta = \theta_M = \theta_{01} + \vartheta_1$.

Under this assumption a new heat-elimination line (line 2, dashed on Figure 4-1), will correspond to the following equation

$$\varphi_{II,2} = \frac{1}{\vartheta_2}(\theta - \theta_{02}) = \frac{2}{\vartheta_1}\left(\theta - \theta_{01} - \frac{\vartheta_1}{2}\right) \tag{4-2}$$

Therefore, the line 2 will pass through the same point $\theta = \theta_m$ for $\varphi = 1$ as the line 1 does, and through the point $\theta = \theta_{02} = \theta_{01} + (\theta_m - \theta_{01})/2$ for $\varphi = 0$ which is again on the middle of the segment $\theta_{01} - \theta_m$. As is seen from Figure 4-1, the point of intersection II in the region of the high stationary level, corresponding to combustion, can correspond to the new intersection of the curves $\varphi_I(\theta)$ and $\varphi_{II}(\theta)$. It is essential that such a displacement of the stationary level into the region beyond the ignition point should refer not only to the initial curve $\varphi_I(\theta)$ (solid line) but also to a number of them down to a certain dashed curve on Figure 4-1a. If the exceptionally rapid growth of the parameter τ_{sK} in the $\varphi - \theta$ diagram (Figure 2-10) is recalled here, then it becomes evident that the transition from the solid heat-liberation curve to the dashed curve on Figure 4-1a can correspond to a decrease in the value of τ_{sKi}, the "ignition delay" time, by a whole order.

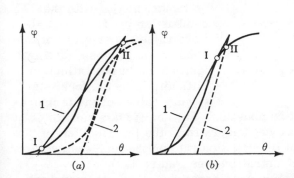

(a) (b)

Fig. 4-1. Influence of mixing a fresh mixture with combustion products at a stationary combustion level and critical ignition and extinction phenomena. (a) Ignition; (b) departure from extinction; 1—line of elimination of heat for a fresh mixture; 2—line of elimination of heat for a (1:1) mixture of initial and final combustion products.

Shown on Figure 4-1b for the same example is the possible departure from a practically unstable state near extinction (I) to a more stable combustion region (II) when the initial products are mixed with the final products.

In the general case, if the mixing of the fresh mixture with the products of its complete combustion occurs in the proportion 1:a, the new value of the initial temperature on the $\varphi - \theta$ diagram will be

$$\theta_{02} = \frac{\theta_{01}(1 + a) + a\vartheta}{1 + a} = \theta_{01} + \frac{a}{1 + a} \qquad (4\text{-}3)$$

and the new value of the mixture heat productivity will be correspondingly

$$\vartheta_2 = \frac{\vartheta_1}{1 + a} \qquad (4\text{-}4)$$

A change in the stationary region for different values of the number a is shown on Figure 4-2. As is seen from this graph, starting with a certain minimum value a_{min}, the mixture ignition, being absent for a given value of τ_{sK} in the initial conditions, can always be guaranteed. Let us note that the assumption on mixing

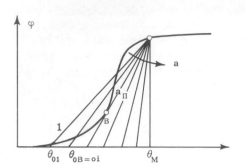

Fig. 4-2. Influence of mixing a fresh mixture with the combustion products on ignition.

with the complete combustion products, used in these examples for simplicity of the computation, is understandably not at all obligatory since the qualitative character of the phenomena remains the same.[1]

Hence, mixing with the combustion products will always raise the stability of the combustion process, facilitate ignition and make extinction difficult, raise the local stationary values of the temperature and completeness of combustion. Physically, this results directly from the predominance, remarked in the introduction, of the exponential dependence of the reaction rate on the temperature over its dependence on the concentration (see Figure 1-7).

In particular, these simple considerations clarify the physical substance of the means of "attaching" the tongue, known for a long time in furnace technology, by means of introducing a poorly streamlined body (Figure 4-3a) into the flow. As is known, a zone of reverse currents is built up behind the latter. Turbulent mixing of the combustion products, returning because of circulation, and the incoming fresh mixture, occurs on the boundary of this zone. This mixing guarantees, as does the "diffusion effect" for a sudden broadening in the channel (Figure 4-3b), stable ignition within definite limits of the flow velocity, i.e., the stay time τ_{sK}. It is very probable that precisely this phenomenon[2] would basically explain the so-called "flameless combustion" (31), say.

A similar continuous incendiary mechanism is realized in very different jet furnaces also, for example, in coal-dust furnaces. In this case, the jet issuing from the burner into the chamber filled with hot combustion products (Figure 4-3c) draws them back to the heart of the jet and creates a turbulent boundary layer in which ignition is accomplished. Moreover, the same mechanism, as G. F.

[1]For example, the mixing of the initial mixture with the combustion products for a certain value $\varphi < 1$, and $\theta = \theta_{01} + \varphi\vartheta < \theta_m$, respectively, in the first example, would yield $\theta_{02} = \theta_{01} + \varphi\vartheta/2$; the line $\varphi_{II}(\theta)$ would be rotated through a smaller angle around the point $\varphi = 1$; $\theta = \theta_m$ [$\vartheta_2 = \vartheta_1(1 - \varphi/2)$], i.e., the final effect of the mixing would be rather weaker than at $\varphi = 1$.

[2]Possibly in conjunction with the radiation which leads to abrupt heating of the wall, which in turn does not permit the gases in the eddy zone to be cooled despite the low velocity.

Knorre (25) indicated, apparently plays a fundamental part (probably again jointly with radiation) in the ignition of coal particles or of hot gases (carbon monoxide, volatile gases) also in the solid-fuel layer because of the formation of stagnant, circulating zones when the flow separates around the individual pieces of coal. Let us also note that return of the combustion products to the fresh-mixture region is still more essential in the burning of liquid fuel since it leads to an acceleration in fuel evaporation.

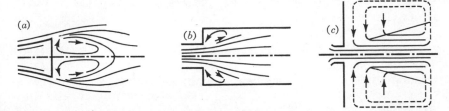

Fig. 4-3. Examples of tongue stabilization because of premixing of the combustion products with the fresh mixture. (a) Poorly streamlined body (screen); (b) abrupt broadening (diffusor effect); (c) free turbulent jet.

If the reasoning on the difference between lean and rich mixtures, presented in Chapter 2 (Figures 2-8 and 2-9) is recalled, then it becomes qualitatively conceivable that the ignition conditions of rich mixtures will be more reliable when the combustion products with the usual values of the stoichiometric number χ_0 (of the order of 10 to 15) are mixed, than for lean mixtures. For example, a lean mixture (α'), with $\alpha' > 1$ and $\alpha'' = 1/\alpha' < 1$, can be ignited stably at a significantly higher value of the time τ_{sK}, i.e., at a lesser value of the velocity than for the rich mixture (α'').

A more detailed survey of these or other similar specific cases of flame stabilization (25) is beyond the scope of this book.

It is not difficult to consider the question of the role of secondary air (mixing of the combustion products of a rich mixture with air) analogously to the influence of the mixing of a fresh mixture with combustion products, by the same method of investigating the intersection of the curves in the $\varphi - \theta$ diagram. However, it will be more expedient to investigate this problem later in connection with a concrete example of the combustion process (section 5-3).

Now, let us turn to the general case of heat supply without relating it to the return of the combustion products any more. For simplicity, let us start from a linear dependence of the quantity of heat supplied as a function of the difference in temperature; let us consider the heat supply source to be the complete combustion zone $(\varphi = 1)$ at the temperature $\theta_m = \theta_0 + \vartheta$.

Let the quantity of heat supplied per kg of mixture be

$$Q_w = \alpha F (T_m - T)\tau_s \tag{4-5}$$

where, as in Chapter 3, α is the heat-transfer coefficient (heat supply in this case); $F(m^2/kg)$ is the magnitude of the specific surface receiving the heat.

The heat-balance equation per kg of mixture, taking (4-5) into account, is

$$\varphi q c_0 = c_p(T - T_0) - \alpha F(T_m - T)\tau_s \tag{4-6}$$

or, solving for φ

$$\varphi = \frac{c_p}{q c_0}(T - T_0) - \frac{c_p}{q c_0}\frac{\alpha}{c_p k_0} \cdot k_0 \tau_s (T_m - T) \tag{4-6'}$$

Transforming to nondimensional variables

$$\theta = \frac{RT}{E}; \quad \theta_0 = \frac{RT_0}{E}; \quad \vartheta = \frac{R_q c_0}{E c_p}$$

$$\tau_{sK} = k_0 \tau_s = \frac{\tau_s}{\tau_k}; \quad \theta_m = \frac{RT_m}{E} = \theta_0 \vartheta$$

and introducing the additional parameter

$$\beta = \frac{\alpha F}{c_p k_0} \tag{4-7}$$

where β is the nondimensional heat-transfer coefficient, we obtain

$$\varphi_{II} = \frac{1}{\vartheta}(\theta - \theta_0 - \beta \tau_{sK}(\theta_m - \theta_0)) \tag{4-8}$$

or, taking the equality $\theta_m = \theta_0 + \vartheta$ into account

$$\varphi_{II} = \frac{1 + \beta \tau_{sK}}{\vartheta}(\theta - \theta_0) - \beta \tau_{sK} \tag{4-8'}$$

It is seen from (4-8) that, in the presence of heat supply, the product[3] of the dimensionless heat-transfer coefficient β and the stay time τ_{sK} also enters into the expression for $\varphi_{II}(\theta)$ in addition to the previous variables.

As an illustration, let us solve (4-8') with respect to the combustion temperature

$$\theta = \theta_0 + \frac{\varphi + \beta \tau_{sK}}{1 + \beta \tau_{sK}}\vartheta \tag{4-9}$$

---

[3] Since τ_{sK} occurs independently in the equation for $\varphi_I(\theta)$, it is not expedient to introduce the product $\beta \tau_{sK}$ as a criterion in the general case.

As is usual, (4-9) for $\varphi = 1$ yields

$$\theta = \theta_0 + \vartheta = \theta_m$$

which corresponds physically to the assumption of an internal heat redistribution during the process (but not of an external heat supply source independent of the reaction).

In the other extreme case, we have from (4-9) for $\varphi = 0$

$$\theta_{\varphi = 0} = \theta_0 \frac{\vartheta}{1 + 1/\beta\tau_{sK}} \tag{4-10}$$

As in the adiabatic process, we have for $\beta = 0$ (absence of a heat supply for $\alpha = 0$) or for $\tau_{sK} = 0$ (heat supply equal to zero at the first moment of mixture inflow $\tau_s = 0$): $\theta_{\varphi = 0} = \theta_0$. However, it follows from (4-10) for $\beta \neq 0$ and $\tau_{sK} \neq 0$ (i.e., $\alpha > 0$ and $\tau_s > 0$): $\theta_{\varphi = 0} > \theta_0$; particularly as $\tau_{sK} \to \infty$ the line $\varphi_{II}(\theta)$ becomes parallel to the vertical axis as $\theta_{\varphi = 0} \to \theta_m$.

Hence the presence of heat supply leads to two effects: to a change in the slope of the line of resultant heat elimination $\varphi_{II}(\theta)$, i.e., to the replacement of the real heat productivity ϑ by the reduced quantity

$$\vartheta_{eff} = \frac{\vartheta}{1 + \beta\tau_{sK}} \tag{4-11}$$

and to a change in the intersection of the line $\varphi_{II}(\theta)$ with the horizontal axis, i.e., as if replacing the real value of the initial mixture temperature θ_0 by its reduced, effective value

$$\theta_{0, eff} = \theta_{\varphi = 0} = \theta_0 + \frac{\beta\tau_{sK}}{1 + \beta\tau_{sK}} \vartheta \tag{4-10'}$$

For a given value of the heat-transfer coefficient β, the lines

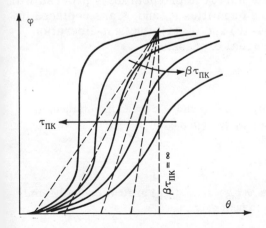

Fig. 4-4. Influence of heat supply on the stationary levels of the combustion process. Upper arrow shows the rotation of the heat-elimination lines as the stay time or the heat-transfer coefficient increases for a given time τ_{sK}; lower arrow, change in the heat-liberation curves as the stay time increases.

$\varphi_{II}(\theta)$ on the $\varphi - \theta$ diagram seem to rotate around the point $\varphi = 1$; $\theta = \theta_m$ toward increasing values of the temperature (Figure 4-4) as the stay time τ_{sK} increases. Now, there are not one line $\varphi_{II}(\theta)$ and a family of curves $\varphi_I(\theta)$ as occurred in the adiabatic process, but two families: the lines $\varphi_{II}(\theta)$ and the curves $\varphi_I(\theta)$ (Figure 4-4) correspond to different values of the parameter τ_{sK} in the $\varphi - \theta$ diagram.

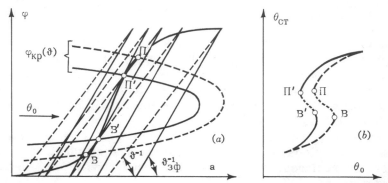

Fig. 4-5. Influence of the initial temperature on the stationary combustion temperature with heat supply. Dashed line, adiabatic process; solid line, process with heat supply; (a) intersection of the curves in the $\varphi - \theta$ diagram ($\varphi_{cr}(\theta)$); the curve $\vartheta = \text{const}$; dashed line for the real value of ϑ; solid line for the effective value of ϑ; (b) curve of the stationary values of the combustion temperature.

If we speak of the construction of the curves of the stationary values of the temperature and the completeness of combustion[4] as a function of the initial temperature θ_0 for given values of ϑ, τ_{sK}, and β (Figure 4-5) or of the heat productivity of the mixture ϑ for given values of θ_0, τ_{sK}, and β (Figure 4-6), then the problem will be completely analogous to the adiabatic problem for a process with heat supply if the values of the quantities θ_0 and ϑ are replaced by their effective values from (4-10) and (4-11); the heat-liberation curve $\varphi_I(\theta)$ here retains its usual expression

$$\varphi_I = \frac{\tau_{sK}}{\tau_{sK} + e^{1/\theta}} \tag{2-14}$$

[4]Let us note that the similarity of the φ and θ curves is retained, at first glance, only if the parameter θ_0 is replaced by its effective value $\theta_{0\,\text{eff}}$ from (4-10)

$$\varphi = \frac{\theta - \theta_{0\,\text{eff}}}{\theta \ - \theta_{0\,\text{eff}}}$$

In general, the stationary curves $\theta(\tau_{sK})$ and $\varphi(\tau_{sK})$ are not mutually similar for constants θ_0, ϑ, and β with heat exchange.

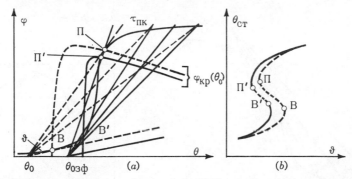

Fig. 4-6. Influence of mixture heat productivity on the stationary combustion temperature with heat supply (τ_{sK} = const; θ_0 = const; β = const). Dashed line, adiabatic process; solid line, process with heat supply; (a) intersection of the curves in the $\varphi - \theta$ diagram ($\varphi_{cr}(\theta)$); (b) the curve θ_0 = const; dashed line for real values of $\theta_{0\,cr}$; solid line for effective values of $\theta_{0\,cr}$.

The quantity ϑ_{eff} is less than the actual characteristic of the the mixture heat productivity ϑ; the quantity $\theta_{0\,eff}$ is larger than the actual value θ_0. In this connection, as also follows from very simple considerations, the effect of heat supply leads to earlier ignition by comparison with the adiabatic process

$$\theta'_{oe} < \theta_{oead}; \quad \vartheta_i < \vartheta'_{iad}$$

and later extinction

$$\theta'_{oe} < \theta_{oead}; \quad \vartheta'_i < \vartheta_{iad}$$

The quantities with the primes here refer to a process with heat supply, and with the subscript *ad* to the adiabatic process (Figures 4-5 and 4-6). In other words, heat supply extends the limits of stable combustion in comparison with the combustion process both with respect to the initial temperature and in terms of the heat productivity or the composition of the mixture. This means that ignition occurs for a smaller value of θ_0, other conditions remaining the same; in its turn, extinction occurs for stronger cooling, i.e., again for a smaller value of θ_0. Similarly, ignition and extinction with heat supply occur for a respectively leaner ($\alpha > 1$ case) or richer ($\alpha < 1$ case) mixture than in the absence of heat supply. Let us also note that heat supply, according to the effect on the $\varphi_{II}(\theta)$ lines, is analogous to the case of mixing a fresh mixture with the combustion products (Figures 4-1 and 4-2).

Shown on Figure 4-7 is a construction of the stationary combustion temperature curve as the heat-emission coefficient β and the constants θ_0, τ_{sK}, and ϑ are varied. Graphically, the problem re-

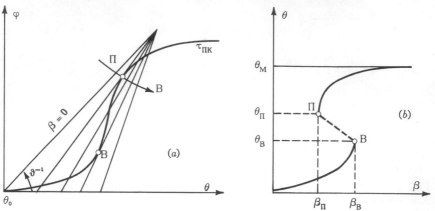

Fig. 4-7. Effect of heat-transfer coefficient (heat supply) on the stationary combustion temperature (θ_0 = const; τ_{sK} = const; ϑ = const). (a) Intersection of the curves in the $\varphi - \theta$ diagram; (b) curve of the stationary combustion temperature.

duces to the investigation of the conditions for the intersection of the family of $\varphi_{II}(\theta)$ lines for a parameter with one $\varphi_I(\theta)$ curve. This is analogous to the preceding in the other cases.

As follows from the above-mentioned Figure 4-4, the construction of the stationary temperature curve as a function of the stay time τ_{sK} for constant θ_0, ϑ, and β reduces graphically to looking for the point of intersection of the family of $\varphi_I(\theta)$ curves with the family of $\varphi_{II}(\theta)$ lines during the successive transition from one pair of curves to the other. This case is shown separately in Figure 4-8; here also, the presence of heat supply increases the stability of the process; the latter is evident both from the physical meaning

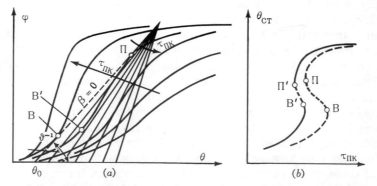

Fig. 4-8. Effect of stay time on the stationary combustion temperature with heat supply (θ_0 = const; ϑ = const; β = const). Dashed line, adiabatic process; solid line, process with heat supply; (a) intersection of the curves in the $\varphi - \theta$ diagram; (b) curve of the stationary combustion temperature.

of the phenomena and from the geometrical, and from the "counter" motion of the $\varphi_I(\theta)$ and $\varphi_{II}(\theta)$ curves in the $\varphi - \theta$ diagram as τ_{sK} increases.

The conditions corresponding to the more complex case of the hysteresis process are shown on all the graphs (Figures 4-5 to 4-8). In addition, naturally, a noncritical process is also possible; the construction of similar curves for this case or their interpretation does not cause any difficulty. Let us also note that the assumption on the equality of the heat source temperature to a quantity T_m, introduced for simplicity, does not limit the conclusions obtained in any way. For example, if it is assumed that the fresh mixture obtains heat from a source whose temperature is $T_1 < T_m$ (by abutting the red-hot chamber walls, etc., say), then this just leads to a change in (4-8)

$$\varphi_I = \frac{1}{\vartheta}\,(\theta - \theta_0 - \beta\tau_{sK}\,(\theta - \theta_0))$$

i.e., to new effective values of $\theta_{0\,\text{eff}}$ and ϑ_{eff}, namely:

$$\theta_{\varphi=0} = \frac{\theta_0 + \beta\tau_{sK}\,\theta_1}{1 + \beta\tau_{sK}}$$

$$\theta_{\varphi=1} = \frac{\theta_0 + \vartheta + \beta\tau_{sK}\,\theta_1}{1 + \beta\tau_{sK}}$$

The behavior of the solution and the conclusions, in principle, remain the same in this case as in the $\theta_1 = \theta_m$ case. Consequently, let us return to the interpretation of the effect of heat supply on heterogeneous combustion without considering the process for $\theta_1 = \theta_m$.

The basic Eqs. (3-10) for $\varphi_I(\theta)$ and (4-8) for $\varphi_{II}(\theta)$ remain the same in this case as for the combustion of a well-mixed mixture when the parameter τ_{sK} is replaced by the nondimensional time τ_{DK}. The invariance of the first of these for the quantity $\varphi_I(\theta)$ is evident since this expression is defined entirely by the heat-liberation law. As regards the second expression, for $\varphi_{II}(\theta)$, to derive it we shall write the heat-balance equation for unit surface of the solid phase

$$\alpha_D(c_0 - c)q = \alpha(T - T_0) - \alpha_1(T_m - T) \tag{4-12}$$

The coefficient α_1 is not related to the convective-heat-transfer process in the boundary layer but rather is a linearized radiation-heat-transfer coefficient.

Let us rewrite (4-12) as

$$\varphi = 1 - \frac{c}{c_0} = \frac{c_p}{qc_0} \cdot \frac{\alpha}{\alpha_D c_p}(T - T_0) - \frac{c_p}{qc_0}\frac{\alpha_1}{c_p k_0}\frac{k_0}{\alpha_D}(T_m - T) \tag{4-12'}$$

or, after introducing the nondimensional variables

$$\theta = \frac{RT}{E}; \quad \vartheta = \frac{Rqc_0}{Ec_p}; \quad \tau_{DK} = \frac{k_0}{\alpha_D}$$

and the new complementary parameter[5]

$$\beta = \frac{\alpha_1}{c_p k_0} \tag{4-13}$$

the nondimensional heat-emission coefficient, taking (3-14) into account: $\alpha = \alpha_D c_p$ (for $a \approx D$), to the final form

$$\varphi_{II} = \frac{1}{\vartheta}(\theta - \theta_0 - \beta\tau_{DK}(\theta_m - \theta_0)) \tag{4-14}$$

which agrees with (4-8) when the parameter τ_{sK} is replaced by τ_{DK}. Consequently, all the results and graphs, given in this paragraph for the combustion of a well-mixed mixture with heat supply, are retained completely for the heterogeneous process also.

The conclusions obtained in this manner for both problems (combustion of a well-mixed mixture and the combustion of coal, say), which reduce basically to a rise in combustion stability with heat supply, i.e., to making ignition easier and extinction more difficult, are perfectly natural physically. The quantitative side of the question, particularly the determination of the critical values of the variables in the process with heat supply, does not merit detailed analysis. Consequently, let us be limited to the remark that all the results, which refer to adiabatic combustion, are retained for heat supply if the effective values of the mixture heat productivity ϑ_{eff}, from Eq. (4-11), and the initial temperature $\theta_{0\ eff}$, from (4-10) replacing the actual values ϑ and θ_0, are introduced in all the final expressions (see Tables 2-1 and 2-2).

As is seen from the above, Figures 4-5 to 4-8, heat supply, in addition to the previously mentioned rise in combustion stability, leads to a broadening of the region of the uncritical process and to a corresponding contraction of region of the hysteresis process.

[5]Expressions (4-7) and (4-13) differ externally by the values of the kinetic constants k_0 (1/sec) for a homogeneous reaction in (4-7) and k_0 (m/sec) for a heterogeneous reaction in (4-13). In substance, the parameter β has the same value in both cases. Thus, for example, if we transform in (4-13) to the effective reaction-rate constant referred to unit volume and if the specific heat c_p is referred to a kilogram of gas, then the expression for β agrees exactly with (4-7).

4-2. ON RADIANT HEAT TRANSFER

The combustion process in the general case is accompanied by complex heat exchange. Specifically, let us consider coal combustion in this section (a heterogeneous process in the isolated element of surface of the solid phase) taking radiant heat transfer into account. As before, the results of the solution can be carried over completely to the combustion of a well-mixed mixture. Because of the complexity related to the introduction of the fourth power of the temperature into the computations, the limiting case of very intense radiant heat emission will be investigated mainly below, so that by comparison the convective term in the heat-elimination equation can be neglected.

Let us recall that the latter, as was shown in Chapter 3, substantially expresses the heat susceptibility of the combustion products of the reacting gas and is related to the gas exchange Eq. (3-14) for the simplest, but practically most important case of $a \approx D$. Hence neglecting convection comparable to radiation is equivalent to neglecting the heat susceptibility of the combustion products. Thus the limiting case under consideration is limited to the region of comparatively low heating of the combustion products and of the coal surface, and such low values of the velocity that the part of radiation in heat elimination is large in comparison with convection.[6]

This simplification permits the basic peculiarities induced in the process by radiation to be explained and permits relations to be obtained which, in addition to those obtained earlier for purely convective heat emission (i.e., the adiabatic process) represent the two limiting cases. The general case of combined heat transfer by convection and radiation is hence intermediate with respect to the limiting cases; heat transfer solely by convection or solely by radiation.

As before, let us start with the heat-balance equation referred to unit reacting surface. Equating the heat being liberated to the heat eliminated (by convection and radiation), we obtain

$$\alpha_D(c_0 - c)q = k_0 e^{-E/RT} cq = \alpha(T - T_D) + c_{np}(T^4 - T_0^4) \quad (4\text{-}15)$$

where c_{np} is the reduced radiation coefficient, taking into account the degree of blackness of the surfaces[7] radiating and receiving heat and the view factor between them.

It has been assumed, for simplicity, in (4-15) that the tempera-

---

[6]Let us recall that we speak of a relative effect, i.e., of the significant influence of radiation with a low reaction rate near the critical ignition and extinction conditions.

[7]Here, as well as later, the radiation of furnace gases is neglected.

ture of the cold surface equals the temperature T_0 of the reacting gas far from the coal surface. Let us be limited as before to the $a \approx D$ case and, correspondingly, to $\alpha = \alpha_D \cdot c_p$ (3-14). Equating the first two expressions in (4-15) and introducing nondimensional variables, we obtain, as before, an expression for the $\varphi_I(\theta)$ curve of heat liberation in the usual form [Eq. (3-10)]

$$\varphi_I = \frac{\tau_{DK}}{\tau_{DK} + e^{1/\theta}} \tag{4-16}$$

We obtain an expression for $\varphi_{II}(\theta)$ from the equality of the first and third expressions in (4-15), taking (3-14) into account

$$\varphi_{II} = \frac{1}{\vartheta}[\theta - \theta_0 + \sigma\tau_{DK}(\theta^4 - \theta_0^4)] \tag{4-17}$$

where, in addition to the notation encountered earlier, it has been assumed that

$$\sigma = \frac{E^3}{R^3} \frac{c_{np}}{k_0 c_p}$$

We call the quantity σ the nondimensional radiant-heat-transfer coefficient or, briefly, the radiation coefficient. As before, the remaining nondimensional variables in (4-16) and (4-17) have the same value as above

$$\theta = \frac{RT}{E}; \quad \theta_0 = \frac{RT_0}{E}; \quad \vartheta = \frac{R_q c_0}{Ec_p}; \quad \tau_{DK} = \frac{k_0}{\alpha_D}; \quad \varphi = 1 - \frac{c}{c_0}$$

Hence the problem with combined heat emission by convection and radiation reduces to an investigation of the intersection and tangency conditions in the $\varphi - \theta$ diagram of the $\varphi_I(\theta)$ curves of (4-16) and the $\varphi_{II}(\theta)$ curves of (4-17). Here what is new in comparison with the previous work is the appearance of the fourth powers of the temperature and, correspondingly, of the nondimensional radiation coefficient σ (instead of the parameter β in the problem of heat exchange according to a linear law of the temperature dependence for a heat supply, section 4-1, or heat emission, see below).

As already mentioned, let us first consider the limiting case of very intense heat emission by radiation for which the convective elimination of heat in the right side of (4-17) can approximately be neglected in comparison with the radiant

$$(\theta - \theta_0) \ll \sigma\tau_{DK}(\theta^4 - \theta_0^4)$$

Under this assumption, we write the expression for $\varphi_{II}(\theta)$ as follows instead of (4-17):

$$\varphi_{II} \approx \frac{\sigma \tau_{DK}}{\vartheta}(\theta^4 - \theta_0^4) \tag{4-18}$$

In order to look for stationary levels of the process and for critical conditions, let us return to the $\varphi - \theta$ diagram. Since the curvature of the fourth-power parabola, $\varphi_{II}(\theta)$, according to (4-18), is small in comparison with the curvature of the exponential curve $\varphi_I(\theta)$, the character of the intersection of the heat-liberation and -emission curves, exactly as the number of critical conditions, also remains the same as in the case of convection alone. The influence of a change in one of the parameters, namely, the initial temperature θ_0 (for constant ϑ, τ_{DK}, and σ) or the mixture heat productivity ϑ (for constant θ_0, τ_{DK}, and σ) remains qualitatively the same as on Figures 2-3a, b, e, f, and 2-4; replacement of the $\varphi_{II}(\theta)$ line on Figure 2-3 by a fourth-degree parabola just changes the quantitative side of the process, which is considered in detail below.

The case of varying the radiation coefficient σ (for constant θ_0, ϑ, and τ_{DK}) is shown diagrammatically on Figure 4-9. An increase in σ here leads to a reduction in the stationary values of the temperature and the completeness of combustion, and to extinction for large enough values of σ; a decrease in σ leads to an increase in φ and θ and ignition. Graphically, the problem reduces to the intersection of one $\varphi_I(\theta)$ curve with a family of $\varphi_{II}(\theta)$ parabolas according to (4-18).

As regards a variation of the last parameter, the nondimensional time, the character of the intersection of the $\varphi_I(\theta)$ and $\varphi_{II}(\theta)$ curves and, respectively, the curves of the stationary values of φ

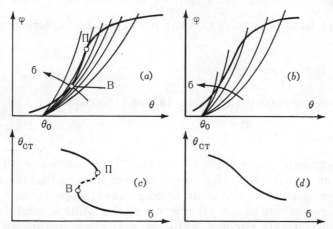

Fig. 4-9. Influence of the radiation coefficient on the stationary value of the combustion temperature. (a) and (b) Intersection of the curves in the $\varphi - \theta$ diagram; (c) and (d) curves of the stationary values of the temperature.

and ϑ, recalls Figure 2-3c and d and Figure 2-4 for convection only, in a comparatively narrow range of very high values of τ_{DK} (for which convective heat emission can be neglected, i.e., heat absorption of the combustion products of the reacting gas) however, with a substantial predominance of the region of the noncritical process (see below). A more detailed investigation of the influence of this parameter while neglecting heat absorption is of no interest since this assumption has no meaning for small τ_{DK}.

This question will be considered later when taking into consideration the combined effect of heat absorption (convective elimination of heat related to gas exchange for coal, $\alpha = \alpha_D c_p$) and heat emission independent of gas exchange.

Basically, no other new, qualitative, phenomena occur in the limiting case of intense heat elimination by radiation as analyzed here; the basic (quantitative) influence of radiation reduces to a sharp cutoff of the region of the hysteresis process.

In order to prove this, let us turn to an investigation of the critical conditions for the limiting case of radiation only. Equating the values of $\varphi_I(\theta)$ (4-16) to $\varphi_{II}(\theta)$ (4-18) and also the first derivatives with respect to the temperature $(d\varphi_I/d\theta = d\varphi_{II}/d\theta)$, we obtain from the system of equalities

$$\frac{\tau_{DK}}{\tau_{DK} + e^{1/\theta}} = \frac{\sigma \tau_{DK}}{\vartheta}(\theta^4 - \theta_0^4)$$

and

$$\frac{1 - \varphi}{\theta^2}\varphi = \frac{4\sigma \tau_{DK}}{\vartheta}\theta^3 = \frac{4\varphi\theta^3}{\theta^4 - \theta_0^4}$$

We obtain, first, an expression for the critical completeness of combustion

$$\varphi_{cr} = 1 - \frac{4\theta^5}{\theta^4 - \theta_0^4} \tag{4-19}$$

The curves constructed using (4-19), and the curves

$$\varphi_{cr, ad} = 1 - \frac{\theta^2}{\theta - \theta_0} \tag{2-23}$$

for the adiabatic process $((\sigma = 0)$ in (4-17)) are shown on Figure 4-10 in the $\varphi - \theta$ plane. By comparison it is seen that the character of these curves is the same in both cases; in particular, in the range of low values of the parameter θ_0 the ignition conditions vary comparatively slightly, while the extinction conditions differ significantly.

Also plotted on Figure 4-10 are the characteristic lines for a process with radiation. The first of these lines, the boundary of

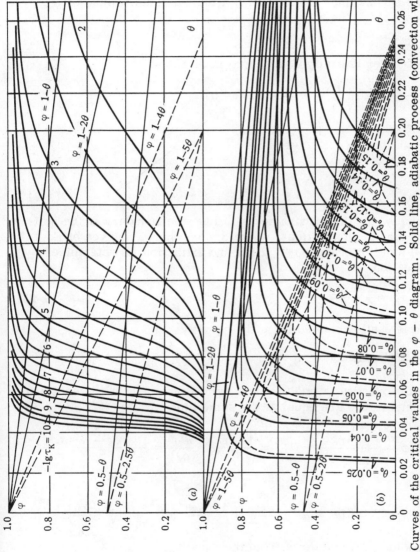

Fig. 4-10. Curves of the critical values in the $\varphi - \theta$ diagram. Solid line, adiabatic process (convection with hetero-geneous combustion); dashed line, heat emission by radiation; (a) heat-liberation curve; (b) curves of critical values ($\theta_{0\,cr}$ = const).

123

the hysteresis region, which corresponds to the limiting extinction conditions (for $\theta_0^4 \ll \theta^4$), is plotted according to the equation

$$\varphi_{cr, \, lim} = 1 - 4\theta \qquad (4\text{-}20)$$

which results directly from (4-19).

The second line, the boundary of the maximum values of φ_{cr}, corresponds to the equation

$$\varphi_{cr, \, max} = 1 - 5\theta \qquad (4\text{-}21)$$

The latter is easily obtained from (4-19)

$$\frac{d\varphi_{cr}}{d\theta} = 20 \, \theta^4(\theta^4 - \theta_0^4) - 16 \, \theta^8 = 0$$

from which

$$\theta = \sqrt[4]{5} \, \theta_0; \quad \theta_0 = \theta/\sqrt[4]{5} \qquad (4\text{-}22)$$

and

$$\varphi_{cr, \, max} = 1 - 5\theta = 1 - 5\sqrt[4]{5} \, \theta_0 \qquad (4\text{-}21')$$

Finally, the third characteristic line, the boundary of the ignition and extinction regions, which divides the φ_{cr} curves of Eq. (4-19) into two branches, ignition and extinction, is determined by the equation

$$\varphi_{ie} = \frac{1}{2} - \frac{5}{2}\theta \qquad (4\text{-}23)$$

which is easily obtained from the equality

$$\frac{d^2\varphi_I}{d\theta^2} = \frac{d^2\varphi_{II}}{d\theta^2}$$

when the quantity φ and the first derivatives of φ with respect to the temperature are equal at the same time

$$\varphi_I = \frac{\tau_{DK}}{\tau_{DK} + e^{1/\theta}}; \quad \frac{d\varphi_I}{d\theta} = \frac{1 - \varphi}{\theta^2} \, \varphi; \quad \frac{d^2\varphi_I}{d\theta^2} = \frac{1 - 2\varphi - 2\theta}{\theta^2} \frac{d\varphi_I}{d\theta}$$

and

$$\varphi_{II} = \frac{\sigma\tau_{DK}}{\vartheta}(\theta^4 - \theta_0^4); \quad \frac{d\varphi_{II}}{d\theta} = \frac{4\sigma\tau_{DK}\theta^3}{\vartheta}; \quad \frac{d^2\varphi_{II}}{d\theta^2} = \frac{3}{\theta} \frac{d\varphi_{II}}{d\theta}$$

from which (4-23) follows from the equality

$$\frac{1 - 2\varphi - 2\theta}{\theta^2} = \frac{3}{\theta}$$

Equating (4-23) and (4-19)

$$1 - \frac{4\theta^5}{\theta^4 - \theta_0^4} = \frac{1 - 5\theta}{2}$$

We also find a relation between the values of θ and θ_0 when the critical ignition and extinction phenomena coincide, after simple manipulations

$$\theta_{0,\,i,\,e} = \theta \sqrt[4]{\frac{1 - 3\theta}{1 + 5\theta}} \tag{4-24}$$

Let us compare the results obtained with the adiabatic case. The boundaries of the characteristic regions in the whole range in which the critical phenomena exist are shown on Figure 4-11. This graph

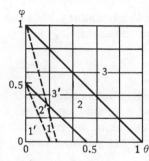

Fig. 4-11. Characteristic regions in the diagram. Hysteresis process region. 1—Convection and 1'—radiation, ignition; 2—convection and 2'—radiation, extinction; 3—convection and 3'—radiation, region of the noncritical process; solid line, boundary of the regions for heat emission by convection (adiabatic problem); dashed line, boundary of the regions for heat emission by radiation.

indicates the abrupt cutoff of the region of the hysteresis process. In particular, we obtain from Eqs. (4-20), (4-23), and (4-25)

$$\theta_{e\,\max} = 0.25; \quad \theta_{i\,\max} = 0.2$$

and

$$\theta_{0\,cr\,\max} = 0.2\sqrt[4]{0.2} = \frac{1}{5\sqrt[4]{5}} \approx 0.134$$

instead of the limiting critical values of θ_{cr} and $\tau_{0\,cr}$, which equal for convection (Chapter 2)

$$\theta_{e\,\max} = 1; \quad \theta_{i\,\max} = 0.5; \quad \theta_{0\,cr\,\max} = 0.25$$

In order to compare both limiting cases of heat loss by convection (the adiabatic process for a gas and by radiation in the $\theta_{cr} - \tau_{DK\,cr}$ coordinates), we obtain from Eqs. (4-19) and (4-16)

$$\frac{\tau_{DK}}{\tau_{DK} + e^{1/\theta}} = \frac{\theta^4 - \theta_0^4 - \theta^5}{\theta^4 - \theta_0^4}$$

an expression of the critical value of the nondimensional time

$$\tau_{DK,\,cr} = \frac{\theta^4 - \theta_0^4 - 4\theta^5}{4\theta^5} e^{1/\theta} \tag{4-25}$$

and also from Eqs. (4-16) and (4-24)

$$\frac{1 - 5\theta}{2} = \frac{\tau_{DK}}{\tau_{DK} + e^{1/\theta}}$$

an expression of the boundary critical value of the parameter τ_{DK} when ignition and extinction coincide

$$\tau_{DK, i\text{-}e} = \frac{1 - 5\theta}{1 + 5\theta} e^{1/\theta} \qquad (4\text{-}26)$$

and, finally, from Eqs. (4-16) and (4-20)

$$1 - 4\theta = \frac{\tau_{DK}}{\tau_{DK} + e^{1/\theta}}$$

an expression for the limiting value $\tau_{DK\,cr}$ on the boundary between the regions of the hysteresis and noncritical processes:

$$\tau_{DK\,lim} = \frac{1 - 4\theta}{4\theta} e^{1/\theta} \qquad (4\text{-}27)$$

A comparison of these dependences for convection and radiation is presented in Figure 4-12 in the $\theta_{cr} = \theta(\theta_0, \tau_{DK})$ coordinates. The critical ignition-temperature values for heat emission by radiation are insignificantly higher for identical values of the parameters θ_0

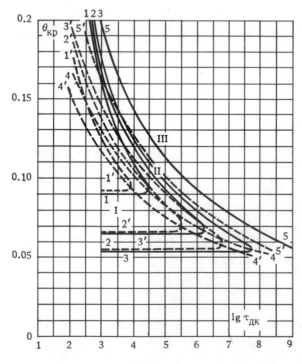

Fig. 4-12. Comparison of the dependences of the critical ignition and extinction temperatures for heat emission by convection and radiation. Solid line, convection; dashed line, radiation; 1-1 and 1'-1', $\theta_0 = 0.08$; 2-2 and 2'-2', $\theta_0 = 0.06$; 3-3 and 3'-3', $\theta_0 = 0.05$; 4-4 and 4'-4', curves of coincident ignition and extinction; 5-5 and 5'-5', boundaries of the hysteresis region; I—ignition; II—extinction (hysteresis region); III—region of noncritical process.

and τ_{DK}, but substantially lower for extinction than for heat emission by convection. Physically, this means that ignition can occur, for given values of the blast rate and initial gas temperature, at a somewhat higher heating in the case of heat emission by radiation while extinction occurs for considerably lower values of the temperature (since the growth of the latter is limited by intense heat emission) than in the adiabatic process (for heat emission by convection). Qualitatively, the influence of the τ_{DK} parameter is identical in both cases.

Finally, let us also compare the boundaries of the characteristic regions in the $\theta_{cr} = \theta(\theta_0 \vartheta)$ coordinates. The relation between the values of θ and θ_0 for ignition and extinction coincident was obtained above as Eq. (4-24). As has been shown earlier in detail, the boundary curve in this diagram (see Figure 2-14) corresponds to neglecting burn-up; $\varphi = 0$; $\vartheta = \infty$. We have from Eq. (4-19) for $\varphi = 0$

$$\theta_{0,\,\varphi\,0} = \theta\sqrt[4]{1 - 4\theta} \qquad (4\text{-}28)$$

(instead of the Semenov formula (1-19) for the convection case). A comparison of both cases is given on Figure 4-13. Here again, the sharp cutoff of the region of hysteresis is seen; this is particularly abrupt for the extinction region.

Now let us return to the case of the combined effect of heat emission by convection and by radiation, i.e., to taking into account the thermal capacity of the combustion products and heat emission by radiation. Let us show that the critical ignition and extinction conditions, which refer to this case, are included between the limiting cases of convection alone and of radiation alone, in the $\varphi - \theta$ plane.

Fig. 4-13. Characteristic regions of the process in the $\theta - \varphi$ plane. Solid line, boundary of the region for convection; dashed line, boundary for radiation; 1— (convection) and 1'—(radiation), ignition; 2—(convection) and 2' (radiation), extinction, hysteresis process region; 3— (convection) and 3' (radiation), region of the noncritical process.

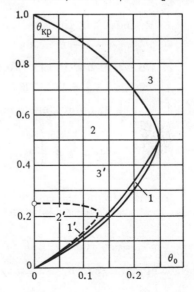

We obtain an expression for the critical completeness of combustion

$$\varphi_{cr} = 1 - \frac{\theta^2 + 4\sigma\tau_{DK}\theta^5}{\theta - \theta_0 + \sigma\tau_{DK}(\theta^4 - \theta_0^4)} \qquad (4\text{-}29)$$

from the conditions of the tangency of the curves $\varphi_I(\theta)$ (4-16) and $\varphi_{II}(\theta)$ (4-17) in the form of the equalities

$$\frac{\tau_{DK}}{\tau_{DK} + e^{1/\theta}} = \frac{1}{\vartheta}(\theta - \theta_0 + \sigma\tau_{DK}(\theta^4 - \theta_0^4)) \quad (\varphi_I = \varphi_{II})$$

and

$$\frac{1 - \varphi}{\varphi^2}\varphi = \frac{1 + 4\sigma\tau_{DK}\theta^3}{\vartheta} = \frac{\varphi(1 - 4\sigma\tau_{DK}\theta^3)}{\theta - \theta_0 - \sigma\tau_{DK}(\theta^4 - \theta_0^4)} \left(\frac{d\varphi_I}{d\theta} = \frac{d\varphi_{II}}{d\theta}\right)$$

In the absence of radiation $(\sigma \to 0)$ (4-29) transforms into (2-23); $\varphi_{cr} = 1 - (\theta^2/(\theta - \theta_0))$ for convection; and for $\sigma\tau_{DK} \to \infty$, it transforms into (4-19) for radiation. Hence, for a given value of the parameter θ_0, the curves $\varphi_{cr}(\theta)$ in the $\varphi - \theta$ diagram transform continuously from curves for convection (2-23) through all the intermediate values to the curve (4-19) for radiation as the nondimensional time increases within the interval $0 \leqslant \tau_{DK} \leqslant \infty$. The location of the critical curve $\varphi_{cr}(\theta)$ in the $\varphi - \theta$ plane in the $\theta_0 =$ const, $\tau_{DK} =$ const case is determined by the radiation coefficient o.

All the characteristic lines of the diagram are warped simultaneously with the curve $\varphi_{cr}(\theta)$ as the product $\sigma\tau_{DK}$ increases. The equations of these curves, obtained similarly to the above, can be represented as follows:[8]

1. Boundary of the hysteresis process $(\theta_0 \ll \theta)$:

$$\varphi_{cr,\,lim} = 1 - \theta - 3\theta\psi \qquad (4\text{-}30)$$

2. Curve of maximum values of φ_{cr} $(d\varphi_{cr}/d\theta = 0)$

$$\varphi_{cr,\,max} = 1 - 2\theta - 3\theta\psi \qquad (4\text{-}31)$$

3. Curve of coincident ignition and extinction $(d^2\varphi_I/d\theta^2 = d^2\varphi_{II}/d\theta^2)$

$$\varphi_{i-e} = \frac{1}{2} - \theta - \frac{3}{2}\theta\psi \qquad (4\text{-}32)$$

[8]Let us note that the equations of the characteristic lines in the general case (and also in particular cases) are related by simple relations

$$\varphi_{cr,\,max} = \varphi_{cr,\,lim} - \theta; \quad \varphi_{i-e} = \frac{1}{2}\varphi_{cr,\,max} = \frac{1}{2}(\varphi_{cr,\,lim} - \theta)$$

which simplify their derivation considerably.

For brevity, we used the following notation in all these formulas

$$\psi = \frac{4\sigma\tau_{DK}}{1 + 4\sigma\tau_{DK}} \qquad (4-33)$$

in which $\psi = 0$ for $\sigma\tau_{DK} = 0$; $\psi = 1$ for $\sigma\tau_{DK} = \infty$. In conformance with this, the two first terms remain in (4-30) to (4-32) for $\sigma\tau_{DK} = 0$ and they now, naturally, are in agreement with Eqs. (2-24), (2-25), and (2-26) for convection alone. The expressions (4-30) to (4-32) transform into (4-20), (4-21), and (4-23) for $\sigma\tau_{DK} = \infty$ and $\psi = 1$.

The curves of the critical values of $\varphi_{cr}(\theta)$ in the $\varphi - \theta$ plane on Figure 4-10, for $0 < \sigma\tau_{DK} < \infty$, will be within the limiting curves $\sigma\tau_{DK} = 0$ (convection) and $\sigma\tau_{DK} = \infty$ (radiation) just as are the other critical curves (for example the boundary lines for the $\varphi - \theta$ region of the hysteresis process on the $\theta_{cr} - \theta_{0,cr}$ diagram on Figure 4-13, and others).

Before supplying the summary of the investigation, let us return to the question of the influence of the τ_{DK} parameter on the combustion process under the combined effect of heat emission by convection and radiation. Without analyzing this question rigorously, let us consider the characteristic example of the intersection of the $\varphi_I(\theta)$ and the $\varphi_{II}(\theta)$ curves in the $\varphi - \theta$ diagram on Figure 4-14a. The appropriate curves of the stationary values of φ and θ as a function of τ_{DK} are shown on Figure 4-14b and c for constant θ_0, ϑ, and σ.

As is seen from the graph, new critical ignition and extinction phenomena (conditionally, "heat exchange" i_T and e_T) can occur at high values of τ_{DK} for complex heat exchange in addition to the usual (conditionally, "adiabatic" i_A and e_A) conditions. As the values of τ_{DK} increase correspondingly, the $\varphi_I(\theta)$ and $\varphi_{II}(\theta)$ curves are shifted to one side, toward the origin. Consequently, conditions can occur for various "rates" of this displacement when the $\varphi_{II}(\theta)$ curve "overtakes" the $\varphi_I(\theta)$ curve so that it loses the common point on the upper level (extinction occurs) or, conversely, "remains" thereon so that it again arrives at a stable combustion region (ignition occurs). Such a character of the stationary-values curves with two pairs of critical phenomena, one in the low-value region of τ_{DK} ("adiabatic" ignition and extinction) and the other in the high-value region of τ_{DK} ("heat-exchange" ignition and extinction), corresponds, say, to the arrangement of the experiment with the carbon rod described in section 3-3. In addition, other kinds of stationary-value curves of φ and θ are also possible, depending on the τ_{DK} parameter; for example, either one or the other hysteresis loop or both together can degenerate, in separate cases, into a continuous smooth curve, etc.

Common to all these cases is the combustion temperature drop

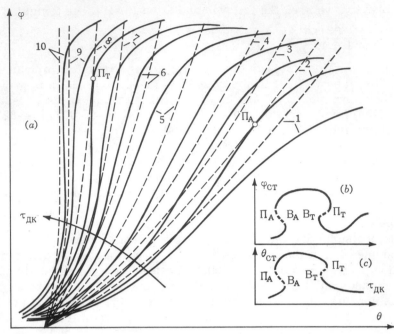

Fig. 4-14. Dependence of stationary values of the temperature and completeness of combustion on the nondimensional time for heat emission by convection and radiation. (a) Intersection of the curves in the $\varphi - \theta$ diagram; solid line, heat-liberation curves; dashed line, heat-emission curves; (b) and (c) stationary values of the completeness of combustion and the temperature (curves for the adiabatic process with heat emission just by convection are shown dashed); i_A and e_A—adiabatic ignition and extinction; i_T and e_T—heat-exchange ignition and extinction.

in the presence of appreciable heat loss and the rise in the nondimensional time τ_{DK}. Physically, as has already been mentioned, this means that cessation of combustion will always occur in a wide range of gas velocities with intense heat emission both in the region of very small velocities, where the part of heat emission is always large (larger τ_{DK} values), and also in the region of high velocities close to the adiabatic region in connection with the inevitable transition of the reaction into an intermediate and then into a kinetic combustion region with an unlimited intensification of diffusion. The stable combustion region corresponds, in all cases, to a certain range of the relative air velocity. It also corresponds to a relatively broad variation of the particle size. Stable combustion is here also always limited, in principle, both by very small (small τ_{DK} with intense diffusion) and by very coarse particles (large τ_{DK} with relatively strong cooling).

These conclusions also apply to the thermal combustion region of a well-mixed mixture. In addition to the (adiabatic) critical phenomena analyzed in Chapter 1—ignition for a rise in the stay time and extinction for its drop—the presence of intense heat emission leads to "heat-exchange" ignition for a drop in the stay time (reduction of the quantity of heat being emitted) and to "heat-exchange" extinction for an increase in the stay time (an increase in the heat losses); hence the first critical phenomena are observed in the region of low values of the stay time τ_{DK} and the second (the heat-exchange) are observed in the high-value region. A quantitative analysis of the relations describing these phenomena for heat emission by radiation is very awkward; consequently, a more simple, quantitative analogy of the problem of the influence of heat emission subject to a linear dependence on the temperature difference will be analyzed in the next section. Let us cite some brief conclusions. The influence of heat emission by radiation leads to a sharp reduction of the hysteresis region and to the appearance of qualitatively new, critical ignition and extinction phenomena absent in the adiabatic process or in the process with heat supply. Physically, these ("heat-exchange") critical phenomena are close to those mentioned in the previous chapter in the problem on the combustion of unmixed components (see Figures 3-10, 3-11, for example). The practical value of these phenomena is great since they indicate the possibility of a contradictory influence of the individual parameters (gas velocity, particle size for the hysteresis process, stay time, i.e., forcing the process for the combustion of a well-mixed mixture, etc.) on the total process, mainly in its initial stages near ignition and the yield of the stable combustion region. Heat emission plays an especially large part in the initial zone of the combustion process in the consumption of liquid fuel and of two-component liquid mixtures in connection with the expenditure of heat by evaporation. The analysis of these processes, however, is outside the problems of this book.

4-3. PROCESS WITH HEAT LOSS

It has been shown in the previous paragraph that heat loss not only reduces the combustion stability, i.e., decreases the stationary values of the temperature and the completeness of combustion, but also, if the heat emission is sufficiently intense, leads to qualitatively new critical phenomena which are missing in the adiabatic process. These peculiarities of the process with heat loss, considered in detail below, are of great theoretical and practical interest; apparently, if they are not considered along with other phenomena (mixing, heat supply, etc.), it is impossible to explain correctly the dependences and relations observable in furnace apparatus.

Let us investigate the problem in detail by an example of the combustion of a well-mixed mixture for the simple linear law of the temperature dependence of the heat loss. For simplicity let us assume, as in the case of heat emission by radiation, that the temperature of the medium receiving the heat equals the initial mixture temperature. The problem in such a form was first solved by Zel'dovich and Zysin (13a and 15) by using the series expansion of the exponential (in the expression $\exp(-E/RT)$, see section 3-3) proposed by Frank-Kamenetskii. The method of solution used by Zel'dovich and Zysin (15) is the direct investigation of the curves of the stationary regions.

The solution of the same problem of the influence of heat loss, presented below,[9] differs first in its use of the exact formula for the temperature dependence of the reaction rate and second in the replacement of the direct investigation of the curves of the stationary states by the more graphic and physically surveyable investigation of the critical conditions. Basically, the results obtained reproduce the solution of Zel'dovich and Zysin (15). In particular, making the temperature dependence of the reaction rate more precise did not lead to any substantial divergence from the results of the approximate computation. This latter is completely understandable since we speak of phenomena which occur, basically, in the low-temperature range near ignition.

The use of a zero-dimensional model of a combustion process which is accompanied by intense heat loss, is most suitable for investigating the states of a mixture in individual, isolated sections of the combustion chamber. It can also be extended approximately to combustion in the chamber as a whole if we speak of a process very relaxed in production; however, the first diagram (for example, the delivery of the phenomenon under consideration to the initial section of the chamber, to the ignition zone) is of great enough practical interest.

As in many of the cases analyzed earlier, the problem of looking for the stationary states reduces mathematically to an investigation of the conditions for the intersection (in the particular case of critical regions, for the tangency) of the heat-liberation curve $\varphi_I(\theta)$ from Eq. (4-16) and the heat-loss curve $\varphi_{II}(\theta)$ in the $\varphi - \theta$ plane. We write the equation of the latter curve (the heat balance of the system) in nondimensional form by analogy with Eq. (4-8) for a

---

[9]The problem in such form was solved by M. S. Natanzon under the supervision of the author. In particular, Natanzon performed a considerable portion of the computations and constructions presented in this and the next paragraphs.

process with heat supply

$$\varphi_{II}(\theta) = \frac{1}{\vartheta}(\theta - \theta_0 + \beta\tau_{SK}(\theta - \theta_0)) = \frac{1 + \beta\tau_{SK}}{\vartheta}(\theta - \theta_0) \qquad (4\text{-}34)$$

Equation (4-34) differs from (4-8) for heat loss, first, in the sign of the additional component (in heat emission, the heat being liberated in the process of the reaction occurs as a rise in the heat content of the gaseous reaction products and as the loss of heat to the cold medium; in heat supply, the total of the heat supplied from outside and the heat being liberated in the reaction occurs as a rise in the heat content of the reaction products). In addition, $\theta > \theta_0$ in both terms on the right side of (4-34), where the same value of θ_0 has been assumed, for simplicity. The three equations, the equality (4-16) and the two equalities in (4-34), contain six variables (φ, θ, θ_0, ϑ, τ_{SK}, and β). In the $\tau_{SK} = $ const case, an investigation of the process when one of the three parmeters θ, ϑ, β varies while the other two are constant, in principle, is in no way different from the cases analyzed earlier. The influence of heat emission is here experienced in the replacement of the effective characteristic of the heat productivity of the mixture ϑ by a reduced (diminished) value determined from the formula

$$\vartheta_{eff} = \frac{\vartheta}{1 + \beta\tau_{SK}} \qquad (4\text{-}35)$$

i.e., it leads (as in the mixing problem) to a reduction in combustion stability and to a decrease in the region of the hysteresis process. The influence of a change in the heat-emission coefficient β is completely analogous to the effect of the radiation coefficient σ in the previous section (Figure 4-9). Finally, all the quantitative relations for $\tau_{SK} = $ const, obtained in section 2-4 for the critical conditions or for coincident ignition and extinction (see Tables 2-1 and 2-2) for a process proceeding adiabatically, are also retained for the process with heat elimination by replacing the value of ϑ by ϑ_{eff} using Eq. (4-35).

In this connection let us return directly to the basic problem of an investigation of the process with heat emission, to the explanation of the possible curves of the stationary values of the temperature and completeness of combustion as a function of the nondimensional time τ_{SK} (or τ_{DK}, respectively, for heterogeneous combustion). The next section of this chapter will be devoted to an investigation of the influence of heat loss for variable τ_{SK} on the critical ignition and extinction conditions, and to a delimitation of the characteristic regions of the progress of the process.

The physical content of the question, as is seen from the brief considerations presented at the end of the previous paragraph, reduces to the following: The quantity of heat eliminated from the combustion products rises as the stay time τ_{SK} increases [see Eq. (4-34)]. In this connection, the values of the stationary temperature and the completeness of combustion are naturally lowered and ignition is made difficult and extinction is facilitated. In the limit, the process transforms into a region in which critical phenomena are lacking. This tendency in the process for an increase in τ_{SK} and the relative growth in heat emission is counteracted by the tendency, usual for the adiabatic process, to a rise in combustion stability (Figure 2-4c and d, etc.), to facilitate ignition, etc., as the stay time increases. Consequently, the region of stable combustion seems to be bounded on two sides in a wide range of stay-time values; by the influence of heat emission for high values of the stay time and by limited mixture burn-up for low values. This limitation can proceed in both cases both as critical phenomena and as a smooth (noncritical) reduction of the stationary level; other more complex shapes of the stationary-value curves, first mentioned by Zel'dovich and Zysin (15) and analyzed below, are also possible.

As regards the graphical solution, the peculiarities of the latter when heat emission is taken into account were shown graphically by the example of Figure 4-14 for heat emission by radiation. The picture remains qualitatively the same for a linear heat-elimination law: As τ_{SK} increases, the corresponding $\varphi_I(\theta)$ and $\varphi_{II}(\theta)$ curves, whose intersection determines the stationary region, are shifted toward the origin (in particular, the lines $\varphi_I(\theta)$ rotate counterclockwise around the point $\theta = \theta_0;\ \varphi = 0$).

The various conditions of intersection and tangency of the $\varphi_I(\theta)$ curves and the $\varphi_{II}(\theta)$ lines can be combined graphically at different places in the $\varphi - \theta$ plane for different values of the process parameters $\theta_0, \vartheta, \beta$. As τ_{SK} increases, just as for heat emission by radiation (Figure 4-14), cases of one curve "overtaking" or "lagging" the other are possible, which lead to additional critical ignition and extinction phenomena.[10]

The most typical examples of the intersection of the heat-liberation and -elimination curves are given on Figures 4-15 to 4-19. The $\varphi_I(\theta)$ curves on each of these graphs are drawn by fine lines;

[10]The role of the "angular velocity" of the lines $\varphi_{II}(\theta)$, determined by the derivative of the angular coefficient of the line with respect to τ_{SK}, is essential in these phenomena

$$\frac{\partial(1/\vartheta_{eff})}{\partial \tau_{SK}} = \frac{\partial}{\partial \tau_{SK}}\left(\frac{1 + \beta\tau_{SK}}{\vartheta}\right) = \frac{\beta}{\vartheta}$$

that is, the ratio of the heat-loss coefficient and the mixture heat-production coefficient.

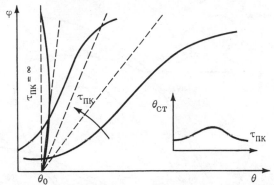

Fig. 4-15. Example of the construction of the curve of the stationary states for heat loss as a function of stay time. Solid line, heat-liberation curve; dashed line, heat-loss curve; thick line, stable state.

the $\varphi_{II}(\theta)$ curves by dashed and the curves of stationary (stable) states by thick lines. The latter are shown separately, to a small scale, on Figures 4-15 to 4-19 for the combustion temperature θ_{st} as a function of the stay time τ_{SK}. The limiting case of a continuous, noncritical variation of the stationary levels as the parameter τ_{DK} varies is shown on the first of the graphs of Figure 4-15. The opposite limiting case of the hysteresis process, which is identical to an adiabatic process in the nature of the critical phenomena, where ignition (i_A) occurs with an increase and extinction (e_A) with a decrease in stay time, is pictured on the last graph of this series, Figure 4-19. Let us note that, in contrast to the adiabatic process, the combustion temperature in all the Figures

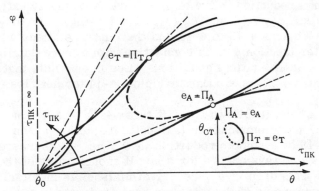

Fig. 4-16. Example of the construction of the curve of the stationary states for heat loss as a function of stay time. Solid curved line, heat-liberation curve; dashed curved line, heat-loss curve; solid line, stable states; dashed line, unstable states; e_A and e_T—adiabatic and heat-exchange extinction.

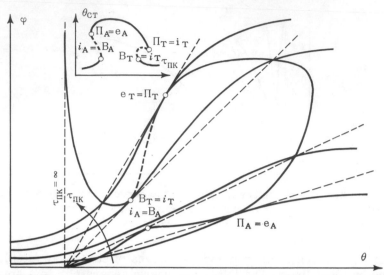

Fig. 4-17. Example of the construction of the curve of the stationary states for heat loss as a function of stay time. Solid curved line, heat-liberation curve; dashed curved line, heat-loss curve; solid line, stable states; dashed line, unstable states; i_A and i_T—adiabatic and heat-exchange ignition; e_A and e_T—adiabatic and heat-exchange extinction.

(4-15 to 4-19), and particularly in the last, approaches the initial value ($\theta \approx \theta_0$) because of cooling, as the stay time increases without limit (but not to the maximum temperature $\theta_m = \theta_0 + \vartheta$, as in the adiabatic case; naturally, the completeness of combustion approaches unity in all cases; $\varphi \to 1$ as $\tau_{SK} \to \infty$ although the growth of φ after a reduction in the temperature is naturally extremely slow; similar $\varphi_{st}(\tau_{SK})$ and $\theta_{st}(\tau_{SK})$ are lacking). The origin of the graphs on Figures 4-16 to 4-18 and their interrelations will be discussed later (section 4-4) in connection with a more detailed investigation of the critical conditions. Let us only note that one of them (Figure 4-17) is similar to Figure 4-14 for heat loss by radiation.

On the whole, it follows from Figures 4-15 to 4-19 that a drop in the stationary temperature (adiabatic extinction e_A on Figures 4-16 to 4-19 or a smooth reduction in θ_{st} as τ_{SK} decreases on Figure 4-15) always occurs for a small enough value of the stay time τ_{SK}. This drop in θ_{st} as τ_{SK} diminishes is inevitable since the maximum value of the effective heat productivity of the mixture is bounded by the real value of ϑ

$$\vartheta_{\text{eff min}} = \vartheta_{\text{eff}} \tau_{SK \to 0} = \frac{\vartheta}{1 + \beta \tau_{SK}} \to \vartheta$$

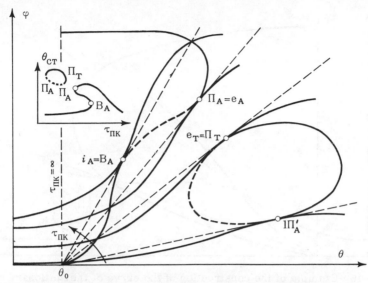

Fig. 4-18. Example of the construction of the curve of the stationary states for heat loss as a function of stay time. Solid curved line, heat-liberation curve; dashed curved line, heat-elimination curve; solid line, stable states; dashed line, unstable states; i_A—adiabatic ignition; e_A and e_T—adiabatic and heat-exchange extinction.

Therefore, the adiabatic line $\varphi_{II} = (\theta - \theta_0)/\vartheta$ serves as the limit for the $\varphi_{II}(\theta)$ lines as $\tau_{SK} \to 0$, while the horizontal axis $\varphi_I \tau_{SK \to 0} \to 0$ serves as the limit for the curves

$$\varphi_I = \frac{\tau_{SK}}{\tau_{SK} + e^{1/\theta}} \text{ as } \tau_{SK} \to 0$$

Because of the increase in the portion of heat eliminated for a sufficiently high value of τ_{SK}, a drop in the magnitude of θ_{st} (heat-exchange extinction e_T in Figure 4-17 or the continual reduction in temperature as τ_{SK} increases, Figures 4-15 and 4-19, or finally, both along with different values of τ_{SK}, on Figures 4-16 and 4-18) will again occur.

The most favorable conditions for the realization of the combustion region correspond, therefore, to a certain average value of the stay time; in particular, the ignition conditions (i_A on Figures 4-17 to 4-19 and i_T on Figure 4-17) correspond thereto. A peculiarity of the stationary-value curves shown on Figure 4-16 (two extinctions and no ignition) and on Figure 4-18 (three extinctions and one ignition) is the presence of closed sections of the curves bounded by two extinctions e_A and e_T in their stable parts, in the low- and high-value regions of τ_{SK}, respectively.

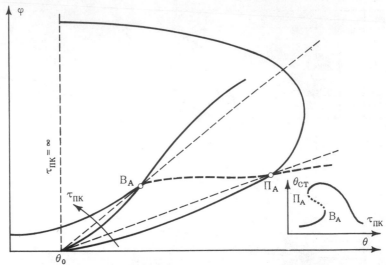

Fig. 4-19. Example of the construction of the curve of the stationary states for heat loss as a function of stay time. Solid curved line, heat-liberation curve; dashed curved line, heat-elimination curve; solid line, stable states; dashed line, unstable states; i_A and e_A—adiabatic ignition and extinction, respectively. $(B_A = i_A; \Pi_A = e_A)$

Apparently these "inadmissible" states (to which ignition does not lead) can be realized always, in practice, in the quasi-stationary combustion process preceding the given state; more details will be given later.

Let us present certain relations which are required to construct curves of the stationary values and to explain the results shown on Figures 4-15 to 4-19. From the equality of $\varphi_I(\theta)$ (4-16) and $\varphi_{II}(\theta)$ (4-34)

$$\frac{\tau_{SK}}{\tau_{SK} + e^{1/\theta}} = \frac{1 + \tau_{SK}}{\vartheta}(\theta - \theta_0)$$

or after transforming from the quadratic equation in τ_{SK}

$$\tau_{SK}{}^2 - \frac{\vartheta - (\theta - \theta_0)(1 + \beta e^{1/\theta})}{\beta(\theta - \theta_0)}\tau_{SK} + \frac{e^{1/\theta}}{\beta} = 0$$

we express the stay time thus:

$$\tau_{SK} = \frac{\Delta}{2} \pm \sqrt{\frac{\Delta^2}{4} - \frac{e^{1/\theta}}{\beta}} \tag{4-36}$$

Here, for brevity, the symbol Δ denotes the coefficient of τ in the preceding equation.

The equality (4-36), along with one of the expressions (4-16) or

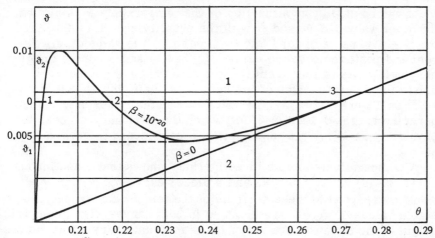

Fig. 4-20. Example of the function $\vartheta = \mathcal{A}(\theta)$ (for $\theta_0 = 0.02$; $\beta = 0$ and $\beta = 10^{-20}$). 1—Region of real and positive values of the stay time; 2—region in which a stationary process is impossible.

(4-34), is a system of parametric equations which permits the following functions to be constructed:

$$\varphi = \varphi(\theta); \quad \tau_{SK} = \tau(\theta) \quad \text{and} \quad \varphi = \varphi(\tau_{SK})$$

Let us note that certain inequalities guaranteeing compliance with the physically obvious conditions,[11] $\tau_{SK} \geqslant 0$; $\theta \geqslant \theta_0$, should be taken into account in constructing these curves.

It is seen from (4-36) that $\tau_{SK} \geqslant 0$ for $\Delta > 0$, i.e., for

$$\vartheta_1 \geqslant (\theta - \theta_0)(1 + \beta e^{1/\theta}) \tag{4-37}$$

In addition, there must also be

$$\frac{\Delta^2}{4} \geqslant \frac{e^{1/\theta}}{\beta}$$

for τ_{SK} to be real, or after substituting the value of Δ

$$\vartheta_2 \geqslant (\theta - \theta_0)(1 + \sqrt{\beta e^{1/\theta}})^2 \tag{4-38}$$

Since, from (4-38) and (4-37), the difference in the minimum values of ϑ_2 and ϑ_1 is positive

$$\vartheta_2 - \vartheta_1 = 2(\theta - \theta_0)\beta e^{1/\theta} > 0$$

compliance with the second condition (4-38) is necessary and sufficient. It is seen from Figure 4-20, on which a curve of the mini-

[11]Noncompliance with these inequalities leads to the appearance of complex roots in the computations of the stationary-value curves (see Figure 4-20).

mum values of ϑ_{min} as a function of the temperature θ is plotted
for given values of θ_0 and β with the equality sign in (4-38), that
the $\vartheta - \theta$ plane is divided into two regions. The value of τ_{SK} is
real and positive above the curve $\vartheta_{min} = \vartheta(\theta)$ and becomes imaginary below. As is seen from the graph, a range of values $\vartheta_1 = \vartheta = \vartheta_2$
exists for a certain value of the heat-loss coefficient $\beta > 0$ ($\beta =$
10^{-20} on Figure 4-20, say), in which two mutually unrelated temperature ranges 0-1 and 2-3, for which the stationary process is
physically real (τ_{SK} real and positive), correspond to each value
of ϑ.

A comparatively simple investigation[12] shows that a continuous
curve $\tau_{SK}(\theta)$ for $\theta_0 \leqslant \theta \leqslant \theta_1$ and a closed curve $\tau_{SK}(\theta)$ for $\theta_2 \leqslant$
$\theta \leqslant \theta_3$ correspond to these sections of the temperature range if un-
stable values of $\tau_{SK}(\theta)$ are included in both curves. The geometric
origin of the isolated sections of the stable stationary-value curves
on Figures 4-16 and 4-17 thereby become understandable. Physically, as already remarked, the stationary states, corresponding
to these isolated sections bounded by extinction from both sides,
can be realized in the previous process of establishing equilibrium
for the other parameters θ_0, ϑ, or β. The combustion regions obtained here are stable (which results from the intersection of the
$\varphi_I(\theta)$ and $\varphi_{II}(\theta)$ curves in the $\varphi - \theta$ plane on Figures 4-16 and
4-17); however, the combustion process is inevitably disrupted, and
extinction occurs, for a noticeable increase or decrease in the stay
time. It is essential that the transition to these isolated states be
impossible for those values of θ_0, ϑ, and β which correspond, say,
to Figures 4-16 or 4-17. Its realization is possible only with the
change in at least one of the parameters, assumed to be constant
on Figures 4-15 to 4-19, the initial temperature, the mixture heat
productivity, and the heat-emission coefficient.

For greater clarity, let us recall that the stationary value of

---

[12] Let us write (4-36) as $\tau_{SK} = (\Delta/2)(1 \pm \sqrt{1 - 4\,e^{1/\theta}/\beta\Delta^2})$ and let us expand it in a series near $\theta \to \theta_0$, $\Delta \to \infty$. We obtain two approximate values
corresponding to the two signs in front of the radical:

$$\tau'_{SK\,0} \approx \Delta/2 \to \infty; \quad \tau''_{SK\,0} \approx e^{1/\theta}/\beta\Delta \to 0 \quad \text{for} \quad \theta \to \theta_0$$

Hence, the $\tau_{SK} = \tau(\theta)$ curve passes through the whole possible range of values of τ_{SK} $(\theta)(0 \leq \tau_{SK} \leq \infty)$ on the 0-1 section as the temperature varies
$\theta = \theta_0$ to $\theta = \theta_1$. The values of τ_{SK} on section 2-3 of Figure 4-20 coincide
on the boundaries $\tau_S = \Delta/2$ in the $\theta_2 \leq \theta \leq \theta_3$ range of temperature values;
this is the case of equal roots in (4-36). Since the quantity τ_{SK} is here
bounded by certain minimum and maximum values, then the curve of the
function $\tau_{SK} = \tau(\theta)$ must be closed in this range of temperature values.
Isolated curve sections are obtained correspondingly for stable states.

the temperature (or completeness of combustion) from the heat-balance equation $\varphi_I(\theta) = \varphi_{II}(\theta)$, that is

$$\frac{\tau_{SK}}{\tau_{SK} + e^{1/\theta}} = \frac{1 + \beta\tau_{SK}}{\vartheta}(\theta - \theta_0)$$

depends on four variables

$$\theta_{st} = \theta(\theta_0, \vartheta, \beta, \tau_{SK})$$

If, say, a spatial (three-dimensional) dependence of the stationary value of the temperature on two variables, $\theta_{st} = \theta(\theta_0, \tau_{SK})$ say, were to be constructed for unchanged values of β and ϑ, then the isolated portions of the θ_{st} curves, which would be obtained in certain $\theta_0 =$ const cross-sections, would merge into a certain surface, "accessible" by means of ignition or a smooth rise as the third variable, θ_0, varies. Actually, we speak of a more complex "hypersurface" in five-dimensional space, consequently, the presence of isolated sections of the curves in the $\theta - \tau_{SK}$ plane means only the impossibility of realizing the corresponding stationary states for given values of the parameters θ_0, ϑ, and β in addition to innumerable sets of "paths" which lead to these states for a motion outside the $\theta - \tau_{SK}$ plane.

It is not difficult to present also simple practical examples which illustrate this phenomenon. For example, it is known that many combustion chambers continue to operate stably when elevated in altitude after having been ignited on the ground. However, at a certain altitude, reignition, after the process has been cut off, seems to be impossible although it had been easy to accomplish with a reduction in altitude. The following example is still more graphic. It is well known that the ignition limits (for example, loading, mixture composition, or excess-air coefficient) are always considerably more narrow than the stable combustion limits. Consequently, a very small stay time can be arrived at by working with a definite excess of air to the combustion chamber and gradually boosting it, for example; however, reignition seems to be possible only for an increase in the stay time (a decrease in consumption) or for an improvement in the mixture composition.

In conclusion, let us note that the examples, analyzed in this section, of the stationary-value curves of the temperature and the completeness of combustion as a function of stay time refer completely to heterogeneous combustion also and, in any case qualitatively, are also retained for the more complex case of heat loss by radiation, as is seen, for example, from a comparison of Figures 4-17 and 4-14.

4-4. INFLUENCE OF HEAT EMISSION ON CRITICAL CONDITIONS

The emergence of complex-shaped curves of the stationary states (Figures 4-16 to 4-18) and the transition from a curve of one shape to another becomes considerably clearer when investigating the critical ignition and extinction conditions for a process with heat elimination. The most indicative, in this sense, is the dependence of the critical value of the mixture heat productivity on the rest of the parameters: $\vartheta_{cr} = (\theta_0, \theta, \beta)$, which is obtained by eliminating the quantities φ and τ_{SK} from the condition that the heat-liberation and -elimination curves be tangent in the $\varphi - \theta$ plane. In order to derive this dependence, let us note that the value $\tau_{SK\,cr} = \tau(\theta, \theta_0)$ for a process with heat elimination has the same form as in the adiabatic problem:[13]

$$\tau_{SK,\,cr} = \frac{\theta - \theta_0 - \theta^2}{\theta^2}\, e^{1/\theta} \tag{2-33}$$

Substituting (2-33) into the equation $\varphi_I(\theta) = \varphi_{II}(\theta)$ in the form

$$\frac{1 + \beta\tau_{SK}}{\vartheta}(\theta - \theta_0) = \frac{\tau_{SK}}{\tau_{SK} + e^{1/\theta}}$$

we obtain after simple manipulation, an expression for the critical value of the mixture heat productivity

$$\vartheta_{cr} = (\theta - \theta_0)^2 \left(\frac{\beta e^{1/\theta}}{\theta^2} + \frac{1}{\theta - \theta_0 - \theta^2}\right) \tag{4-39}$$

and for the critical value of the heat-emission coefficient

$$\beta_{cr} = \frac{\theta^2}{e^{1/\theta}}\left[\frac{\vartheta}{(\theta - \theta_0)^2} - \frac{1}{\theta - \theta_0 - \theta^2}\right] \tag{4-40}$$

[13]Actually from (4-16) and (4-34) there follows:

$$\frac{d\varphi_I}{d\theta} = \frac{1 - \varphi}{\theta^2}\,\varphi; \quad \frac{d\varphi_{II}}{d\theta} = \frac{1 + \beta\tau_{SK}}{\vartheta} = \frac{\varphi}{\theta - \theta_0}$$

that is

$$\varphi_{cr} = 1 - \frac{\theta^2}{\theta - \theta_0} \tag{2-23}$$

as in the adiabatic process. Furthermore, from the equality

$$1 - (\theta^2/(\theta - \theta_0)) = \tau_{SK}/(\tau_{SK} + e^{1/\theta})$$

there results

$$\tau_{SK} = (\theta - \theta_0 - \theta^2)\, e^{1/\theta}/\theta^2 \tag{2-33}$$

Let us note that both formulas (2-23) and (2-33) are not applicable to a process with heat supply (section 4-1).

There follows from (4-39) and (4-40) in the particular case $\beta = 0$ (adiabatic process)

$$\vartheta_{cr} = \frac{(\theta - \theta_0)^2}{\theta - \theta_0 - \theta^2} \qquad (4\text{-}41)$$

which agrees with the formula presented in Table 2-1.

Let us consider the graph, corresponding to (4-39), in $\theta - \vartheta$ coordinates.

Shown on Figure 4-21 are a number of characteristic curves $\theta_{cr} = \theta(\vartheta)$ with the parameter β for one value of θ_0.

The range of variation of θ_{cr} on this graph must satisfy the inequality $\theta - \theta_0 - \theta^2 \geqslant 0$ from the physical conditions $(\theta \geqslant \theta_0; \vartheta \geqslant 0)$.

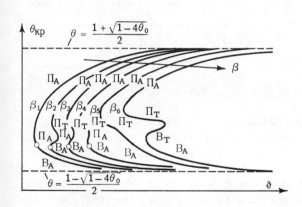

Fig. 4-21. Dependence of the critical temperature θ_{cr} on the mixture heat productivity ϑ for a given value of the initial temperature θ_0 and different values of the heat-loss coefficient $(\theta < \beta_1 < \beta_2 \ldots < \beta_6)$. i_A and e_A —adiabatic; i_T and e_T —heat-exchange ignition and extinction. $(B = i;$ $\Pi = e.)$

Evidently the limiting values of θ_{cr} correspond to the equality sign in this expression, i.e., correspond to neglecting burn-up $(\varphi \rightarrow 0; \vartheta \rightarrow \infty)$. Under this assumption, we again arrive at the Semenov formula (2-28)

$$\theta_{cr \, \varphi \rightarrow 0} = \frac{1 \pm \sqrt{1 - 4\theta_0}}{2}$$

(the minus sign is ignition and the plus, extinction).

Two lines, corresponding to $\theta_{cr} = (1 \pm \sqrt{1 + 4\theta_0})/2$, are the asymptotes on Figure 4-21 for all curves of the critical conditions $(\beta = $ const). These curves correspond to (4-39), but they are shown diagramatically on Figure 4-21; in particular, sections of the curves, corresponding to critical conditions which differ in character,[14] are

---

[14]Actually, the temperature range in which the critical conditions act is small and very close to the limiting line $\theta_{B_{\vartheta \rightarrow \infty}}$ (more accurately, it is located in the ignition region between this line and the curve where ignition and extinction coincide). Shown on Figure 4-22 to scale is one curve $\theta_{cr} =$

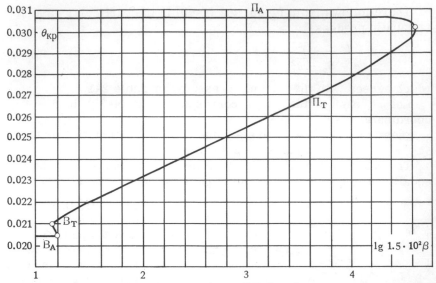

Fig. 4-22. Example of the function $\theta_{cr} = \theta(\beta)$ for $\theta_0 = 0.02$ and $\vartheta = 0.012$.

distorted (stretched), the "adiabatic," i_A and e_A, and the "heat-exchange", i_T and e_T. As before, a division is made here depending on the influence of τ_{SK}: For adiabatic critical conditions—ignition as the stay time increases, extinction as it decreases; for heat-exchange critical conditions, the converse. As the heat emission coefficient β increases on Figure 4-21 (in the direction of the arrows), a deformation occurs of the critical curves, which leads to a change in the number of extremums $(d\vartheta_{cr}/d\theta = 0)$ and in their mutual location. Thus, there is one minimum ϑ_{cr} for the curve marked β_1 and corresponding to low values of the heat-loss coefficient (including $\beta = 0$, the adiabatic process); two minimums and one maximum for the curves β_2, β_3, and β_4, etc. These extremum values divide the critical curves into individual sections each of which corresponds to a definite critical condition (i_A, e_A, i_T, etc.; these values are written on each of the curves on Figure 4-21).

Now if some value of the heat productivity of the mixture $\vartheta = $ const is selected in addition to the rest of the parameters, then the number of critical conditions in the stationary dependence $\theta = \theta(\tau_{SK})$ can be estimated by means of the intersection of a line parallel to the vertical axis on Figure 4-21 and one of the curves ($\beta = $ const; $\theta_0 = $ const).

$\theta(\beta)$ for $\theta_0 = 0.02$ and $\vartheta = 0.012$. For this curve $\theta_{B_{\vartheta \to \infty}} \approx 0.0205$; $\theta_{S_{\vartheta \to \infty}} = 0.98$; the whole range of critical conditions (for a given value of ϑ) does not go beyond the value $\Delta \approx 0.031$.

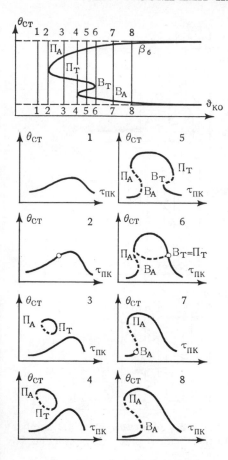

As is seen from Figure 4-21, in the general case the number of such intersections of the lines β = const and ϑ = const for a value θ_0 = const selected for the diagram can vary between zero and four. The tangency of these curves at the extremum points of the curve β = const corresponds to the coincidence of any pair of critical conditions. It is necessary that the curves β = const shift toward increasing values of the mixture heat productivity ϑ as the heat-loss coefficient β increases. The range of values in which critical phenomena are absent is thereby broadened as the heat-loss increases. On the other hand, any of the curves β = const will always intersect the line ϑ = const in two points corresponding to the adiabatic ignition (i_A) and extinction (e_A) conditions, for a sufficient increase in the mixture heat productivity.

Hence, an increase in the heat emission leads to broadening of the noncritical process, a rise in heat productivity, to broadening of the hysteresis region (the "adiabatic" conditionally).[15] The character of the change in the stationary-temperature-value curves as a function of stay time for an

Fig. 4-23. Stationary-value curves $\theta_{st} = \theta(\tau_{SK})$ for various values of the mixture heat productivity at a constant heat-emission coefficient (case 6 of Figure 4-21). i_A and e_A — adiabatic; i_T and e_T —heat-exchange ignition and extinction, respectively.

increase in ϑ and given values of β and θ_0 is shown sketchily on Figure 4-23, as an example. At the top of this graph is shown one of the β = const curves (a β_6-type curve on Figure 4-21) and its

---

[15]In contrast to the authentic adiabatic process ($\beta = 0$) in which $\theta \rightarrow \theta_M$ as $\tau_{SK} \rightarrow \infty$, the temperature always drops in the $\beta > 0$ case for $\tau_{SK} \rightarrow \infty$ and will, in the long run, tend to the initial value: $\theta \rightarrow \theta_0$.

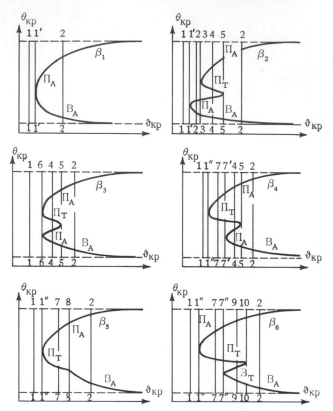

Fig. 4-24. β = constant curves in the $\theta_{cr} - \vartheta_{cr}$ diagram. Identical numbers over the ϑ = const lines correspond to the types of stationary-value curves with the same shape (Figure 4-25).

intersection is shown with a number of lines ϑ = const. Presented below on a series of graphs are the corresponding curves of the stationary temperature values $\theta_{st} = \theta(\tau_{SK})$.

As is seen from Figure 4-24 on which are also separately shown sketchily all the curves β = const listed on Figure 4-21, the various conditions for the intersection of the β = const curves and the ϑ = const lines can be reduced to approximately ten variations. The latter, as is seen from Figure 4-25, are distinguished by the shape of the stationary-temperature-value curves as a function of the stay time. In particular, cases 1, 7, 9, 4, and 2 correspond to the examples presented earlier on Figures 4-15 to 4-19. As will be shown below, these cases are most typical for the development of heat loss; examples of the degeneration of a closed curve of stationary regions into an isolated point (cases 3 and 6 on Figure 4-25 correspond to tangency of the β = const and ϑ = const curves at the

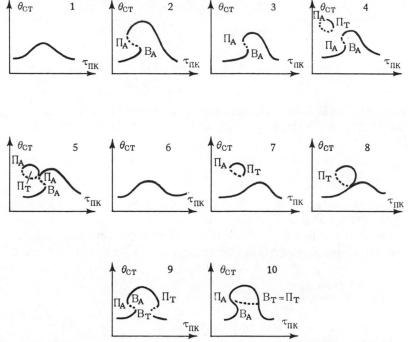

Fig. 4-25. Various types of stationary-temperature-value curves as a function of stay time. *Remarks*: 1. Numbers on the graphs correspond to the lines $\vartheta = \text{const}$ on Figure 4-24; 2. cases 1, 7, 9, 4, and 2 correspond to Figures 4-15, 4-16, 4-17, 4-18, and 4-19.

point $e_A = e_T$ on Figure 4-24 for the β_2 and β_3 curves) can be noted from the other graphs.[16] Also to be noted is the junction of the closed section with the continuous (case 8) or hysteresis (case 4) curve, etc.

It follows from the graphs presented (Figure 4-21 and others) that a change in the number of critical conditions, i.e., a transition from one kind of stationary curve $\theta_{st} = \theta(\tau_{SK})$ to another, corresponds to an extremum in the $\vartheta_{cr} = \vartheta(\theta)$ dependence. Let us express this condition analytically.

There results from (4-39) that the derivative $d\vartheta/d\theta$ becomes zero

$$\frac{d\vartheta}{d\theta} = (2\theta\theta_0 + \theta_0 - \theta)\left[\frac{1}{(\theta - \theta_0 - \theta^2)^2} - \frac{\beta e^{1/\theta}}{\theta^4}\right] = 0$$

[16]It is understood that these regions, noted in the work cited above (15), have no practical value because of instability for infinitesimal changes in the parameter τ_{SK}!

if

$$2\theta\theta_0 + \theta_0 - \theta = 0$$

or

$$\frac{(\theta - \theta_0 - \theta^2)^2}{\theta^4}\beta e^{1/\theta} = 1; \quad \beta = \frac{\theta^4 e^{-1/\theta}}{(\theta - \theta_0 - \theta^2)^2}$$

Evidently both these expressions correspond to the condition of the two critical phenomena being coincident. The first of them yields

$$\theta = \frac{\theta_0}{1 - 2\theta} \tag{2-27}$$

i.e., corresponds to the condition of ignition and extinction coincidence in the adiabatic process (see Table 2-2).

Substituting this value of the temperature in (4-40) for the heat-loss coefficient β, we obtain the equation of a line in $\beta - \vartheta$ coordinates

$$\beta_{\lim} = \frac{e^{2 - 1/\theta_0}}{4\theta_0^2}\left[\vartheta - \frac{4\theta_0^2}{1 - 4\theta_0}\right] \tag{4-42}$$

In the particular case that heat loss is lacking ($\beta = 0$), there follows from (4-42):

$$\vartheta_{i-e} = \frac{4\theta_0^2}{1 - 4\theta_0}$$

which, naturally, agrees with the formula mentioned in Table 2-2.[17]

Taking this formula into account, we rewrite (4-42) thus:

$$\beta_{\lim} = \frac{e^{2 - 1/\theta_0}}{4\theta_0^2}(\vartheta - \vartheta_{ie}) \tag{4-42'}$$

The second solution of the equation $d\vartheta/d\theta = 0$ leads to parametric equations for the second boundary curve on the $\beta - \vartheta$ plane after it is substituted in (4-39)

$$\beta = \frac{\theta^4 e^{-1/\theta}}{(\theta - \theta_0 - \theta^2)^2}; \quad \vartheta = \frac{(\theta - \theta_0)^3}{(\theta - \theta_0 - \theta^2)^2} \tag{4-43}$$

Shown on Figure 4-26, which is a development of the diagram proposed in the cited work of Zel'dovich and Zysin (15), is the division of the $\beta - \vartheta$ plane ("heat loss-heat producitivity") into five characteristic regions by means of the line (4-41) and the

[17]Zel'dovich and Zysin (15) give $\vartheta = 4\theta_0^2$ approximately instead of (4-42), i.e., reiterate the result of Frank-Kamenetskii $\vartheta_{ie} = 4$ [see (51) and section 3-3], which is obtained by expanding the exponential in series.

curve (4-43), with a regression point. Indicated on the separate sections of the boundary curves is the coincidence of the critical conditions to which these curves correspond (for example, $i_A = e_A$; $e_A = e_T$, etc.). The progress of the process for each of the five regions on the $\beta - \vartheta$ diagram can be briefly characterized as follows:

1. Region of the uncritical process (Figure 4-15)

2. Region of mutual superposition of the uncritical process (continuous curve) and the closed curve bounded by extinction on both sides (Figure 4-16)

3. Region of hysteresis-process development in which there are two ignitions and two extinctions in a wide range of values of τ_{SK} (Figure 4-17)

4. Region of superposition of the hysteresis ("adiabatic") process and a closed curve; for this region one ignition and three extinctions are characteristic (Figure 4-18)

5. Region of the hysteresis (conditionally "adiabatic") process with one ignition and one extinction (Figure 4-19)

Shown by dashes on this same Figure 4-26 are the values $\beta = \beta_1, \beta_2, \ldots \beta_6$ corresponding to the six characteristic curves on Figure 4-21 with numbers, corresponding to the values $\vartheta = \text{const}$ on Figure 4-24, written thereon.

The diagram sketched on Figure 4-26 which divides the $\beta - \vartheta$ plane into characteristic regions of the thermal process refers to

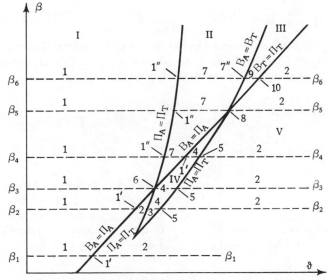

Fig. 4-26. "Heat loss-heat production" diagram, $\beta - \vartheta$. Points on the dashed lines ($\beta = \text{const}$) marked by the numbers 1, 2, 3, ... 10 correspond to regions mentioned in Figures 4-24 and 4-25.

a certain definite value of the initial mixture temperature θ_0. As θ_0 increases, the intersection of the line (4-41), the fundamental boundary between the uncritical and hysteresis types of processes, will shift toward the larger values of the heat productivity ϑ. There follows from (4-42) for $\theta_0 \, {}_{cr \, max} = 0.25$: $\vartheta_{ie} \to \infty$. Rotation of these curves will also occur as θ_0 increases, in addition to the shift of the lines (4-41), i.e., to broadening of the region of the uncritical process. In order to characterize the influence of the parameter θ_0 on the whole more clearly, let us find the equation of the envelope for lines of ignition and extinction coincidence (4-41).

From (4-41) in the form

$$4\beta e^{(1-2\theta_0)/\theta_0} \theta_0^2 - \vartheta + \frac{4\theta_0^2}{1-4\theta_0} = F(\beta, \vartheta, \theta_0) = 0$$

we have

$$\frac{\partial F}{\partial \beta} = 4\beta e^{(1/\theta_0)} - 2(2\theta_0 - 1) + \frac{8\theta_0(1 - 2\theta_0)}{(1 - 4\theta_0)^2} = 0$$

or finally

$$\beta = \frac{2\theta_0 e^{2 - (1/\theta_0)}}{(1 - 4\theta_0)^2} \tag{4-44}$$

After substituting (4-44) into (4-39), we obtain

$$\vartheta = \frac{4\theta_0^2}{(1 - 4\theta_0)^2}(1 - 2\theta_0) \tag{4-45}$$

The expressions (4-44) and (4-45) are a parametric description of the equation of the envelope of the lines (4-41). The shape of this envelope is shown on Figure 4-27 for small values of ϑ.

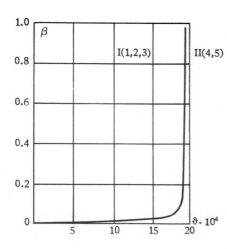

Fig. 4-27. Envelope of the lines dividing the $\beta - \vartheta$ plane into two regions: I = 1 + 2 + 3 and II = 4 + 5. (Arabic numbers are from Figure 4-26.) $\theta_{01} < \theta_{02} < \dots \theta_{05}$.

Processes corresponding to regions I″, II, and III on Figure 4-26 are possible in region I adjoining the vertical axis on this graph but processes of type IV and V cannot occur for any values of θ_0. A more graphical illustration of the influence of θ_0 is given in Table 4-1 presented below of the values of $\vartheta_{ie,\,ad}$ and K (i.e., the segment on the ϑ axis cut off by the line (4-41) and the slope of this line) from (4-41) in the form

$$\beta_{\lim} = K(\vartheta - \vartheta_{\lim,\,ad}); \quad K = \frac{e^{2-(1/\theta_0)}}{4\theta_0{}^2}$$

As is seen from the values presented in Table 4-1 and the schematic diagram on Figure 4-27, the region of the hysteresis (adiabatic) process II on Figure 4-27 is very small for low values of θ_0 and is located near the horizontal axis: as θ_0 increases, this region is shifted sharply toward the more intense heat loss and it advances simultaneously toward higher values of the mixture heat productivity.

The results obtained yield a detailed picture of the influence of heat loss on the stationary region of the process. Very important here are the limitation of the combustion region at high values of τ_{SK} (τ_{DK}, correspondingly for heterogeneous combustion) and the presence of special critical ignition and extinction conditions, specific only for a process with heat emission.

It is extremely essential that the latter (i_T and e_T) owe their origin to the contradictory influence of the parameter τ_{SK} on the character of the process, namely, to a rise in the completeness of combustion (i.e., heat liberation) and a rise in heat loss as τ_{SK} increases. Just the first tendency is observed in the adiabatic process, which is related to the growth of τ_{SK}; correspondingly, the process can be uncritical or hysteresis (adiabatic, i_A and e_A).

Table 4-1.

θ_0	0	0.05	0.10	0.15	0.20	0.25
ϑ	0	0.0125	0.0667	0.225	0.225	—
K	0	1.2×10^{-6}	0.0085	0.10	0.10	0.55

The identical result (two regions of progress of the process in the β - ϑ diagram, namely I and V on Figure 4-26) is obtained also in the other limiting case, when heat susceptibility is neglected. Actually, if it is assumed in (4-34) that

$$\theta - \theta_0 \ll \beta\tau_{SK}(\theta - \theta_0), \text{ i.e., } \beta\tau_{SK} \gg 1$$

and, correspondingly,

$$\varphi_{II} \approx \frac{\beta\tau_{SK}}{\vartheta}(\theta - \theta_0) \tag{4-46}$$

then from the equality $\varphi_I(\theta) = \varphi_{II}(\theta)$ in the form

$$\frac{\beta\tau_{SK}}{\vartheta}(\theta - \theta_0) = \frac{\tau_{SK}}{\tau_{SK} + e^{1/\theta}}$$

taking into account the formula

$$\tau_{SK,\,cr} = \frac{\theta - \theta_0 - \theta^2}{\theta^2}\,e^{1/\theta} \tag{2-33}$$

there follows

$$\vartheta_{cr} = \beta\frac{(\theta - \theta_0)^2}{\theta^2}\,e^{1/\theta} \tag{4-47}$$

Equating the derivative $d\vartheta_{cr}/d\theta$ to zero, we arrive at the condition for ignition and extinction coincidence[18] $\theta_{i-e} = \theta_0/(1 - 2\theta_0)$

$$\theta_{i-e} = \frac{\theta_0}{1 - 2\theta_0} \tag{2-27}$$

from which after simple manipulations, we obtain

$$\beta_{lim} = \frac{e^{2 - 1/\theta_0}}{4\theta_0^2}\,\vartheta \tag{4-48}$$

A line passing through the origin and parallel to the line (4-41) corresponds to this formula in the $\beta - \vartheta$ diagram because of the equality of the slopes K in (4-41) and (4-48).

It is not difficult to obtain a similar result also for the limiting process with radiant heat loss which exceeds the heat susceptibility considerably. In the case that

$$\theta - \theta_0 \ll \sigma\tau_{SK}(\theta^4 - \theta_0^4)$$

[18] $\dfrac{d\vartheta}{d\theta} = \dfrac{\beta}{\theta^4}\left\{\left[2(\theta - \theta_0)\,e^{1/\theta} - (\theta - \theta_0)^2\,\dfrac{e^{1/\theta}}{\theta^2}\right]\theta^2 - 2\theta(\theta - \theta_0^2)\,e^{1/\theta}\right\} = 0$

from which after combining

$$\theta - \theta_0 - 2\theta\theta_0 = 0$$

that is

$$\theta = \frac{\theta_0}{1 - 2\theta_0}; \quad \theta_0 = \frac{\theta}{1 + 2\theta}$$

for

$$\varphi_{II} \approx \frac{\sigma \tau_{SK}}{\vartheta}(\theta^4 - \theta_0^4) \qquad (4\text{-}18)$$

from the equality $\varphi_I(\theta) = \varphi_{II}(\theta)$ in the form

$$\frac{\sigma \tau_{SK}}{\vartheta}(\theta^4 - \theta_0^4) = \frac{\tau_{SK}}{\tau_{SK} + e^{1/\theta}}$$

taking into account the formula

$$\tau_{SK,\,cr} = \frac{\theta^4 - \theta_0^4 - 4\theta^5}{4\theta^5} e^{1/\theta} \qquad (4\text{-}25)$$

there follows

$$\vartheta_{cr} = \frac{(\theta^4 - \theta_0^4)}{4\theta^5} e^{1/\theta} \sigma \qquad (4\text{-}49)$$

We obtain for the boundary curve from the condition $d\vartheta_{cr}/d\theta = 0$

$$\frac{d\vartheta}{d\theta} = \frac{\sigma}{4\theta^5}\left\{\left[2(\theta^4 - \theta_0^4) - 4\theta^3 e^{1/\theta} - \frac{e^{1/\theta}}{\theta^2}(\theta^4 - \theta_0^4)^2\right]4\theta^5 \right.$$
$$\left. - 5\theta^4(\theta^4 - \theta_0^4)^2 e^{1/\theta}\right\} = 0$$

from which there follows after manipulation

$$\theta_0 = \theta\sqrt[4]{\frac{1 - 3\theta}{1 + 5\theta}} \qquad (4\text{-}24)$$

i.e., the relation encountered earlier for coincidence of ignition and extinction (section 4-2). After having substituted (4-29) into (4-49) for ϑ_{cr}, we obtain the following parametric expressions for the boundaries of the regions of the uncritical and the hysteresis processes:

$$\sigma_{lim} = \frac{1 + 5\theta}{2} e^{-1/\theta}\vartheta; \quad \theta_0 = \theta\sqrt[4]{\frac{1 - 3\theta}{1 + 5\theta}}$$

i.e., again the equation of a line in $\sigma - \vartheta$ coordinates passing through the origin.

Hence, in both limiting cases of convection and radiation, neglecting the heat susceptibility leads to the retention of just two basic kinds of processes, the uncritical and the hysteresis (i_A and e_A), just as in the adiabatic process. Apparently, the same regions are retained in the general case of heat loss by radiation too (as is shown by a graphical investigation of the stationary states, see Figure 4-14, for example) as in heat loss by convection (Figures 4-15 to 4-19, etc.). In connection with the sharp influence of radiation, complex heat exchange can also be expected in this case with respect to an increase in not only the region of the uncritical process I but also the regions II and III on Figure 4-26, i.e., a process with heat-exchange critical phenomena as well as with heat-exchange and adiabatic phenomena. Moreover, as was mentioned in detail above, heat loss by radiation considerably shortens the whole region of existence of the critical conditions (Figure 4-13, etc.).

All these results refer both to the combustion of a well-mixed mixture and to the heterogeneous process as well. For the latter, the combustion of coal, say, they mean, first, a limitation of the combustion region from both the high values of the velocity side (or small particle size) and the low values of the velocity side (or the large particle size).

Let us also note that the case of additional heat loss considered in this paragraph, which is subject to the linear law

$$\varphi_{II} = \frac{1 + \beta \tau_{DK}}{\vartheta}(\theta - \theta_0) \tag{4-18}$$

also refers directly to the heterogeneous combustion process with heat elimination by heat conduction from the combustion surface. This is seen, for example, from the equation of heat balance of unit surface in the form

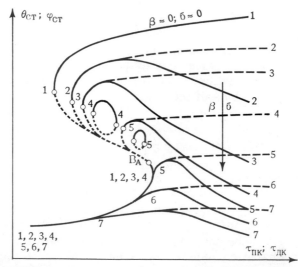

Fig. 4-28. Influence of heat loss on the curves of the stationary values of the temperature and completeness of combustion as a function of nondimensional time. ($\beta_1 < \beta_2 < \ldots \beta_7$.) Solid line, temperature; dashed line, completeness of combustion.

$$\alpha_D(C_0 - C)q = \alpha(T - T_0) + \frac{\lambda_T}{\delta}(T - T_0) \qquad (4\text{-}49')$$

where λ_T is the coal heat-conductivity coefficient; δ is the reduced wall thickness. If the equality

$$\alpha_1 = \frac{\lambda_T}{\delta} \qquad (4\text{-}50)$$

is denoted in the latter, then (4-49') transforms directly into (4-18). This case, say, corresponds to experiments on the combustion of a coal channel (8, 34, 36, 40), which, as is known, is one of the simplest models of an underground gas generator.

On the whole, the influence of heat elimination in all cases of a process with intense heat elimination is first expressed in the diminution of the region of stationary combustion and in the reduction of the combustion temperature. The range of values of the nondimensional time (τ_{SK} for the combustion of a well-mixed mixture; τ_{DK} for coal combustion), corresponding to comparatively high values of the temperature, is simultaneously abbreviated. This general result has been shown simplified,[19] for an example on Figure 4-28 in the form of a series of curves of the stationary temperature values as a function of the nondimensional time for increasing values of the heat-transfer coefficient (β for heat transfer by convection or σ for transfer by radiation) for given values of the initial mixture temperature and heat productivity. Figure 4-28 graphically shows one of the possible cases of successive change in the curves $\theta_{st} = \theta(\tau_{SK})$ as the heat loss increases, in particular, the formation of isolated sections for the hysteresis (4-4) or the continuous (5-5) curves. Shown by dashes on this same graph are curves of the stationary values of the completeness of combustion $\varphi_{st} = \varphi(\tau_{SK})$, which are approximately similar to the $\theta_{st}(\tau_{SK})$ curves on the left up to the maximum of the temperature (including the isolated sections) and which diverge afterward, after the initial temperature drop. Under intense heat-loss conditions, an increase in the completeness of combustion after a reduction in the temperature cannot actually occur.

4-5. REMARK ON DISCONTINUOUS OSCILLATIONS

In concluding the chapter, let us dwell briefly on one of the questions, which although not related exclusively to heat-exchange conditions, is, however, of considerable interest in connection with the

[19] For simplicity, the ignition point (i_A) for the hysteresis curves, 1, 2, 3, and 4 is superposed on Figure 4-28 and the lines of the nondimensional time-dependence of θ (solid line) and the completeness of combustion (φ) (dashed) up to the maximum value of the temperature are also combined.

peculiarities of the hysteresis process. We speak of the formation of oscillatory combustion regions which are sometimes observed in the consumption of a gaseous or liquid fuel and, considerably more rarely, of a solid fuel. Let us first note that the problem of flame oscillation, detected at the end of the last century during investigations of flame propagation in burning mixtures filling long tubes (46), did not receive a complete solution.

Special kinetic schemes for the progress of two successive chemical reactions with different temperature dependence were proposed in the work of Frank-Kamenetskii, Sal'nikov, and others (50). It had been shown that such a two-stage reaction mechanism can lead to the build-up of a self-oscillating process under definite conditions in a certain range of the variables.

In addition to such purely kinetic conceptions of the nature of oscillations during combustion, the idea of a two-stage process can underlie other (aerodynamic, diffusion, or thermal) schemes of the oscillatory process.

Apparently, the following can clarify the simplest of these. Let us imagine, for example, the successive accumulation of the combustible mixture in the chamber, its ignition and very rapid, almost instantaneous complete combustion, repeated accumulation, ignition, etc.

The "ignition lag" used in this scheme, which leads to a significant accumulation of the combustible mixture, can be caused by the conditions of air and fuel supply, by the character of the mixture formation, and finally, by kinetic properties of the mixture. The reverse influence of the change in state in the chamber (pressure rise during ignition, etc.), on the delivery of fuel and air to the chamber, and on the flow of the combustion products can also be of great value. Finally, a hydraulic diagram of the chamber, flame stabilization conditions, a supply system for the combustible mixture, etc., are essential to the investigation of specific cases.

Without discussing the question in all its complexity here, let us limit ourselves to an indication of one of the possible oscillation diagrams, related directly to the peculiarities of the thermal region during the hysteresis combustion process. Insignificant deviations from the average steady state are always inevitable in an actual furnace process. Oscillations of the region which arise continuously and displace eath other, can be caused, for example, by disturbances in the uniformity of the air or fuel supply, which would lead to oscillations in the consumption and composition of the mixture, of the humidity, etc., of the fuel, temperature, and the degree that the mixture is well-mixed, mixing or heat-exchange conditions, etc.

In particular, these oscillations make impossible the realization, under actual conditions, of an average between the oxidation and the

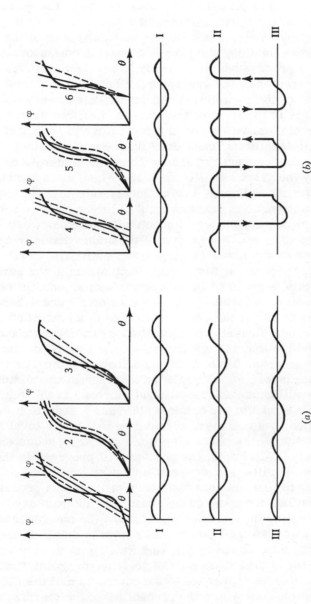

Fig. 4-29. Examples of oscillatory processes. (*a*) Small oscillation case; (*b*) discontinuous oscillations case; 1 and 4—oscillations of the parameter θ_0; 2 and 5—τ_{SK}; 3 and 6—ϑ; I(*a* and *b*) fluctuations of one of the parameters; II(*a*) and III(*a*) resultant oscillations of the temperature and completeness of combustion near the upper (II) and lower (III) levels; II(*b*) and III(*b*) discontinuous oscillations of the temperature and completeness of combustion with the transition from one level to another.

157

combustion of the stationary region which is unstable to infinitesimal deviations. Analogous considerations, referring to finite deviations, can also explain the possibility of building up an original unstationary combustion region in the form of discontinuous oscillations of the temperature and completeness of combustion.

For example, let us assume that the value of one of the parameters of the process, the initial temperature, the mixture heat productivity, the heat-transfer coefficient, or finally, one of the characteristic times (mixing, stay, etc.), fluctuates continuously with time during a process which is steady on the average. Depending on the character of the average equilibrium state, these oscillations of one of the parameters can lead either to very insignificant fluctuations in the level of the process, i.e., two values of the completeness of combustion and of temperature in the chamber, or to sharp, intermittent transitions from the upper stable level to the lower and conversely. These simple considerations are illustrated by the graphs on Figure 4-29. When, as is shown on the upper diagrams of Figure 4-29a, fluctuations near the equilibrium state do not lead to a transition out of the critical ignition and extinction regions, insignificant, practically harmonic, oscillations of the values of φ and θ near one of the stable levels of the process, the upper or the lower (Figure 4-29a), will also correspond to small (harmonic, for simplicity) fluctuations of the parameter. Precisely this is realized in the operation of any stable region of the combustion process. If, as is shown on Figure 4-29b, small oscillations of one of the parameters lead to a transition out of the critical regions, then sharp, discontinuous oscillations containing the successive interchange of ignition and extinction, can be built up in the process. Thus, if we start from a combustion state (upper stable level), for example, an increase in the mixture heat productivity will cause an insignificant increase in the value of φ and θ, then a return to the original state and a reduction in φ and θ, accompanied by a collapse, a transition to a lower level for the opposite deviation of the parameter (for example, a reduction of heat productivity). After this, the process will progress in the reverse sequence: ignition will occur at the lower level, etc.

The circumstance that the real stationary process can proceed with certain deviations from the quasi-stationary diagram used here in no way changes the qualitative picture of the phenomenon, in substance. Let us also note that as was shown in detail in preceding paragraphs, the influence of mixing (more exactly, the commensurability of the mixing time and the reaction-progress time) as well as of heat loss is expressed in the contraction of the hysteresis loop in connection with which the probability of the mechanism of the discontinuous fluctuations considered increases; the very same also refers to the supplementary (heat-exchange) critical ignition and extinction conditions related to intense heat emission.

This simple diagram of an unstationary oscillatory process with the subsequent transition from one stable level to another and back does not certainly include many questions essential to the process progress for specific conditions: the influence of the pressure variation on the process in the chamber, the delivery of the fresh mixture and the elimination of the combustion products, the general picture of the gas motion in the chamber, and certain others, whose review is beyond the scope of this book.

Chapter 5

Examples of a Computation with the One-dimensional Diagram

5-1. SIMPLEST EXAMPLES OF THE BURN-UP CURVES

For comparison, let us consider certain very simple cases of a computation performed for the one-dimensional model of the process. Let us start from the following assumption: Let us imagine that the burning of each element of a well-mixed combustible mixture moving in a "direct-flow" chamber (a cylindrical tube, say) occurs under conditions of complete insulation from the rest of the furnace space. This assumption means, first, the absence of intermixing of the fresh mixture and the combustion products and second, the absence of heat exchange between the separate zones of the chamber. Evidently the case being considered corresponds to a limiting scheme of the process opposite the zero-dimensional model (total mixing and equalization of the temperature and concentration in the space) used in the preceding four chapters.

Let us consider the concentration and temperature across any chamber cross section to be uniform and independent of time; the first assumption is rigorous only for an elementary stream-tube and corresponds, for a stream of finite dimensions, to the introduction of average values of the variables across the cross section into the computation; the second corresponds to a stationary process.

Let us start with adiabatic combustion of a well-mixed mixture. Let us write the reaction-rate equation (for $n = 1$) for a certain stay-time element of the mixture in the chamber as

$$-\frac{dc}{d\tau_S} = kc = k_0 e^{-E/RT} c \tag{5-1}$$

The time element $d\tau_S$ is here related to the chamber length x and the mixture velocity w by the usual relation

$$d\tau = \frac{dx}{w} \tag{5-2}$$

where it can be assumed for small values of velocity

$$\frac{w}{w_0} \approx \frac{T}{T_0} \tag{5-3}$$

where w_0 and T_0 are velocity and temperature in the initial section of the chamber.

160

Introducing, as before, the nondimensional variables

$$\varphi = 1 - c = 1 - c/c_0; \quad \tau_{SK} = \tau_S/\tau_K; \quad \theta = RT/E$$

for the simplest case of a first-order reaction, we obtain instead of (5-1)

$$\frac{d\varphi}{d\tau_S} = (1 - \varphi) \, e^{-1/\theta} \tag{5-4}$$

We use the following relation for the adiabatic process to relate the variables φ and θ

$$-q \, dc = c_p dT; \quad d\varphi = \frac{d\theta}{\vartheta}$$

where, as before,

$$\vartheta = \frac{Rqc_0}{Ec_p}$$

Integrating, we obtain as before

$$\varphi = \frac{\theta - \theta_0}{\vartheta}; \quad \theta = \theta_0 + \varphi \tag{5-5}$$

The dependence of the completeness of combustion on the mixture stay time in the chamber can then be expressed as

$$\tau_{SK} = \int_0^\varphi \frac{e^{1/(\theta_0 + \varphi\vartheta)}}{1 - \varphi} \, d\varphi \tag{5-6}$$

Similarly, the relation between the temperature and the time is

$$\tau_{SK} = \int_{\theta_0}^\theta \frac{e^{1/\theta}}{\theta_m - \theta} \, d\theta \tag{5-7}$$

where, as before,

$$\theta_m = \theta_0 + \vartheta$$

is the maximum combustion temperature.

The construction of the curve of the temperature- or completeness-of-combustion[1] variation as a function of stay time for given values of the parameters θ_0 and θ_m (or ϑ), therefore, reduces to the calculation of the integrals (5-6) or (5-7). These latter are not difficult to evaluate graphically or numerically or, finally, by

[1] The $\theta(\tau_{SK})$ and $\varphi(\tau_{SK})$ curves in the process under consideration are similar, just as in the total mixing case, since it follows from (5-5) that

$$\varphi = (\theta - \theta_0)/(\theta_m - \theta_0) = (T - T_0)/(T_m - T_0) \tag{5-5'}$$

transformation to tabulated functions.[2] Similarly, the problem of calculating the curve of the variation of θ (or φ) along the chamber length is also solved, in principle, by starting from the expression

$$\xi = \frac{1}{\theta_0} \int_{\theta_0}^{\theta} \frac{\theta \, e^{1/\theta} \, d\theta}{\theta_m - \theta} = \frac{1}{\theta_0} \int_0^{\varphi} (\theta_0 + \vartheta \, \varphi) \, \frac{e^{\frac{1}{\theta_0 + \vartheta \varphi}}}{1 - \varphi} \, d\varphi \qquad (5\text{-}8)$$

which is obtained from (5-2) and (5-3). In formula (5-8)

$$\xi = \frac{k_0 \chi}{w_0} = \frac{\chi}{w_0 \, \tau_K} \qquad (5\text{-}9)$$

is the reduced (nondimensional) coordinate.

The characteristic curves $\theta - \theta (\tau_{SK})$ are shown on Figure 5-1 for intensely and slightly exothermal reactions. In the first case, the curve $\theta (\tau_{SK})$ is extremely steep for a certain value of the time for a large enough value of the parameter ϑ and it rises almost vertically to the value $\theta \to \theta_m$. The temperature rise in the case of a low value of ϑ occurs comparatively slowly; combustion is practically absent. These two sharply differentiated processes agree qualitatively with the hysteresis and uncritical processes in the zero-dimensional scheme, where this agreement is especially good for the slightly exothermal reactions. It is natural to call the instant corresponding to the sharp rise in the curve $\theta (\tau_{SK})$ or $\varphi (\tau_{SK})$ for the intensely exothermal process (curve 1 on Figure 5-1), the critical ignition time.

If we repeat the imaginary experiment with the combustion in a telescopic chamber described in section 2-3, i.e., with a continuous

---

[2] For example, substituting $y = \exp(1/\theta)$ (i.e., $\theta = (1)/(\ln y)$); $d\theta = -(dy)/(y \ln^2 y)$ into (5-7) changes it to

$$\int_{\theta_0}^{\theta} \frac{e^{1/\theta} \, dy}{\theta_m - \theta} = li(y) - li(y_0) \qquad (5\text{-}7')$$

where $y_0 = \exp(1/\theta)$; $y_m = \exp(1/\theta_m)$ and the symbol $li(y) = \int_0^y \frac{dy}{\ln y}$ denotes the logarithm integral whose values can be taken from appropriate tables or calculated approximately by using the series

$$li(y) = C + \theta \ln (\ln y) + \frac{\ln^2 (y)}{2 \cdot 2!} + \frac{\ln^3 y}{3 \cdot 3!} + \cdots (0 < y < \infty)$$

where $C = 0.577$ is Euler's constant.

Let us note also that the function $li(e^y) = Ei(y)$; consequently, it is convenient to substitute $li(y) = li(e^{1/\theta}) = Ei(1/\theta)$ in (5-7). (Tables of values of the latter function are given, for example, in Jahnke and Emde, *Tables of Functions.*)

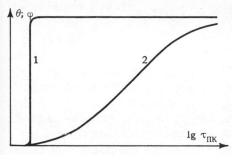

Fig. 5-1. Curves of the variation of temperature and completeness of combustion as a function of time (one-dimensional problem). 1—Intensely exothermal process; 2—slightly exothermal process.

increase and decrease in the length of the chamber, then the curve 1 on Figure 5-1 will describe the dependence of the combustion temperature in the output cross section ξ for both a lengthening and a shortening of the chamber. This means that the ignition and extinction conditions coincide in the one-dimensional model; "inertia" of combustion is missing.

As should have been expected, the zero-dimensional model is a better approximation to reality since the hysteresis character of the curve $\theta = \theta(\tau_{SK})$, typical for strongly exothermal reactions, is always observed in experiment and under real conditions.

Let us turn to a numerical example for a more detailed comparison of these two schemes. Compared on Figure 5-2 in $\varphi - \tau_{SK}$ coordinates are three pairs of curves showing the dependence of the stationary values of the completeness of combustion on the nondimensional time, referred to one initial temperature value and three heat-productivity values. The first two values of ϑ in the zero-dimensional scheme correspond to the hysteresis process, the third to the limiting case of ignition and extinction coincidence. The

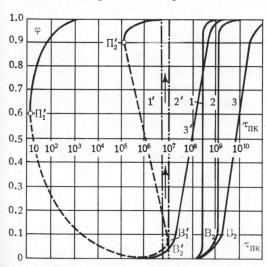

Fig. 5-2. Curves of the time-dependence of the temperature computed by the one-dimensional (1, 2, 3) and the zero-dimensional (1', 2', 3') schemes for adiabatic combustion of a well-mixed mixture ($\theta_0 = 0.05$; 1 and 1'—$\vartheta = 0.5$; 2 and 2'—$\vartheta = 0.05$; 3 and 3'—$\vartheta = 0.0125$).

curves denoted by the numbers 1, 2, and 3 have been calculated by using (5-6) and the curves 1', 2', and 3' by using

$$\tau_{SK} = \frac{\varphi}{1 - \varphi} \, e^{\frac{1}{\theta_0 + \vartheta \varphi}} \tag{2-14}$$

As is seen from the graph, the curves calculated under the assumption of total mixing of the fresh mixture with the combustion products (zero-dimensional model), even if two of them, 1' and 2', diverge from the hysteresis shape, i.e., if only the process of increasing φ is considered, considerably outstrip the curves computed for the same values of θ_0 and ϑ under the assumption of isolated combustion (curves 1, 2, 3) in all three cases. This example again stresses the value of mixing the fresh mixture with the combustion products, which shortens the critical ignition time a great deal. It is understood that a similar result, a considerable acceleration in the development of the process, can also be achieved if the delivery of heat to the fresh mixture is independent of mixing with the combustion products. Without dwelling on the details of the computations, let us note that the rise in curve 1 on Figure 5-1 occurs at a significantly smaller value of the time for an intense heat supply, and that curve 2 approximates the shape of curve 1, in particular, acquires a sharp, practically vertical slope (ignition). A more complex investigation is essential in the one-dimensional scheme of the process with heat loss, as performed by Todes and Melent' ev (48). In substance, the solution of the problem reduces to obtaining a time-dependence of temperature as a curve with a maximum; for small values of τ_{SK} the low temperatures near the initial value of the temperature are related to low reaction rate, and low temperature for high values of the time are due to cooling. In qualitative respects, the results are similar to those obtained above for the zero-dimensional model; a detailed interpretation is made difficult by the complexity of the relationships and by the necessity of relying on graphical or numerical methods of computation for specific values of the parameters.

Now, let us consider the second limiting case, diffusion combustion. We assume for the approximate computation,

$$- \frac{dc}{d\tau_S} = \frac{c}{\tau_D}$$

where, as before, τ_D is the characteristic mixing time. Transforming to nondimensional variables

$$\frac{d\varphi}{d\tau_{SD}} = 1 - \varphi \tag{5-10}$$

and integrating, we obtain

$$\varphi = 1 - e^{-\tau_{SD}} \qquad (5\text{-}11)$$

Presented on Figure 5-3 is a comparison of the curves $\varphi = \varphi(\tau_{SD})$ for diffusion combustion, calculated using (5-11) for a one-dimensional scheme and using $\varphi = (1)/(1 + \tau_{SD})$ (3-33) for the zero-dimensional scheme. It is natural that a more rapid rise in the completeness of combustion is obtained in this case (we speak, in substance, of reactions whose rate is independent of temperature) in the absence of the fresh mixture being mixed with the combustion products. As was remarked in Chapter 3 (see section 3-5), the assumption of diffusion combustion corresponds to the range of high-temperature values, consequently, the initial sections of the curves 1 and 2 on Figure 5-3 are drawn dashed.

Let us also consider the purely approximate character of the $\varphi = \varphi(\tau_{SK}, \tau_{SD})$ curves for the general combustion case (see section 3-4). Retaining the same simplifying assumption on the successive progress of the mixing and the reaction, and summing, respectively, the values of the time τ_K' and τ_D in the expression for the reaction rate

$$-\frac{dc}{d\tau_S} = \frac{c}{\tau_K \, e^{1/\theta} + \tau_D} \qquad (5\text{-}12)$$

or in the nondimensional form

$$\frac{d\varphi}{d\tau_{SK}} = \frac{1 - \varphi}{e^{1/\theta} + \tau_{DK}} \qquad (5\text{-}12')$$

we arrive at the expression ($\theta = \theta_0 + \vartheta \, \varphi$ for an adiabatic process)

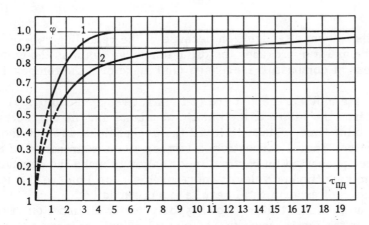

Fig. 5-3. Curves of the time dependence of the completeness of combustion for a computation by the one-dimensional (1) and the zero-dimensional (2) scheme for diffusion combustion.

$$\tau_{SK} = \int\limits_{0}^{\frac{1}{\theta_0 + \vartheta\varphi}} \frac{e^{1/\theta}}{1 - \varphi} \, d\varphi - \tau_{DK} \ln(1 - \varphi) \qquad (5\text{-}13)$$

or in dimensional form

$$\tau_S = \tau_K \int\limits_{0}^{\frac{1}{\theta_0 + \varphi}} \frac{e^{1/\theta}}{1 - \varphi} \, d\varphi - \tau_D \ln(1 - \varphi) \qquad (5\text{-}13')$$

The first of the terms on the right in (5-13') corresponds to the time the reaction progresses according to (5-6); the second is the mixing time according to (5-11'); in conformance with the assumption made on the sequence of the diffusion and reaction processes, the total time consists of the sum of the times of the component processes. Shown schematically on Figure 5-4 are examples of the construction of the burn-up curve $\varphi = \varphi(\tau_S)$ by summing the abscissas of the appropriate corresponding values on the diffusion (1) and kinetic (2) curves. As is seen from the graph, the total curve (3) is very close to the kinetic curve in the initial section and departs substantially therefrom after ignition because of the retarding role of the diffusion and it approaches the diffusion curve again as the completeness of combustion increases (and therefore, the temperature also).

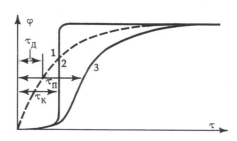

Fig. 5-4. Burn-up curves computed according to the one-dimensional scheme. 1—Diffusion combustion; 2—kinetic combustion; 3—general case.

The examples presented are of illustrative, methodological value since the values of the kinetic constants and the characteristic mixing time, which are in all the expressions, are not known in practice. In this connection, a further close examination of the relations presented (in particular, attempts to make the dependence of the mixing time on velocity more precise, etc.) before the accumulation of experimental results is not expedient.

Let us just note that by knowing the velocity distribution of the flow over the length, from (5-3), for a constant-pressure process, a velocity, equal in magnitude to the velocity at the ignition point and directed opposite the flow of the fresh mixture, can be treated as the effective rate of flame propagation from the condition of stationarity of the phenomena. This will be considered in detail below.

5-2. SCHEMATIC COMPUTATION OF A MUFFLE BURNER

As an example of the method, which illustrates the use of certain of the conceptions of the thermal combustion theory developed above —in particular, the influence of the supply of heat on the development of the process—let us carry out a schematic computation of the combustion in a flow of an air-dust mixture. Let us start from the one-dimensional model of the phenomenon and, for simplicity, from the same assumptions on the kinetics of the process as made in Chapter 3 for the thermal region of coal combustion.

Let us assume that a mixture of air and pulverized coal, for simplicity, coal substantially free of volatile matter (anthracite, say) enters a certain channel of constant cross section, which simulates a coal-dust muffle burner, say.

Combustion of the air-dust mixture would not occur in practice at a low initial temperature in the absence of special ignition in the continuously adiabatic process considered in the previous section. Theoretically it would require a channel many hundreds of kilometers long for its development.[3] Actually, a comparatively rapid development of the process is guaranteed by a continuous supply of heat from the flame zone to the fresh air mixture. This heat supply is accomplished, basically, by a mixture with the combustion products and also by radiation.

Let us try to project the principle of the computation scheme of such a process to preheat the fresh mixture solely by radiation and let us illustrate it by certain numerical results which are of methodological value.

The substance of the computation consists of the approximate separation of the process into two successive stages: a stage of inert heating of the mixture prior to ignition and a stage of active combustion.

To be definite, let us assume that we speak of an air mixture with a noticeable lack of air ($\alpha < 1$). Let us consider, therefore, that the burn-up of the oxidizer, the oxygen in the air, in an atmosphere of excess fuel occurs completely but that the burn-up of the coal is comparatively negligible. In this connection, constant (average) values of the particle size can be introduced into the computation.

[3] The theoretical length of a burner without heat supplied to the mixture is of the order of 1,000 km (!) for the values of k_0, E, and $T_0 = 400°$ abs, used later for an example of the computation.

When computing the first zone of the process, the section of firing the mixture, let us assume in addition that very intensive heat exchange occurs between the coal and the air (the heat-transfer coefficient by convection is of the order of $\alpha \approx 10^3$ kcal/m³ hr deg for coal dust) and it leads to an almost instantaneous equalization of the coal and air temperatures. Let us also neglect the velocity of the carbon particles relative to the gas flow.

After determining the curve of the temperature variation according to the time or the burner length because of heating by radiation, let us compute the burn-up of the oxygen in the air. To do this, let us substitute the time dependence of the temperature, found from a computation of the initial heating, in the reaction equation. The instant of ignition can always be found for such a two-stage computation with a high degree of accuracy and the burn-up of the oxygen also can be determined; but with a certain lag in the instant of the termination of the combustion, since the actual temperature rise in the combustion process occurs considerably more rapidly than during inert initial heating. This distortion can, in principle, be reduced to a minimum by successive approximations; however, in practice, the second approximation is completely sufficient. This reduces to a construction of the temperature curve on the active section starting from the results on burn-up obtained in a first approximation for a given temperature curve. Shown on Figure 5-5, schematically, are curves of the variation of the temperature of the mixture and the oxygen concentration, corresponding to the computation scheme used.

Let us first form the general heat-balance equation of a mixture element

$$-\frac{dc}{d\tau_S} \cdot q = k'_{\text{eff}}\, cq = c'_p\, \frac{dT}{d\tau_S} - c_r\, (T_m{}^4 - T^4) \qquad (5\text{-}14)$$

On the left in this system of equations is the rate of oxygen consumption expressed according to formula (3-7) by means of the effective constant of the heterogeneous reaction rate

$$k_{\text{eff}} = \frac{1}{\dfrac{1}{k} + \dfrac{1}{\alpha_D}}$$

referred to unit volume of mixture by multiplying the specific carbon surface per unit volume. On the right side of (5-14) is the difference in the increment of the mixture heat content (c'_p is reduced specific heat of the dust and the air) and the quantity of heat supplied by radiation from the flame (c_r—reduced coefficient of radiation calculated according to the specific surface of the carbon and ash particles receiving the radiant heat, with the degree of blackness, view angle, etc., taken into account).

Let us transform (5-14) to nondimensional variables used in this book

$$\frac{d\varphi}{d\tau_{SK}} = \frac{1 - \varphi}{\tau_{DK} + e^{1/\theta}} \tag{5-12'}$$

from which, as in the preceding section

$$\tau_{SK} = \int_0^\varphi (e^{1/\theta} + \tau_{DK}) \frac{d\varphi}{1 - \varphi} \tag{5-15}$$

and

$$\frac{d\varphi}{d\tau_{SK}} = \frac{1}{\vartheta} \left[\frac{d\theta}{d\tau_{SK}} - \sigma\,(\theta_m^4 - \theta^4) \right] \tag{5-16}$$

It is not difficult to see that (5-16) is a generalization of (4-17), obtained by passing to infinitely small changes in the variables, exactly as in (5-12) with respect to (3-45).

Let us approximately integrate the system of Eqs. (5-12) and (5-16), as mentioned before, by neglecting any heat liberation due to reaction in the first section of the process in the low-temperature range. Hence, assuming a zone of inert mixture heating for the first section of the burner

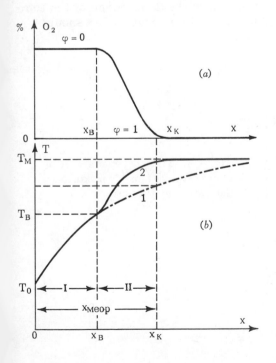

Fig. 5-5. Computation scheme of a burner. (a) Curve of the drop in the oxygen concentration; (b) curve of the temperature rise; I—"inert" heating section $O - x_B$; II—active combustion section, $x_B - x_K$; 1—computed heating curve; 2—actual temperature-rise curve.

$$\frac{d\varphi}{d\tau_{SK}} = 0; \qquad \frac{d\theta}{d\tau_{SK}} = \sigma \left(\theta_m^4 - \theta^4\right) \tag{5-17}$$

we obtain

$$\frac{\tau_{SK}}{\sigma} = \int_{\theta_0}^{\bar{\theta}} \frac{d\theta}{\theta_m^4 - \theta} = \frac{1}{\theta_m^3} \cdot \int_{\bar{\theta}_0}^{\bar{\theta}} \frac{d\bar{\theta}}{1 - \bar{\theta}^4}$$

where $\bar{\theta} = \theta/\theta_m$ or after evaluating the elementary integral

$$\theta_m^3 \frac{\tau_{SK}}{\sigma} = \frac{1}{4} \left[\ln \frac{1 - \bar{\theta}_0^2}{(1 - \bar{\theta})(1 + \bar{\theta}_0)}\right.$$

$$\left. + 2 \left(\arctan \bar{\theta} - \arctan \bar{\theta}_0\right)\right] \tag{5-18}$$

The results of the computation are shown on Figure 5-6.

In order to transform from the curve of the time variation of the temperature to the curve of its variation with burner length, an average dust-air-flow velocity can be introduced into the computation in a first approximation

$$\frac{w_{av}}{w_0} = \frac{T_0 + T_m}{2T_0} = \frac{1}{2}\left(1 + \frac{\theta_m}{\theta_0}\right) = \frac{1}{2}\left(1 + \frac{1}{\theta_0}\right)$$

In this case, in order to transform to the dependence of the temperature on the length, the abscissa scale on Figure 5-6 should

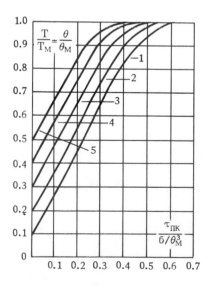

Fig. 5-6. Time dependence of the temperature of an air mixture in the initial heating process.

simply be changed. However, it is not difficult to make more rigorous computation if it is assumed, as in the preceding section

$$\xi = \frac{k_0 x}{w_0}; \quad d\xi = \frac{k_0}{w_0}\, dx = \frac{k_0}{w_0}\, w d\tau_S = \frac{w}{w_0}\, d\tau_{SK} = \frac{\theta}{\theta_0}\, d\tau_{SK}$$

In conformance with this there can be written instead of (5-17)

$$\frac{\theta}{\theta_0}\, \frac{d\theta}{d\xi} = \sigma\,(\theta_m{}^4 - \theta^4);$$

$$\xi = \frac{\sigma}{\theta_0} \int_{\theta_0}^{\theta} \frac{\theta\, d\theta}{\theta_m{}^4 - \theta^4} = \frac{\sigma}{\theta_0 \theta_m{}^4} \int_{\bar{\theta}_0}^{\bar{\theta}} \frac{\bar{\theta}\, d\bar{\theta}}{1 - \bar{\theta}^4} \tag{5-19}$$

or finally

$$\theta_m{}^3 \frac{\xi}{\sigma} = \frac{1}{4\bar{\theta}_0} \ln \frac{1 + \bar{\theta}^2}{1 - \bar{\theta}^2} \cdot \frac{1 - \bar{\theta}_0{}^2}{1 + \bar{\theta}_0{}^2}$$

The appropriate curves are shown on Figure 5-7.

Returning now, for example, to Eq. (5-12′) or to a similar equation for the variation of θ along the chamber length, let us

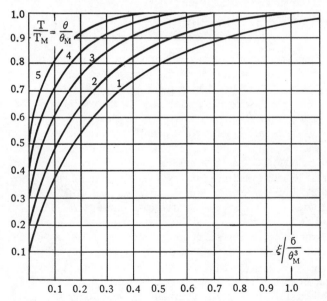

Fig. 5-7. Dependence of the temperature of an air mixture on the burner length in the firing process.

Curve No.	1	2	3	4	5
T_0/T_m	0.1	0.2	0.3	0.4	0.5

consider the variables θ and τ_{SK} related by the Eq. (5-17). Under this assumption, it can be rewritten as:

$$\frac{d\varphi}{1-\varphi} = \frac{d\theta}{(\tau_{DK} + e^{1/\theta})\sigma(\theta_m{}^4 - \theta^4)} \tag{5-20}$$

or finally

$$\varphi = 1 - e^{-\int_{\theta_0}^{\theta} \frac{d\theta}{(\tau_{DK} + e^{1/\theta})(\sigma)(\theta_m{}^4 - \theta^4)}} \tag{5-21}$$

Graphical integration of the last expression yields a relation between the variables φ and θ, which permits the dependence $\varphi = \varphi(\tau_{SK})$ also to be determined using Eq. (5-18). In order to make the temperature curve on the active combustion more precise, heat supply can be neglected on this section now and the more precise dependence of $\theta(\tau_{SK})$ can be constructed according to the $\varphi(\tau_{SK})$ curve from the adiabatic relation

$$d\varphi = \frac{d\theta}{\vartheta}; \quad \varphi \approx \theta_i + \vartheta\varphi$$

Further improvements have no practical meaning. Hence, the problem is in principle solved.

Results of a computation for a numerical example are shown on Figures 5-8 to 5-11.[4] Thus, curves of the oxygen burn-up (drop in

---

[4] The computation method was developed by the author in 1944 in connection with a rough design of a muffle burner being made by Engineer A. F. Ivanitskii (TEP, MES USSR), which uses A Sh (anthracite slag) dust for firing boilers. The following data were used in the example of the computation: fuel, anthracite slag coal; heat-creating capacity $Q_{p}{}^h = 6,000$ kcal/kg, ash content 20 per cent; theoretical quantity of air $\chi_0 = 8.55$; specific gravity of the coal $\gamma_c = 1,500$ kg/m^3; composition of the combustion products—ratio of $(CO)/(CO_2) = 1.0$; taking the radiation as constant, $C_{ir} = 10^{-8}$ kcal/m^2 hr deg (assuming the view angle of the flame of the order of $\sim 0.15 - 0.2$); kinetic constants of carbon $k_0 = 5.6 \times 10^4$ m/sec, $E = 3 \times 10^4$ kcal/mole; average size of the dust particle $R = 25\mu$; burner efficiency was taken to be = 0.8 on the basis of losses as mechanical (of the order of 7 per cent), in the surrounding medium ($\sim 2 - 3$ per cent) and "direct elimination" (radiation) in the furnace chamber (~ 10 per cent), i.e., the heat-producing capacity of the coal (6,000 kcal/kg) was reduced 20 per cent in computing the flame temperature T_M.

The air-mixture rate in the computation was taken as $w_0 = 6$ m/sec at the beginning of the channel and the initial values of the temperature and the excess air varied thus: $T_0 = 300, 400, 500,$ and $600°$K; $\alpha = 0.15, 0.20, 0.5,$ and 0.7, to which correspond dust concentrations of $\mu = 0.78, 0.39, 0.23,$ and 0.17 kg/kg. Since the choice of the individual quantities is of great importance for the results of the computation, the influence of the

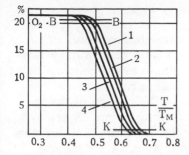

Fig. 5-8. Temperature dependence curves of oxygen burn-up. B-B—Ignition ($\varphi \approx 0.1$); K-K—burn-up ($\varphi \approx 0.99$).

Curve	α	$T_m, °K$	T_0
1	0.7	2,400	400
2	0.5	2,300	400
3	0.3	2,080	400
4	0.15	1,420	400

the percentage of O_2 in a gas-air flow) are shown on Figure 5-8 as a function of the relative temperature T/T_m for different values of the excess air α. The initial air temperature in this example is $T_0 = 400°K$; the value of the flame temperature as a function of the excess air is shown in the legend to Figure 5-8.

Shown on Figure 5-9a is the dependence of the theoretical burner length x_{theor} on the initial mixture temperature T_0 for various values of the excess air. This graph shows the sharp influence of the initial temperature related to the exponential temperature dependence of the reaction rate. Presented on Figure 5-9b is the same dependence with the parameter t_0 for a clearer exposition of the influence of the excess air. It should be noted that the computations showed that the length of the preheat and burn-up zones are approximately identical for all cases; consequently, the halved value of x_{theor} on Figure 5-9 characterizes the absolute length of the active combustion zone ($B - K$ on Figure 5-5).

As was remarked in the preceding footnote, Figure 5-10 shows the influence of separate quantities, previously assigned, on the

---

separate parameters (R, w_0, $Q_p{}^h$, E, $C'_{ir} = (C_{ir})/(\sigma_S)$ where $\sigma_S = 4.96 \times 10^{-8}$ kcal/m^2 hr deg, the efficiency of the burner and the characteristic $\mathcal{E} = (CO_2)/(CO + CO_2)$ for the combustion products) is shown on Figure 5-10 on the basic quantity to be determined in the computation, the total length of the initial heating zone, and the zone of oxygen burn-up x_{theor} for one of the variations in the computations ($T_0 = 400°K$; $\alpha = 0.5$).

Let us also note that $\alpha_D d/D \approx 2$ was used in evaluating the integral (5-21) or

$$\alpha_D \approx D/R = (D_0/R)(T/T_0)^{1/5}$$

Consequently, the nondimensional parameter τ_{DK} was given as

$$\tau_{DK} \approx \frac{K_0}{\alpha_D} \approx \frac{K_0 R}{D_0} \left(\frac{\theta}{\theta_0}\right)^{1/5}$$

i.e., the temperature dependence of the diffusion coefficient D (23) was taken into account.

final results of the calculation, the quantity x_{theor} . Taken as the unit everywhere is the magnitude of x_{theor} for the case $T_0 = 400°$K and $\alpha = 0.5$. This graph shows the approximate character of the whole computation, which generally serves as a preliminary esti- mate of the magnitudes of the quantities which are necessary to an explanation of the influence of the individual parameters.

Finally, shown on Figure 5-11a and b is the change in the ig- nition temperature t_B, determined conditionally from Figure 5-8 for the value of the completeness of oxygen burning $\varphi = 1$ per cent, as a function of t_0 and α. This graph again shows the dynamic character of the ignition phenomenon which depends on the set of factors taking part in the process.

Let us also note that the mixture velocity at $T = T_B$, that is, at the ignition point, characterizes the effective flame propagation rate w_{fl} toward the gas-dust flow. For example, its value at $T = 400°$K for various values of the excess air seems to equal the quantities shown in Table 5-1.

Table 5-1

α	0.15	0.3	0.5	0.7
w_{fl}, m/sec	17.8	19.8	21.6	22.2

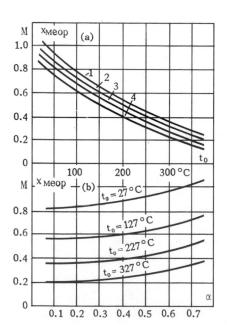

Fig. 5-9. Dependence of the theoretical burner length on the (a) initial temperature and (b) excess air.

Curve	1	2	3	4
α	2.07	0.5	0.3	0.15

In contrast to the adiabatic process (self-ignition, see section 5-1), the flame-propagation rate is explicitly related to the rate of supply of heat toward the fresh mixture.

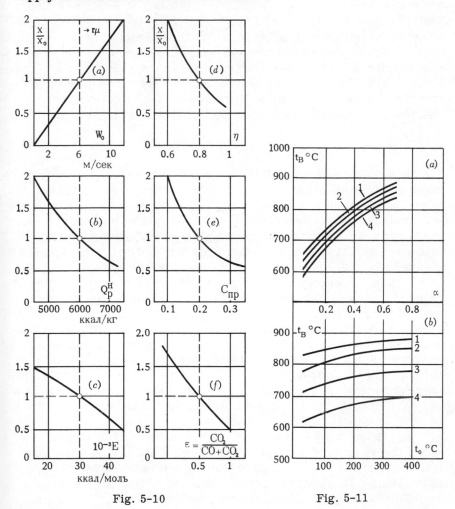

Fig. 5-10   Fig. 5-11

Fig. 5-10. Influence on the theoretical burner length of: Average size of the coal particles and the initial rate (a); heat-creating capacity (b); activation energy (c); burner efficiency (d); reduced radiation constant (e); composition of the combustion products (f). Remark: One parameter is varied on each graph, the values of the rest correspond to the basic computational case: $T_0 = 400°K$; $\alpha = 0.5$; $x_{0 \text{ theor}} = 0.63$ m; $w_0 = 6$ m/sec; $Q_p{}^h = 6,000$ kcal/kg; $E = 3 \times 10^4$ cal/mole; $\eta = 0.81$; $c'_{ir} = 0.2$; $\mathcal{E} = 0.5$.

Fig. 5-11. Dependence of the computed ignition temperature on (a) the excess air and (b) the initial temperature.

The results of the computation as a whole show the expediency of a theoretical estimate of the process and the prospects of similar computations for coal combustion in connection with the development of experimental results. It is clear that the numerical result of the computation will apparently be reasonably probable in order of magnitude and, principally, in the character of the influence of various parameters on the total characteristics of the process, despite the significant arbitrariness in the choice of the initial values. In this connection, let us use the same example of the computation of a muffle burner to illustrate a very important practical question on the rational air distribution along the flame length.

5-3. OPTIMUM THERMAL REGION OF A BURNER

The substance of the question to be considered in this section reduces to the following: it was assumed above in the computation of combustion in a muffle burner that the weight of the air intended for combustion is introduced with the coal dust at the beginning of the burner. In practice, the air supplied to the burner is usually separated into primary air, introduced with the coal dust, and supplementary or secondary air, introduced into the burner at a certain distance downstream. The proper relation of the quantities of primary and secondary air is hence aimed for in an optimum progress of the process. It is seen from the result of the computation presented above that the preheat zone occupies approximately half the theoretical length of the burner. As the quantity of air being presented along with the coal dust decreases, the initial heating of the dust-air flow occurs at a considerably smaller length prior to the beginning of the active process. However, a rational use of the residual (secondary) air is possible only under the condition that it be introduced after complete burn-up of the oxygen of the primary air, moreover, in such a quantity as would not lead to abrupt cooling of the whole mixture considerably below the new value of the ignition temperature. The theoretically optimum operating region of the burner should have been constructed so that the air supply would proceed by insignificant portions (continuously, in the limit) along the flame length, moreover, so that each new portion would be presented after the previous oxygen had been burned up. As regards the choice of the quantity of primary air, the limit to which it can be decreased is set by condensation of the dust-air flow, thus impeding the heating. It can be assumed approximately, for the example under consideration, that $\alpha_1 \approx 0.12 - 0.15$.

Let us compare somewhat the variations of the computation by being oriented to the example selected above ($T_0 = 400°K$, the total excess air coefficient $\alpha = 0.5$). For simplicity in the computation, let us assume that the temperature of the primary and secondary air is identical and equal to T_0 and that the mixing of the secondary air with the dust-gas flow is accomplished practically instantaneously. Let us consider the following three cases as variations of the computation:

1. All the air is introduced simultaneously with the coal dust, $\alpha_1 = \alpha = 0.5$.

2. The air is introduced in two portions, $\alpha_1 = 0.15$ and $\Delta\alpha_2 = 0.35$; here two cases are compared in addition: the introduction of secondary air just prior to ignition of the primary mixture (variation 2a) and after burn-up of the oxygen of the primary air (variation 2b).

3. The air is introduced in three portions, $\alpha_1 = 0.15$, $\alpha_2' = 0.15$, and $\alpha_2'' = 0.2$ (as before, the total excess is $\alpha = 0.5$).

The results of the computation for the separate variations are shown schematically on Figure 5-12. Briefly, they reduce to the following:

Variation 1

The theoretical length of the burner is $x_T \approx 0.63$ m, of which the preheating zone occupies $x_{OB} \approx 0.33$ m and the combustion zone $x_{BK} \approx 0.30$ m. The mixture ignition temperature is $t_B \approx 835°C$.

Variation 2

On the first section, $x_T \approx 0.09$ m for $\alpha_1 = 0.15$; $x_{OB} \approx 0.05$ m; $x_{BK} \approx 0.04$ m. The gas temperature at the end of the section is $t = 1547°C$.

Variation 2a

After the introduction of the secondary air $\Delta\alpha_2 = 0.35$ at the end of the warm-up section for $t = 625°C$, the temperature after mixing drops to $t \approx 320°C$, the repeated warm-up of the mixture and the combustion occur as in the first variation; there is no reduction in the burner length.

Variation 2b

The mixture temperature drops to $t \approx 745°C$ at the end of the combustion zone of the first section ($x = 0.09$ m) when the secondary air $\Delta\alpha_2 = 0.35$ is introduced. Repeated preheating to ignition occurs at the length $\Delta x \approx 0.2$ m, oxygen burn-up at the section of length $\Delta x \approx 0.19$ m. The total theoretical burner length $x_T \approx 0.48$ m, i.e., is approximately 0.76 that in the first variation.

Variation 3

On the first section, $\alpha_1 = 0.15$, the process proceeds just as in the preceding case (variation 2b). After the introduction of the first portion of the secondary air $\alpha'_2 = 0.15$, the temperature must drop to $t \approx 1020°$C because of mixing, which raises the ignition temperature for this mixture ($t_i \approx 760°$C), burn-up occurs very rapidly at the length $\Delta x \approx 0.12$ m, and the temperature rises to $t \approx 1807°$C. The subsequent introduction of the residual air $\Delta\alpha''_2 = 0.2$ must lower the temperature to $t \approx 1140°$C, and combustion occurs practically instantaneously ($\Delta x \approx 0.03$ m). The total theoretical burner length is $x_T \approx 0.24$ m, i.e., it is 0.38 times that in the first variation and is half that in variation 2b.

Hence, an approximate computation shows that the theoretical values of the burner length for the variations 1, 2b, and 3 are in the ratio $1 : 0.76 : 0.38$. A complete comparison of all the variations of the computation is presented on Figure 5-13.

Despite the indisputably approximate character of the computation presented, its results correctly reflect the possibility of a rational construction of the thermal-combustion process. The fundamental idea of the development of such a region lies in the gradual supply of small portions of air to the fuel under compliance with two conditions: (1) A ne' portion of air must be supplied after the oxygen of the preceding portion has been burned up and (2) the quantity of air supplied must be limited in order not to reduce the temperature after mixing substantially below the ignition temperature corresponding to the resultant mixture. Physically, this corresponds to an unusual, successive self-heating of the air introduced by heat liberated during the combustion of the preceding part of the mixture.

It is necessary to note that the technical value of the scheme of the constru'

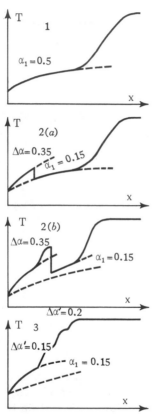

Fig. 5-12. Diagram of the temperature variation along the flame length for various relations between the primary and secondary air. Dashed line, computed preheating curve; solid line, actual temperature curve.

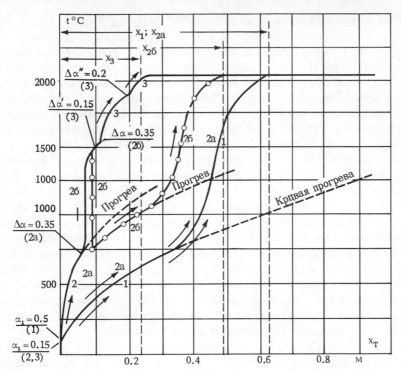

Fig. 5-13. Comparison of various variations of computing burners. Heavy solid line, variation 1; solid line, variation 2a; dashed and dotted line, variation 2b; dashed line, variation 3.

tion of the process is beyond the scope of the specific example of the combustion of a coal-air misture in a muffle burner considered here. Neither does it relate to the scheme of preheating the fresh mixture by flame radiation used in this computation.

Actually, it is not difficult to present a number of examples from combustion practice to which the reasonings presented above refer completely or partially.

The organization of the combustion process in gas-turbine combustion chambers can be one of these examples. As is known (25), the gradual supply of air, guaranteeing the possibility of maximum forcing of the process with very high stability, is accomplished in these chambers.

The question is of the correct supply of secondary air in boiler furnaces—beds and chambers. As G. F. Knorre (25) indicates, the fuel bed in the first layer is a complicated burner system, emitting burning gases in the chamber (volatile, carbon monoxide, etc.). Combustion of these gases, which have a very high temperature, can be effective only with correct supply of secondary air, whose jets must penetrate the whole tongue of flame and must create therein the requisite conditions for rapid combustion (mixture temperature and concentration). As is known, a high-speed sudden blast is fruitful in this respect, while injecting large air masses at low speeds does not create conditions for combustion in the whole space but only leads to a negative result, to intense cooling of the mixture at the tongue edges, and to the increase of losses in connection with the incomplete combustion. In substance, the very same also refers to flame-jet processes.

It is known (25) for example, from practical usage and experience with coal-dust furnaces, that an incorrectly organized return (scatter) of the unburned dust to the chamber can lead to an increase in the losses. As above, this is explained by the introduction of a comparatively large quantity of cold air, which can transport the dust into the process and which can cause a considerable delay or a practically complete cessation of the combustion in the region where it is propagated.

Any kind of detailed selection of all these, or similar cases, is impossible without an analysis of a concrete furnace diagram and the instrinsic "technology" of the furnace process.[5] Since the latter does not enter into the problem of this book, we shall be limited to the references made and turn to an analysis of the physical substance of the question. For a more graphical representation, let us use again the picture of the process in the "completeness of combustion-temperature" plane for a zero-dimensional model. It is easy to reason that the formulation of the problem of the supply of cold air to the heated mixture containing a considerable quantity of unburned fuel is similar to the question considered earlier (see section 4-1) of the mixing of a fresh combustible mixture with heated combustion products. In the latter case, because of the stronger influence of the temperature rise during mixing than of the drop in concentration, the mixing of the combustion products with a fresh mixture guarantees ignition and generally increases combustion stability (see Figures 4-1 and 4-2).

The purpose of the mixing in the example being considered here is to create a combustible mixture of suitable concentration. The accompanying cooling is a negative factor for the rapid development of the process. If it is considered that the mixing is accomplished very rapidly, then from the general considerations, discussed repeatedly above (exponential temperature dependence of the reaction rate and power dependence on the concentration), it

[5] A number of examples and a detailed discussion of the various types of combustion chambers and conditions for the progress of the combustion process are given in the cited book of G. F. Knorre (25).

follows that it is expedient to supply cold secondary air so as to avoid a sharp reduction in temperature.

A development of this statement inevitably leads to a scheme of the gradual supply of air, similar in principle to the above-considered optimum region of operation of a muffle burner.

Let us illustrate these considerations by a sketchy computation applied to the $\varphi - \theta$ plane. Let us assume that we speak of a combustible mixture whose initial temperature equals θ_0, exactly as in the secondary air introduced later.

Let us denote the maximum value of the heat production for a stoichiometric mixture $(\alpha = 1)$ by the symbol ϑ_m. As has been shown in section 2-3,[6] the value of the heat production for any value of $\alpha_1 < 1$ for a rich mixture is determined by the formula

$$\frac{\vartheta_1}{\vartheta_m} = \frac{1 + \chi_0}{1 + \alpha_1 \chi_0} \tag{2-20}$$

where χ_0 is the stoichiometric ratio of oxidizer of fuel. The temperature of reaction products for the complete burn-up of such a mixture $(\alpha_1 < 1)$ will equal

$$\theta_{m_1} = \theta_0 + \vartheta_1 \tag{5-22}$$

Now, let us assume that mixing of the combustion products with the secondary air, injected, for example, in a quantity corresponding to an increase of the excess air by the quantity $\Delta\alpha$ has occurred, where $\Delta\alpha = \alpha_2 - \alpha_1$ if α_2 is the new value of the excess-air coefficient with respect to the initial mixture.

Let us determine the characteristics of the new mixture. Its initial temperature under the simplest assumption of constant specific heat will evidently equal, from the mixing equation

$$\theta_{02} = \frac{(1 + \alpha_1 \chi_0)\theta_{m_1} + \Delta\alpha \chi_0 \theta_0}{1 + \alpha_2 \chi_0} \tag{5-23}$$

Let us determine the difference in the values between θ_{02} and θ_0 which will characterize the preheating of the air during mixing

$$\theta_{02} - \theta_0 = \frac{1 + \alpha_1 \chi_0}{1 + \alpha_2 \chi_0} (\theta_{m_1} - \theta_0)$$

or

$$\frac{\theta_{02} - \theta_0}{\theta_{m_1} - \theta_0} = \frac{1 + \alpha_1 \chi_0}{1 + \alpha_2 \chi_0} \tag{5-24}$$

[6] See formula (2-20).

As is seen from this formula, the value of the initial temperature of the new mixture θ_{02} will vary between the limits $\theta_{02} = \theta_{m_1}$ for $\Delta\alpha = 0$ and $\theta_{02} = \theta_0$ at $\alpha_2 = \infty$ as $\Delta\alpha$ increases (and therefore, as α_2 increases for a given value of α_1), i.e., as the relative portion of the secondary air increases. In particular, the value of $\theta_{02}\Big|_{\alpha=1}$ will equal, from (5-24)

$$\theta_{02}\Big|_{\alpha=1} = \frac{1 + \alpha_1 \chi_0}{1 + \chi_0} \tag{5-25}$$

for $\alpha_2 = 1$ and $\Delta\alpha = 1 - \alpha_1$, i.e., when the combustible mixture being formed during mixing does not contain excess fuel and oxidizer. This value is a minimum for the formation of a rich mixture, i.e., for the $\alpha_2 \geqslant 1$ case and is a maximum, respectively, for a lean mixture ($\alpha_2 \geqslant 1$).

The value of the maximum temperature for complete combustion ($\varphi = 1$) of the new mixture θ_{m_2} is found separately for the case of the formation of a rich $(\alpha_2 < 1)$ and a lean $(\alpha_2 > 1)$ mixture. In the first case we will have

$$\theta_{m_2} = \theta_0 + \vartheta_2 = \theta_0 + \vartheta_m \alpha \frac{1 + \chi_0}{1 + \alpha_2 \chi_0}$$

where ϑ_2 is the total heat productivity of the mixture for $\alpha = \alpha_2 < 1$.

It follows from this equality

$$\frac{\theta_{m_2} - \theta_0}{\theta_m - \theta_0} = \alpha_2 \frac{1 + \chi_0}{1 + \alpha_2 \chi_0} \tag{5-26}$$

As $\Delta\alpha$ increases and, therefore, α_2 increases, the value of θ_{m_2} will increase with $\theta_{m_2} = \theta_{m_1}$ for $\Delta\alpha = 0$ and ending with $\theta_{m_2} = \theta_m$ for $\alpha_2 = 1$.

In order to compute the further variation in the quantity θ_{m_2} for $\alpha_2 > 1$, we should start from the formula

$$\frac{\vartheta_\alpha}{\vartheta_m} = \frac{1 + \chi_0}{1 + \alpha \chi_0} \tag{2-20}$$

where we can write

$$\theta_{m_2} = \theta_0 + \vartheta_m \frac{1 + \chi_0}{1 + \alpha_2 \chi_0}$$

or

$$\frac{\theta_{m_2} - \theta_0}{\theta_m - \theta_0} = \frac{1 + \chi_0}{1 + \alpha_2 \chi_0} \tag{5-27}$$

Hence it follows that as α_2 varies between 1 and ∞, the value of θ_{m_2} will decrease from $\theta_{m_2} = \theta_m$ at $\alpha_2 = 1$ to $\theta_m = \theta_0$ as $\alpha_2 \to \infty$.

After these simple computations, let us turn to the picture of the process in the $\varphi - \theta$ plane. For example, let us speak of the intersection of a certain heat-liberation curve $\varphi_I(\theta)$ on Figure 5-14 with the family of lines $\varphi_{II}(\theta)$, corresponding to various mixing conditions. For greater clarity, the case $\alpha_2 < 1$ is shown separately on Figure 5-14a and the case $\alpha_2 > 1$ on Figure 5-14b. The line 1 in both graphs corresponds to a stoichiometric mixture ($\alpha = 1$) and joins the points $\theta = \theta_0$; $\varphi = 0$, and $\theta = \theta_m$; $\varphi = 1$.

The line $\varphi_{II}(\theta)$ for the initial mixture ($\alpha = \alpha_1$; $\theta = \theta_0$ for $\varphi = 0$ and $\theta = \theta_m$ for $\varphi = 1$) is superposed by dashes. A number of lines corresponding to various values of $\Delta\alpha$, where the direction of the change in $\Delta\alpha$ is shown by an arrow, have been plotted on each of the graphs of Figure 5-14a and b. Now, let us trace the intersection of the lines $\varphi_{II}(\theta)$ and the curve $\varphi_I(\theta)$ on Figure 5-14a, for example. Let us note that a comparison of the various heat-loss lines $\varphi_{II}(\theta)$ with a single (the same for all cases) curve of heat liberation $\varphi_I(\theta)$ does not introduce any noticeable distortions in the end result, although it is approximate, if the generally possible change in the stay time τ_S or time of reaction progress τ_K (because of the change in the excess air) is neglected for various mixing conditions. Actually, the $\varphi_I(\theta)$ curves, which are comparatively close to each other in the φ-θ diagram (see Figure 2-10 and others) differ by an entire order in the values of the parameter τ_{SK}, consequently, a comparatively small change in τ_{SK} cannot substantially affect the character of the intersection of the curves. It is clearly seen from the example on Figure 5-14a that only rapid burn-up of the new mixture[7] corresponds to comparatively small values of $\Delta\alpha$ (just one upper stationary combustion region, line 2); both regions are possible for large values of $\Delta\alpha$: oxidation and combustion; therefore, the first, the lower of them, is accomplished in conformance with the history of the process.

---

[7] The effective values of $\Delta\alpha$ are also limited to very small values because of the insignificance of the heat productivity of the mixture being formed (in the adiabatic process) and, more intensely in practice because of the inevitable heat-losses, which lead to heat-exchange extinction for very small $\Delta\alpha$.

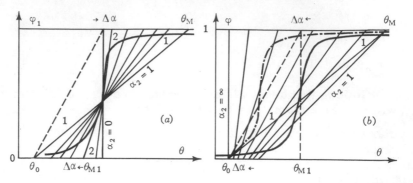

Fig. 5-14. Diagram of the influence of secondary air supply to a rich mixture ($\alpha_1 < 1$) on the combustion process. (a) The case $\Delta\alpha < 1 - \alpha_1$; $\alpha_2 < 1$; (b) the case $\Delta\alpha > 1 - \alpha_1$; $\alpha_2 > 1$.

In this case, an additional supply of heat (for example, by radiation in the computation of the muffle burner, etc.) is necessary for the burn-up of the mixture being formed. It is understood that the concrete conclusions obtained in this example refer only to completely defined conditions of the progress of the process; in particular, they can be changed substantially for another value of τ_{SK} (for example, the dash-dot curve $\varphi_1(\theta)$ on Figure 5-14b), however, their content, in principle, remains the same.

Especially to be noticed is the difference in the behavior of the rich ($\alpha < 1$) and the lean ($\alpha > 1$) mixtures, which appears in this example. This difference once again shows the complexity of the estimation of the character of the combustion process in furnace apparatus in terms of the total process characteristics (for example, the average value of the excess air and its influence on the completeness of combustion, etc.). Only by a deep, primarily experimental, investigation of the local relations in various zones of the chamber is a correct estimate possible of the character of the process and of methods to improve it.

The example considered above, of a theoretical analysis of the combustion process in a muffle burner, and of the related general reasoning about the influence of the heat supply and the effective use of secondary air, shows the fruitfulness of analyzing the thermal region of the combustion process, whose correct application can explain the phenomena observed in practice and can indicate means of effectively acting upon the process. However, the latter at the present time is possible only in close connection with an experimental investigation under concrete conditions, since only experiment can give the quantitative relations necessary for the computation.

Combustion in a muffle burner is characteristic, just as is the example of a process with a change in oxygen concentration along the length. After the burn-up of the oxygen (or, generally, of the mixture component which is found to be inadequate in supply), the combustion process naturally ceases. Combustion is cut off sharply (for a sufficient drop in concentration) in the presence of intense heat emission; heat-exchange extinction occurs. Without considering this question in detail, let us be limited to references to certain work devoted to heterogeneous combustion in a layer or jet. Thus, for example, an approximate analysis of the thermal region of the heterogeneous process has been performed by Frank-Kamenetskii for a coal seam (51) and by Todes and Margolis (49) for the oxidation of iso-octane in a layer of catalyst.

A number of interesting considerations and conclusions on the thermal combustion region in a fuel layer are presented by Z. F. Chukhanov and B. V. Kantarovich (55, 21). A. B. Rezniakov (39) made an attempt to take into account the nonuniformity in the dimensions of coal dust (particles) in a computation of their burn-up time. His analytical development for the thermal combustion region of a jet could be of considerable interest.[8] Finally, a general analysis of the combustion of a layer and jet is given in the cited book by G. F. Knorre (25).

5-4. RELATION BETWEEN THE ZERO-DIMENSIONAL AND ONE-DIMENSIONAL MODELS

Flame Propagation.

Let us try to establish a clearer relation between the two schemes of the process used in the preceding explanations, the furnace (zero-dimensional) and the linear (one-dimensional) schemes. As has been shown above (see section 5-1), the relations of one-dimensional theory are a natural generalization (by a transformation to the analysis of infinitesimals) of the formulas and dependences obtained when using the zero-dimensional model.[9]

---

[8] See also one of the later reports of Z. F. Chukhanov (55a) especially devoted to the ignition and extinction mechanism of coke dust.

[9] For example, let us compare the formulas (2-14)

$$\frac{\varphi}{\tau_{SK}} = (1 - \varphi) \, e^{-1/\theta}$$

and (5-4)

$$\frac{d\varphi}{d\tau_{SK}} = (1 - \varphi) \, e^{-1/\theta}$$

It will be more correct to consider the zero-dimensional scheme as a simplified model of the actual phenomenon corresponding to the transformation from relations written in differential form to the approximate computation by a finite-difference method. Let us explain this by a simple example for the adiabatic combustion process for a well-mixed mixture. Let us assume that a burning mixture of given initial parameters θ_0 and ϑ_0 is presented to a certain combustion chamber; the mixture stay time in the chamber is τ_{SK}. Let us divide the total time the process is in progress into a number of small intervals $\Delta \tau_{SK_1}$, $\Delta \tau_{SK_2}$, etc. The initial mixture parameters for the first time interval as well as for the whole chamber will be $\theta_{01} = \theta_0$; $\vartheta_1 = \vartheta_0$. It is not difficult to determine the stationary values $\theta_{st\,1}$ and $\varphi_{st\,1}$, corresponding to conditions of the reaction progress in this first section of the chamber, from the intersection of the curves $\varphi_1 \theta = \Delta \tau_{SK_1} / (\Delta \tau_{SK_1} + e^{1/\theta})$ and $\varphi_{II} \theta = (\theta - \theta_{01})/\vartheta_1$ in the $\varphi - \theta$ diagram. These values of the temperature and the completeness of combustion, which are the average for the time interval $\Delta \tau_{SK_1}$ in conformance with the averaging method underlying the zero-dimensional model, agree with the final values of θ and φ for the reaction products leaving the isolated element of the combustion chamber.

Consequently, they are the initial values of the parameters for the second section. This latter means that $\theta_{02} = \theta_{st\,1}$ should be taken for the second time interval $\Delta \tau_{SK_2}$ and the partial burn-up of the mixture ($\varphi_{st\,1} > 0$) which occurred in the first section should be taken into account in selecting the new diminished value of the

---

for the adiabatic combustion process of a well-mixed mixture (kinetic region); (3-48)

$$\frac{\varphi}{\tau_{SD}} = 1 - \varphi$$

and (5-10′)

$$\frac{d\varphi}{d\tau_{SD}} = 1 - \varphi$$

for diffusion combustion; (3-45)

$$\frac{\varphi}{\tau_{SK}} = \frac{1 - \varphi}{e^{1/\theta} + \tau_{DK}}$$

and (5-12)

$$\frac{d\varphi}{d\tau_{SK}} = \frac{1 - \theta}{e^{1/\theta} + \tau_{DK}}$$

heat productivity $\vartheta_2 = \vartheta_1 (1 - \varphi_{st\,1})$. The intersection of the curves $\varphi_I(\theta)$ (for $\tau_{SK} = \Delta\tau_{SK_2}$) and $\varphi_{II}(\theta)$ (for $\theta_0 = \theta_{02}$ and $\vartheta = \vartheta_2$) in the $\varphi - \theta$ diagram yields new values $\varphi_{st\,2}$ and $\theta_{st\,2}$ and, therefore, the values $\theta_{03} = \theta_{st\,2}$ and $\vartheta_3 = \vartheta_2 (1 - \varphi_{st\,2})$, which, in turn, permit the initial characteristics of the process for the third time interval $\Delta\tau_{SK_3}$ to be found, etc., up to the very end of the chamber. It is

clear that the less the value of the time element $\Delta\tau_{SK}$ and the larger the number of intervals for a given total magnitude of the stay time, the closer will the results of the computation be to the dependence $\theta = \theta(\tau_{SK})$ obtained for this example by evaluating the integral (5-7).

In the limit, when transforming to an infinite number of elementary time intervals $d\tau_{SK}$, the zero-dimensional model of the phenomenon transforms into the one-dimensional model. Conversely, use of finite differences (zero-dimensional scheme) in the whole chamber is opposite to the limit case in which the total value τ_{SK} has been selected as the stay-time (or chamber-length) element.

Such a construction with the division of the system into a number of elementary sections, of which an example is shown on Figure 5-15, is understandably not limited to the case of the adiabatic process considered here for simplicity. Conversely, the use of the computation by the zero-dimensional scheme in individual elements of the chamber in the presence of complex heat exchange is of great interest if only the distribution of the thermal flows along the separate sections of the chamber can be given with a good enough approximation or if their appropriate dependences can be given. Thus, for example, in the problem of computing a muffle burner, the law of heat supply to the mixture would correspond in the long run to the equation of the curve $\varphi_{II}(\theta)$ for the heat supply which is similar to (4-17), i.e., to the expression

---

for the general case of the intermediate combustion region; (4-17)

$$\varphi = \frac{1}{\vartheta} \left[(\theta - \theta_0) - \sigma\,\tau_{SK} \, (\theta_m{}^4 - \theta^4) \right]$$

and (5-16)

$$d\varphi = \frac{1}{\vartheta} \left[d\theta - \sigma\,(\theta_m{}^4 - \theta^4)\, d\tau_{SK} \right]$$

for the process with heat supply by radiation, etc.

It is evident that the right-hand expressions transform into the left if the differentials $d\varphi$, $d\theta$, and $d\tau_{SK}$ are replaced, respectively, by the differences $\Delta\varphi = \varphi - 0 = \varphi$; $\Delta\theta = \theta - \theta_0$; $\Delta\tau_{SK} = \tau_{SK} - 0 = \tau_{SK}$.

$$\varphi_{II} = \frac{1}{\vartheta_i}\,\theta - \theta_{oi} - \sigma_i \Delta \tau_{SKi}\,(\theta_m - \theta)$$

for a certain ith time interval. In conformance with this, the approximate computation would reduce, in this example, to looking successively for points of intersection of the curves $\varphi_I(\theta)$ and $\varphi_{II}(\theta)$ in the $\varphi - \theta$ diagram in which the initial mixture parameters for each following section would be borrowed from the computation of the preceding section.[10]

The great achievement of the approximate computation by the finite-difference method when the process is divided into a number of sections is the possibility of taking into account the temperature dependence of the physical constants. As regards the tedium related to graphical constructions in the $\varphi - \theta$ diagram, in the long run it is inevitable in the numerical solution of problems of combustion theory. Let us note that use of a one-dimensional computation scheme leads, perhaps, to a still greater volume of numerical and graphical computations. The same problem of the muffle burner or the theory of flame propagation (section 6-3) is an example.

As has already been remarked earlier, use of the zero-dimensional model computation in the individual sections of the chamber is of substantial advantage in a number of cases in comparison with the one-dimensional computation, as well as in respect to the greater approximation to the actual phenomenon, since it permits certain of its essential facets to be estimated in complete form (for example, the mixing of the fresh mixture with the combustion products, etc.), such as show up either very complicatedly, or even impossibly, in the differential equations of the process. Finally, this method is very graphic and the possibility of estimating qualitatively the influence of the separate parameters, shown above by a large number of examples, explains the attention focused on a computation using the zero-dimensional model in the investigations of the thermal combustion region, especially in this book.

Since the basic statements of the theory of thermal flame propagation will be considered in the following chapters, it is expedient to try first to explain qualitatively the physical meaning of this phenomenon by starting from concepts of the zero-dimensional model, although flame-propagation concepts are related to the three-dimensional (in a particular case, linear) problems.

---

[10] Apparently an analogous graphoanalytic method of computing finite differences can also be developed for the approximate solution of three-dimensional problems of thermal combustion theory under the condition of a suitable schematization of the thermal and hydrodynamic processes.

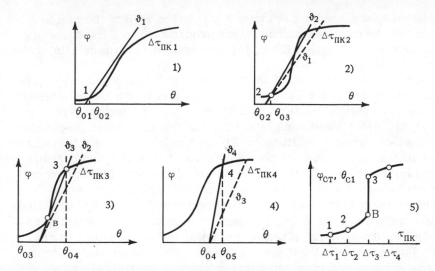

Fig. 5-15. Diagram of the construction of dependences of the temperature and completeness of combustion on the stay time by a finite-differences method (zero-dimensional scheme) for successive time intervals. 1-4—Intersection of the heat-liberation and -elimination curves; 5—dependence of φ and θ on τ_{SK}.

The flame propagation rate against the incident flow of fresh mixture has been mentioned twice in the above-mentioned examples of the computations, in the problems of the progress of the adiabatic reaction (section 5-1) and on the process in a muffle burner (section 5-2). Since stationary processes had been considered in both cases and, therefore, the values of the temperature and concentration in any cross section to the flow planes, i.e., for any value of the space coordinate x, do not change with time, the hydrodynamical scheme of the phenomenon can be inverted and it is possible to transform to a coordinate system bound to the flow, relative to which the mixture will be fixed. Under such a transformation, any state of the reacting mixture will be propagated against the direction of the actual motion at a constant speed, which equals the flow velocity at this point in magnitude.

In particular, for a section in which ignition occurs ($T = T_i$), the thus-introduced magnitude of the linear propagation speed can conditionally be called the rate of ignition propagation or, briefly, the flame rate. Despite the dependence of the velocity on the coordinates in connection with the preheating of the mixture during the reaction, i.e., the change in the density, and for large values of the velocity and pressure, the curve $T = T(x)$ as a whole will be propagated along the direction of the fresh mixture without being deformed, at a constant velocity equal to the rate of the incident cold flow in magnitude. The flame propagation in a fixed burning gas mixture has such a form, for example, if certain details of the phenomena are rejected.

The physical aspects of the flame-propagation phenomenon are closely related to the incendiary mechanism which leads to ignition of the combustible mixture, and by excluding detonation (see section 7-4), are determined completely for the thermal flame propagation by heat-exchange conditions.[11] For example, in the problem of adiabatic self-ignition in the one-dimensional flow of a combustible mixture (section 5-1), the development of the combustion process in conformance with the idealized scheme used occurs isolatedly in each element of the moving mixture which is burning up with time, independently, without the exchange of heat or matter with the residual elements of the stream, and without heat exchange to any solid surfaces. Under these conditions, there is substantially no flame propagation from the burning mixture particles to those not yet in the process. In this case, the concept of the ignition propagation rate becomes formal.

It is not thus with the second of the examples mentioned here. Ignition of a mixture of coal dust and air in a muffle burner, again within the limits of the scheme of the process used, is determined completely by radiant heat flow against the fresh mixture. Only the presence of preliminary mixture heating because of radiation from the flame guarantees the comparatively rapid advance of the fresh mixture into the process (ignition) and, hence, makes possible its subsequent combustion within the practically attainable burner length (of the order of 1 m instead of 10^6 m in adiabatic self-ignition). However, in this case also the introduction of the concept of flame propagation facilitates the analysis of the process very slightly.[12] The magnitude of the flame speed w_{fl} in this example is a complex function of a large number of variables, and no matter which of its concrete values is obtained as a result of computation it is determined by a complicated set of physicochemical phenomena involving the entire process. In particular, the numerical values w_{fl} = 18 to 22 m/sec presented in section 5-2,

[11] The theory of cool flames (50), i.e., chain-approximately-isothermal-flame propagation related to the diffusion of active centers and not by heat transport from the burning to the fresh mixture, is not discussed here or later, in conformance with the general outlook of the book.

[12] In substance, in this example also (as ever for radiation), direct heat transmission from a hotter mixture layer to a less hot layer is lacking, although the fresh mixture, on the whole, is heated and advances into the reaction because of heat supply from the combustion products.

for example, are accidental to a considerable extent and only in-directly characterize the development of the process.

The same holds substantially for any other process under given heat-exchange conditions with the exception of the two typical flame-propagation cases, normal combustion and detonation, con-sidered below.

The whole volume occupied by a process divided into a large number of elements can be represented for any three-dimensional distribution of the variables, no matter how complicated. An in-vestigation of the quasi-stationary state by means of an appropri-ate construction of the heat-liberation and -elimination curves in the $\varphi - \theta$ plane can be used for each such element which seems to represent an elementary flow combustion chamber interrelated by mixture and heat-transport conditions from one chamber to the other. The interconnecting volume elements for which the compu-tation gives the ignition condition in connection with an excess of the quantity of heat being supplied and liberated over the quantity of heat being eliminated, can outline the ignition surface. In con-nection with the stationary character of the process, such a sur-face, on the whole, remains fixed in the flow (we speak, for turbu-lent flow, of a certain average position of the surface obtained by averaging over a sufficiently large time in comparison with the period of turbulent pulsations). This means that a kinematic equi-librium condition can be formulated for each ignition surface ele-ment in the form of the equality of the magnitudes of the velocity vector components normal to the surface and the oppositely direct flame-propagation rate.

Any deviation from this kinematic condition would inevitably lead to the displacement of the appropriate element of the ignition surface to a new equilibrium state. It is obvious that this simple relation, designated by the name of the outstanding Russian phys-icist, Vladimir Aleksandrovich Mikhel'son (32) (see below), as the Mikhel' son law, is not the cause but the consequence of the physi-cal process (heat exchange, at first glance) in the ignition region. The heat-supply mechanism to the fresh mixture under various conditions can be very different; above, for example, such dis-similar phenomena as the mixing of fresh mixture with combustion products (which plays a basic part in flame propagation in a turbu-lent flow), radiant and convective heat supply, heat productivity, etc., have already been mentioned in the review of the individual problems. Consequently, in the general case the ignition surface can be found only as a result of constructing detailed fields of the temperature, space velocity, and concentration. In its turn, the flame-propagation rate is a complicated function of many vari-ables in the majority of problems; consequently, an attempt to assign values of w_{fl} in advance or to treat it as an independent physical variable is clearly inconsistent in the general case.

Besides the propagation rate at each point of the flame front, it is also possible to speak of the total rate of combustion propagation at which the flame front moves in the inverted hydrodynamic scheme, as a single unit, toward the fixed mixture. In this case, the combustion propagation rate evidently agrees in magnitude with, but is opposite in direction to, the velocity of the incident flow of fresh mixture for combustion in a flow. Hence, the problem is reduced to an investigation of the conditions for kindling the fresh mixture at individual (reference) points of the front which guarantee stationary combustion; only in the simplest case of a plane flame front normal to the flow will the propagation rate be the same for all points. In the general case, the ignition picture is very complicated and the introduction of the concept of the combustion propagation rate often falls far short of facilitating its solution.

As has already been remarked, exceptions are slow (normal) combustion and detonation. In the first case, the propagation rate is determined completely by the kinetic equations of the process: heat propagation and diffusion taking into account sources related to the reaction progress. In the second case, detonation, the combustion propagation rate is determined uniquely by the gas-dynamics equations (conservation of mass, momentum, and energy); reliance on the data of chemical kinetics to compute the steady velocity of a detonation wave is superfluous (see section 7-4).

Chapter 6

Normal Combustion

6-1. FLAME PROPAGATION RATE

The flame propagation rate is determined completely by the properties of the combustible mixture and can be considered as a physicochemical constant in two typical cases of flame propagation: for so-called normal or slow combustion and for detonation. As is known, these two kinds of combustion differ radically both in their external characteristics and in the character of the progress, as well as in the mechanism of the fresh-mixture ignition.

The first of these, normal flame propagation, is specified by heat transmission by molecular heat conduction from the hotter layers of flames to the cooler layers. As is known, normal combustion occurs during the flame propagation in fixed hot mixtures or during laminar flow, the normal flame rate is very small, on the order of several centimeters per second and it attains several meters per second (13a, 14, 30) only for the most rapidly burning mixtures of oxygen and hydrogen. The combustion is accompanied by negligible pressure changes and in the majority of cases it can be considered to be isobaric.

The second characteristic case of flame propagation, detonation, is specified by ignition of the fresh mixture during its adiabatic compression in a shockwave. Detonation combustion is propagated at an enormous rate on the order of several kilometers per second and is accompanied by very large pressure drops of tens and hundreds of atmospheres. Considerable destructive effects, sharp noises, etc., are characteristic of the external progress of detonation.

Clear physical representations of these two limiting cases of flame propagation were formulated more than sixty years ago (in 1889) by V. A. Mikhel'son in the dissertation: "On the Normal Ignition Rate of Fulminating Gas Mixtures" (32). In this remarkable work, which only recently obtained complete recognition,[1] V. A.

[1] In this connection it is not without interest to note that in 1890, the great Russian scientist, N. B. Zhukovskii wrote, in referring to the work of V. A. Mikhel'son, "That sympathetic peculiarity of the author, which he manifested in even his earliest work, is exhibited with great clarity in the collection being considered. The unusually simple idea becomes the basis of extremely clever observations and leads to the richest results. The reader will see how all that is thought and obtained by the author did not occur earlier." (N. E. Zhukovskii, *Collected Works*, vol. IX, 1937.)

Mikhel' son wrote, in particular:[2]

Each element of volume of the explosive gas contains all the explosive parts necessary for combustion. In order for the explosion to occur, it is only necessary to make a certain expenditure of energy, which, in general, is insignificant in comparison to the energy of the explosion itself but it is different, depending on how far the gas is from its ignition state and by what means it arrives there. In order that the flame might be transmitted from one layer to another, it would be necessary for the layers already ignited to transmit sufficient energy to the adjoining cold layer so that it would achieve the ignition temperature.

This energy, in the case of an explosive wave, is transmitted as mechanical energy (pressure, impulse) and it only transforms into thermal energy instantaneously in the new layer. The energy required for ignition in the usual combustion case is transmitted from layer to layer directly as heat, i.e., by the heat conduction process.

Characterizing this second kind of slow flame propagation, V. A. Mikhel' son wrote, in particular, that "the normal ignition rate, as I defined it herein, is a quantity which is as characteristic of a gas mixture as is the heat-conduction coefficient, or internal friction, specific heat, etc." Finally, in defining the explosive wave and the normal combustion as "two extreme and typical cases of the ignition of explosive gases," V. A. Mikhel' son also stated: "In addition to these two typical methods of ignition, there evidently exists an innumerable variety of other, intermediate and mixed methods in which both heat conduction and compression play a certain part simultaneously. It can even be said that only the two extremely typical cases are of scientific interest from the physical viewpoint."

Although the experimental side of the question of determining the flame rate is not considered in the later explanation in this book, it should be noted that a number of the most important, fundamental results here are also due to V. A. Mikhel' son. In particular, he had shown that the maximum of the flame propagation rate as a function of the mixture composition lies in the $\alpha < 1$ range, that the very form of this dependence is mapped by a continuous curve with finite curvature (and not by the intersection of two line segments for lean and rich mixtures as assumed earlier), that the experimental determinations of the values of w_{fl} made prior to Mikhel' son (by Bunsen, Le Châtelier, and Mallard, et al.) led to high results; he also developed a detailed theory of the

[2] Here and later, we refer to the book: V. A. Mikhel' son: *Collected Works*, vol. I, *Novyi agronom* Izd., Moscow, 1930, pp. 104, 105, 159.

bunsen burner, a perfected method of determining the normal
flame propagation rate, etc. The majority of these results, as well
as the dissertation of V. A. Mikhel' son itself, have retained their
scientific value up to the present.

The further development of the theory of normal flame propagation and detonation is found in the work of the Soviet scientists
N. N. Semenov, Ia. B. Zel' dovich, K. I. Shchelkin, D. A. Frank-
Kamenetskii, L. N. Khitrin, A. S. Sokolik, V. I. Skobelkin, et al.
(13a, 14, 16, 18, 45, 46, 54, 56, et al.). In particular, Ia. B.
Zel' dovich has created the most rigorous and complete stationary
theory of thermal flame propagation (18), of which a brief explanation is given below in section 6-3.

Despite the fact that neither typical case of flame propagation
is characteristic for furnace technique, their analysis is of methodological value. The applied value of normal flame propagation
is related, first of all, to the study of the properties and behavior
of various combustible mixtures, the kinetics of the combustion
reaction, etc. Detonation theory is related to the study of explosions and explosives, etc. As regards the most important technical case of combustion in turbulent flow, a final theory (13b,
57) is still lacking as yet because of the exceptional complexity
of the question.

Moreover, modern conceptions of the turbulent combustion
mechanism, in particular of the rate of turbulent flame propagation (see section 7-2), can be considered only as the first draft of
the theory of the question, which plays the part of qualitative explanations rather than of theoretical dependences. This position
is due to a considerable extent to an inadequate development of
the general theory of turbulence which must underlie the theory
of turbulent combustion. Consequently, experiment is of decisive
value in this question.

The simplest conception of thermal (normal) flame propagation which it is expedient to hypothesize for a more detailed explanation of the question can be obtained from the following simplified scheme. Let us represent (Figure 6-1) a curve of the
temperature distribution in a one-dimensional flow of a hot gas.
Let us assume that a fresh, well-mixed, combustible mixture
moves continuously in the direction of rising temperature (from
left to right on Figure 6-1). Let us assume the temperature of the
initial (cold) mixture far from the region of intense combustion to
equal T_0 and of the products of complete combustion to be T_m. Following Frank-Kamenetskii (50), let us sketch the curve $T = T(x)$ by
replacing it roughly by a broken line consisting of lines T_0 = const
and T_m = const connected by a tangent drawn through the point of
inflection of the $T(x)$ curve. A thermal flow by heat conduction

flows in the stationary state through unit surface of the isolated gas layer in unit time which equals

$$q_\lambda = \lambda \frac{T_m - T_0}{\delta}$$

where λ is the average heat-conduction coefficient; δ is the conditional thickness of the combustion zone (width of the flame front).

This quantity of heat is continuously removed by the incident gas flow, i.e., is expended in heating it from the initial to the maximum temperature

$$q_\lambda = w c_p \gamma \, (T_m - T_0) \tag{6-1}$$

where w is the velocity of the incident flow, equal in magnitude but opposite in direction to the flame velocity: $w = w_{fl}$. Equating both expressions for the heat flow, we obtain

$$w_{fl} = \frac{a}{\delta} \tag{6-2}$$

where $a = \lambda/c_p$, γ is the average value of the temperature-conduction coefficient. Assuming the quantity δ, conditional width of the flame front, to be equal to the product of the velocity by the mixture stay time in the front to the accuracy of a constant factor, i.e., by the reaction time in a first approximation

$$\delta \approx w_{fl} \tau'_K \tag{6-3}$$

we finally obtain

$$w_{fl} \approx \sqrt{\frac{a}{\tau'_K}} \tag{6-4}$$

In its physical content, the formula obtained is most general; it shows that the rate of flame propagation is proportional to the square root of the ratio of the heat-conduction coefficient a to the characteristic time of the progress of the chemical reaction τ'_K.

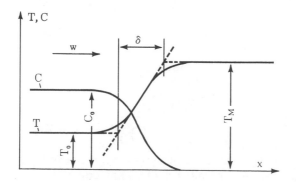

Fig. 6-1. Schematic representation of concentration and temperature in a flame front.

The value of the latter in formula (6-4) can be expressed approximately as a quantity reciprocal to the reaction-rate constant (for $n = 1$)

$$\tau'_K = \frac{1}{k} = \frac{e^{E/RT_m}}{k_0} = \tau_K \, e^{E/RT_m}$$

from which there follows

$$w_{fl} \approx \sqrt{ak_0 e^{-E/RT_m}} \tag{6-5}$$

that is, the normal flame propagation rate increases sharply as the temperature rises. Written more exactly (50), formulas (6-4) or (6-5) must contain the nondimensional factor f which depends on the concrete form of the reaction kinetics

$$w_{fl} = f \sqrt{a/\tau'_K} \tag{6-6}$$

The value of f is less than unity (50). This factor is related, in particular, to the difference between the conditional width of the flame front, defined along the curve $T = T(x)$ on Figure 6-1 (or what is approximately the same, along the curve $c(x)$), and the actual width of the zone in which an intense chemical reaction occurs. Because of the sharp exponential dependence of the reaction rate on the temperature, the burn-up of the fundamental mass of substance in the flame front occurs in the range of temperature values close to the maximum (see Figures 3-2 and 3-3). Consequently, the active reaction zone is always less than the zone of appreciable variation in the temperature and concentration, a zone whose dimensions are related to the processes of material transport by diffusion, and to heat transport by heat conduction. For the same reason, because of the narrowness of the active zone and its closeness to the maximum combustion temperature, the value τ'_K in (6-4), (6-6) should be referred to the quantity T_m

$$w_{fl} \sim \sqrt{\frac{a}{\tau_K}} \, e^{-1/\theta_m}$$

Let us note that formula (6-4) can be obtained very simply from dimensional considerations.[3]

The nonstationary process of the motion of a certain element of the mixture is characterized generally by the following three nondimensional similarity criteria which result from an analysis of the differential equation of heat propagation (33): $a\tau/d^2$, wd/a, $w\tau/a$, one of which (any one) is a combination of two others (here

[3] See (50) for a more exact derivation of formula (6-4) by the methods of similarity theory.

d is a certain characteristic dimension). Let us select any pair of independent criteria and in correspondence with the absence of quantities with the length dimension in the conditions of the problem (a characteristic linear dimension), let us eliminate d [4]

$$\frac{a\tau}{d^2} \left(\frac{wd}{a}\right)^2 = \frac{w^2\tau}{a}$$

Since the process as a whole is stationary and the combustion of any new element, flowing to the flame front with velocity w_{fl} occurs within the same time τ', which as before, can evidently be taken as

$$\frac{w_{fl}^2 \tau_K'}{a} = \text{const}; \quad w_{fl} = \text{const}\sqrt{\frac{a}{\tau_K'}}$$

Formula (6-4) can also be used in reverse order to estimate the value of the characteristic reaction time

$$\tau_K' = \frac{a}{w_{fl}^2}$$

by starting from an experimentally determined value of the normal flame rate w_{fl}. We use such a method, in principle, for example, to take into account the influence of the reaction rate in turbulent combustion (see section 7-2). The complexity of its application is related to the normal flame rate, varying very strongly as a function of the mixture composition and temperature, consequently use of (6-4) can yield only an approximate extimate of the value of τ_K'.

Let us also consider certain simple consequences of the Mikhel'-son law which we will later use, particularly in Chapter 7. The equilibrium condition of an ignition surface for a flame-front element (Figure 6-2, on which the plane case is indicated for simplicity) can be written as the equality

$$w_{fl} = w_n = w \cos \alpha \tag{6-7}$$

where α is the angle between the velocity vector and the normal to the ignition surface element. When the transition is made from a linear combustion rate to a weight γw_{fl} (kg/m² sec), we obtain from (6-7)

$$\gamma w \cos \alpha \, dF = \gamma w_n \, dF = \gamma w_{fl} \, dF_n$$

---

[4] Two additional combinations are possible:

$$\frac{wd}{a} \frac{w\tau}{d} = \frac{w^2\tau}{a} \quad \text{or} \quad \left(\frac{w\tau}{d}\right)^2 : \frac{a\tau}{d^2} = \frac{w^2\tau}{a}$$

or

$$wdF_n = w_{fl} dF \qquad\qquad (6\text{-}7')$$

for the volumetric combustion rate (m³/sec). The meaning of these relations is easily explained by the following example. For instance, let w be the average speed of the gas motion along the pipe whose transverse section equals F_n and let w_f be the normal flame rate directed perpendicularly to the ignition surface F. From the equality

$$wF_n = w_{fl} F \qquad\qquad (6\text{-}8)$$

there follows that any curvature of the flame-front surface leads to an increase in the volume (weight) rate of combustion. In particular, the latter is one of the reasons for the acceleration of the combustion during turbulent motion[5] and during any real motion related to the presence of a velocity profile and the ignition surface curvature, correspondingly. The relation (6-8) is usually called the "area rule" (50). Evidently $F_n = F \cos \alpha$ for a plane flame front and (6-8) agrees with (6-7).

The curvature of the streamline when it intersects the flame front is also of interest in the kinematic propagation of flame. Let us, in a first approximation, identify the ignition surface with the flame front, i.e., let us neglect the width of the latter, which is very insignificant for normal combustion (of the order of parts of a millimeter or several millimeters for slow reactions (13a, 14)). In this case, as is seen from Figure 6-3, the magnitude and direction of the flow velocity vary as the gas passes through the flame front in the general case. It is evident that we can speak of the change in the magnitude of the velocity for a direct flame front normal to the pressure direction (Figure 6-3 a). For the low-velocity case, when the pressure drop at the front can be neglected and we can consider $p_2 \approx p_1$; $\rho_1/\rho_2 = T_2/T_1$, from the continuity condition (for stream tubes or the start of a constant cross section) $\rho_2 w_2 = \rho_1 w_1$ and we can write

$$\frac{w_2}{w_1} = \frac{\rho_1}{\rho_2} = \frac{T_2}{T_1} \qquad\qquad (6\text{-}9)$$

In the case of an oblique front or a curvilinear element (Figure 6-3 b), the relation (6-9) is retained for the normal velocity component w_n, while the tangential component, tangent to the surface of the flame front, remains unchanged. In this connection, "refraction" of the stream line occurs in the flame front; the new direction of

---

[5] However, the quantity w_{fl} is not a physical constant in this case and it can differ radically at various points of the flow.

the velocity vector approaches the normal to the surface (i.e., is removed from the surface itself). If α_1 and α_2 are, respectively, the angles between the velocity vector and the normal along both sides of the flame front (Figure 6-3 b), then from the following version of the continuity equation

$$\rho_1 w_1 \cos \alpha_1 = \rho w \cos \alpha$$

and the condition that the tangential velocity components be constant

$$w_1 \sin \alpha_1 = w \sin \alpha$$

there follows

$$\frac{\tan \alpha_2}{\tan \alpha_1} = \frac{\rho_2}{\rho_1} \qquad (6\text{-}10)$$

or approximately

$$\frac{\tan \alpha_1}{\tan \alpha_2} \approx \frac{T_2}{T_1} \qquad (6\text{-}10')$$

(for example, $\tan \alpha_2 \approx \frac{1}{7}$; $\alpha_2 \approx 8°$ for $\alpha_1 = 45°$ and $T_2/T_1 = 7$).

For large velocities, in particular for detonations, the pressure change $\rho_2/\rho_1 = (P_2/P_1)(T_1/T_2)$ should be taken into account;

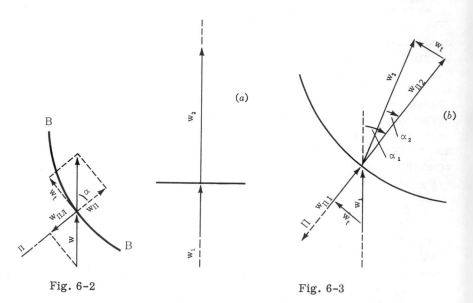

Fig. 6-2   Fig. 6-3

Fig. 6-2. Diagram of kinematic equilibrium of an ignition surface $(B - B)$.
Fig. 6-3. Refraction of the stream line into (a) a normal and (b) an oblique flame front.

expression (6-10′) becomes inapplicable. Condition (6-10), the gas flow "refraction law," is applicable to any surface of discontinuity (flame front or detonation, adiabatic jump, etc.). These questions are considered in more detail in gas dynamics (see also section 7-2).

If the flame front is not perpendicular to the direction of gas motion, then its existence (for a finite extent) is always related to the presence of separate elements of the ignition surface, special "kindling" points, for which the Mikhel' son condition is satisfied with respect to the total vector of the incident flow velocity.

For example, in the case of an oblique flame front (Figure 6-4a) located at an angle α to the mixture flow incident at the constant velocity w, when the thermal flow vector, the heat conduction $q_\lambda = -\lambda\,(dT/dn)$, is directed normally to the surface of the front and the mixture moves at a certain angle to it, any gas jet flowing to the front obtains the heat required for ignition not from the surface element intersecting it but from the previous flame-front elements located above the stream.

A most simple quantitative estimate can be made if the phenomenon is visualized as heat propagation against the mixture flow from a surface of given temperature $T = T_m$, i.e., if it is assumed that the reaction is completed in an infinitesimally thin layer and all the heat being liberated is eliminated by heat conduction and is expended in heating the gas. Similar considerations were used above in deriving formula (6-4).

Let us place the coordinate system at the point 0 of Figure 6-4 and let us direct the t axis tangent, and the n axis normal to the front toward the gas motion.

From the heat-conduction equation in which we shall, for simplicity, consider the physical constants to be fixed such as

$$c_p \gamma w_n \frac{dT}{dn} = \lambda \frac{d^2 T}{dn^2} \tag{6-11}$$

with the boundary conditions

$$T = T_m, \quad \text{for } n = 0$$
$$T = T_0, \quad \text{for } n = -\infty \tag{6-12}$$

we obtain an expression for the temperature distribution in the gas flow in the n direction:

$$T = A + B\, e^{\frac{w_n n}{\alpha}} \; ; \; A = T_0,\, B = T_m - T_0 : \left(\alpha = \frac{\lambda}{c_p \gamma}\right)$$

or finally

$$\frac{T - T_0}{T_m - T_0} = e^{\frac{w_n n}{\alpha}} \tag{6-13}$$

The expression (6-13) agrees in form with the known formula of V. A. Mikhel' son (32) for heating a mixture in the preflame zone (prior to ignition) in front of a direct front. We shall estimate the effective thickness of the gas layer being preheated as the distance along the normal to the front in which the nondimensional gas temperature $(T - T_0)/(T_m - T_0)$ decays e times (Figure 6-4b). From (6-13), the quantity n_0 equals

$$n_0 = \frac{\alpha}{w_n} \tag{6-14}$$

An analogous value of the preheating depth x_0 against a flow in the x direction taking into account both

$$w_n = w \cos \alpha$$

and

$$x_0 = \frac{n_0}{\cos \alpha}$$

will be written as

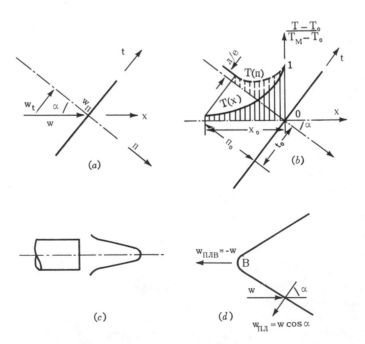

Fig. 6-4. Diagram of an oblique flame front. (*a*) Coordinate system; (*b*) temperature distribution; (*c*) diagram of the flame front in a laminar burner; (*d*) ignition point B.

$$x_0 = \frac{a}{w \cos^2 \alpha} \tag{6-14'}$$

Finally, the effective value of the width of the flame-front section t_0, from which the heat passes into heating the given gas jet, will evidently be

$$t_0 = x_0 \sin \alpha = \frac{a \tan \alpha}{w \cos \alpha} \tag{6-15}$$

Hence, the existence of any element of the oblique flame front in the scheme cited is guaranteed by the presence of a section of size t_0 preceding it. If the flame front is not infinite, then its stationary existence is possible only under the condition that at its extreme point B, the most forward toward the fresh mixture (Figure 6-4d), there is a heat source guaranteeing the supply to the fresh sections of the mixture (in a normal direction to the x axis) of a quantity of heat compensating the absence of the section t_0, i.e., $q = c_p w (T_m - T_0)$ in the scheme used. In its turn, each element of the oblique front, starting from the closest to the ignition source, acts as a kind of preheater for the fresh jets of mixture; the heat required for ignition is transmitted as if by a relay in a direction tangent to the flame front.

Since an additional heat source must evidently also be stationary and fixed in the flow, then local, kinematic equilibrium, the Mikhel' son condition in the form of the equality of the total velocity vector w, and the propagation velocity of the flame from the source w_{fB} in the x direction, $w = w_{fB}$ (see Figure 6-4d), must be conserved while this same condition for any section of the oblique flame front far from the point B is

$$w_n = w \cos \alpha = w_{fl} \tag{6-7}$$

L. N. Khitrin (54) analyzed the stability condition of the flame front in detail in a laminar burner in which the flame cone "holds" its base (the front surface at the base is normal to the motion direction, see Figure 6-4c; a similar problem was analyzed by Frank-Kamenetskii (50) for flame propagation in a fixed gas mixture filling a cylindrical pipe).

Despite the substantial simplifications introduced to simplify the considerations in estimating the phenomenon (to neglect heat liberation because of the reaction, etc.), the substance of the question is clearly explained from the considerations cited. The general (group) flame propagation rate in a stationary flow can evidently be characterized by the quantity $w_{fB} = w_0$, i.e., by the rate of the incident mixture flow while the local values of the propagation rate are determined by (6-7).

The quantities w_{fl} and w_{fB} (for the kindling points) can have a very different nature in the general case, for example, it can be imagined that the role of the ignition source is played by a continuously acting spark feeding the region beyond the poorly streamlined body which guarantees the return of the combustion products and their displacement by the fresh mixture (Figure 4-3), etc. Although the role of such a heat source is substantially less in quantitative respects in the actual process than in the estimate presented (the quantity of heat supplied to 1 kg of mixture in any jet is substantially less than the heat productivity of the reaction $qc_0 = c_p(T_m - T_0)$), however, its existence is responsible for the stationarity of the process. It is evident that combustion in any point of the oblique flame front will inevitably cease after a time $\tau \sim t/w_n$ after "disconnection" of the kindling point; an appropriate flame-front element will be communicated by a flow with the velocity equal to the difference in the values of w and w_n, i.e., equals $w(1 - \cos \alpha)$. Let us note in conclusion that the existence of reference kindling points is of extreme importance for technical combustion processes (see (25), for example) since precisely these points determine the stability of the process as a whole.

6-2. SIMILARITY OF TEMPERATURE AND CONCENTRATION FIELDS

In order to determine the normal flame propagation rate, it is necessary to start from the joint consideration of the heat-conduction and -diffusion equations taking into account heat liberation and the consumption of the initial material during the chemical reaction. Let us briefly recall the form of these equations and let us explain the similarity of the temperature and concentration distributions in addition.

As is known, the heat-conduction and -diffusion equations are particular cases of the laws of energy and mass conservation described as the equations of heat and material balance. Let us visualize a certain isolated element of space in which there is a mixture of two reacting gases and the reaction products. A change in the heat content of the mixture found in this element in an infinitesimal time interval is caused by the following in the general case: First, a certain quantity of gas flows in and out through the boundary of the element bringing in and taking out, respectively, its heat content. This change in the heat content is evidently related to convective flow, i.e., to the general motion of the gas. Second, a molecular heat flow, related to the presence of a temperature gradient, and in the general case, to a concentration gradient also, passes through the boundary of the element; a part of the heat carried along by this flow is retained in the element and goes into the change in its heat content. Third, a certain quantity of heat is liberated within the element because of the chemical reaction. Similar terms enter into the material-balance equation of the iso- lated element. The change in the mixture concentration within an infinitesimal time interval is related in this equation to the con- vective flow of substance through the boundaries of the element, to a molecular flow caused by a concentration gradient and in the general case, by a temperature gradient also, and finally, by the progress of the chemical reaction.

It is assumed, in the considerations presented, that the values of velocity are small, consequently, the kinetic energy of the gases is negligible in comparison with the heat content. Moreover, it is assumed that there is no heat emission by radiation and the gas motion is not turbulent. Taking these remarks into account, let us write the equations of heat and matter (diffusion) propagation with- out derivation in the most brief, vectorial, form (50).

Let us represent the heat conduction equation as

$$c_p \gamma \frac{dT}{d\tau} = c_p \gamma \frac{\partial T}{\partial \tau} + c_p \gamma w \cdot \text{grad } T$$

$$= \text{div} (\lambda \text{ grad } T + k_T D c_p \gamma \text{ grad } c) + Q(c, T) \qquad (6\text{-}16)$$

Similarly, the diffusion equation is

$$\gamma \frac{dc}{d\tau} = \gamma \frac{\partial c}{\partial x} + \gamma w \text{ grad } c$$

$$= \text{div} (D \gamma \text{ grad } c + k_T D \frac{\gamma c}{T} \text{ grad } T) - W(c, T) \qquad (6\text{-}17)$$

On the left in both Eqs. (6-16) and (6-17) is the total (substan- tial) derivative (of the temperature or concentration) with respect to time which consists of two terms, the so-called local and con- vective derivatives, corresponding to the change in these quanti- ties caused by the general motion of the medium

$$\frac{d}{d\tau} = \frac{\partial}{\partial \tau} + \frac{\partial}{\partial x} \frac{dx}{d\tau} + \frac{\partial}{\partial y} \frac{dy}{d} + \frac{\partial}{\partial z} \frac{dz}{d\tau}$$

$$= \frac{\partial}{\partial \tau} + w_x \frac{\partial}{\partial x} + w_y \frac{\partial}{\partial y} + w_z \frac{\partial}{\partial z}$$

The expressions on the right side of (6-16) and (6-17), in the parentheses under the sign of the differential operator[6] div, consist

[6] The scalar div a of the vector a equals div $a = (\partial a_x)/(\partial x) + (\partial a_y)/(\partial y) + (\partial a_z)/(\partial z)$ where a_x, a_y, and a_z are components of the vector a; in its

of two components each. Summed in the heat-conduction equation are the expressions of the molecular heat flow by ordinary heat conduction

$$q_T = \lambda \text{ grad } T$$

and by diffusion heat conduction

$$q_{\text{dif } T} = k_T D c_p \gamma \text{ grad } c$$

Similarly, the first term in the diffusion equation expresses the molecular flow of substance by ordinary diffusion

$$j_D = D \gamma \text{ grad } c$$

and by thermal diffusion

$$j_{\text{thermal } D} = k_T D \frac{\gamma c}{T} \text{ grad } T$$

In addition to the notation encountered earlier, the nondimensional thermal diffusion constant (50) k_T is present in these expressions. Let us note that in the majority of cases the thermal diffusion heat transport is substantially less than molecular conduction and the quantity $q_{\text{dif } T}$ can be neglected in comparison with q_T even when the thermal mass diffusion j_{TD} (28, 50) should be taken into account along with the usual diffusion j_D.

Finally, the last terms in (6-16) and (6-17) express, respectively, the quantity of heat being liberated per unit time per m³ of mixture $Q(c, T)$ and the quantity of material which reacts in unit time in a m³, $W(c, T)$. The quantities Q and W are functions of the temperature and concentration and thereby depend on the space coordinates and time. They are interrelated by means of the mixture heat productivity q in the usual way

$$Q = Wq = Vq\gamma \tag{6-18}$$

where, as before, V is the reaction rate per kg of mixture.

A concrete expression of the reaction rate, i.e., its temperature and concentration dependence, is not essential for the equations written in general form.

Equations (6-16) and (6-17) are not independent since the temperature T and the concentration c are in both equations. In case the cross-molecular flows, thermal diffusion, and diffusion-heat production, are neglected, the interrelation of Eqs. (6-16) and

---

turn, the vector grad φ (where φ is a scalar) equals grad $\varphi = [(\partial \varphi)/(\partial x)] x_1 + [(\partial \varphi)/(\partial y)] y_1 + [(\partial \varphi)/(\partial z)] z_1$ where x_1, y_1, z_1 are unit vectors (directions) of the coordinate axes.

(6-17) is determined by the expression of the reaction rate $W(c, T)$ in both equations.

Let us also note that the equations written in this form assume a general case of the temperature dependence of the physical constants (λ, D, c_p); a significant change in the mixture properties is generally typical for combustion processes. The values of the speed w and its components w_x, w_y, and w_z in (6-16) and (6-17) are assumed to be given; in the general case, the solution of the problem requires the joint integration of the hydrodynamics equations of a compressible fluid (even for small flow velocities in connection with the change in density during preheating), i.e., the motion and continuity equations and (6-16) and (6-17).

Also worth mentioning is a peculiarity of the description of the diffusion equations for a nonisothermal process. We speak of the choice of the dimensionality of the concentration. Along with the nondimensional concentration c (kg/kg), which figures in all the previous computations and in particular in (6-16) and (6-17), the volume concentration c' (kg/m^3) is often used. The quantities c and c' are interrelated by the obvious relation

$$c' = c\gamma = c\frac{P}{RT}; \quad dc' = \gamma dc$$

It is obvious that the first of these, c, varies during the combustion process only in connection with the burn-up of the mixture during the chemical reaction, the second c' also varies in connection with the rarefaction of the gas during heating. Let us clarify this difference by a simple example for a graphical illustration. Let us assume that we speak of a nonisothermal field in an inert gas medium (for example, about the temperature and concentration distributions in air over an electric heater). The value of the nondimensional oxygen concentration c (kg/kg) in all points of the space in this example will obviously be one and the same, but the value of the volume concentration c' (kg/m^3) will be different, namely, large in the region of reduced temperature and less in the region of elevated temperatures. The latter, i.e., the presence of a gradient in c' certainly does not cause any change in composition of the mixture or the occurrence of diffusion exchange (if we neglect thermal diffusion as being practically absent in gas mixtures of approximately the same molecular weights as oxygen and nitrogen, for example).

For isothermal diffusion with γ = const, $dc' = d(\gamma c)$ and use of c or c' is all the same thing, however, for diffusion in a field of variable temperature of which we speak in the computation of combustion processes, the incorrect use of c', the volume concentration, which is sometimes encountered in the literature, can lead to serious errors.[7]

Returning to the fundamental Eqs. (6-16) and (6-17), let us note that k_T can be approximately zero (28, 50) for mixtures which approximate the molecular weight of the individual gases ($\mu_1 \approx \mu_2$) and also identical values of the transport coefficients can be assumed

$$a \approx D \tag{6-19}$$

where, as before, $a = \lambda / c_p \gamma$ is the heat-conduction coefficient; D is the diffusion coefficient.

In this case (for $a = D$), both Eqs. (6-16) and (6-17) can be reduced to a single equation without difficulty.

In connection with the variable value of the specific heat, let us first transform from the temperature and concentration quantities to the appropriate enthalpies.

Let us denote

$$J = \int_0^T c_p \, dT; \quad dJ = c_p \, dT \tag{6-20}$$

as the physical enthalpy (heat content) of the mixture and

$$h = \int_0^c q \, dc; \quad dh = q \, dc \tag{6-21}$$

as the chemical enthalpy of the mixture units. In the new J and h variables, Eqs. (6-16) and (6-17) are written, if (6-18) is taken into account

$$\gamma \frac{dJ}{d\tau} = \gamma \frac{\partial J}{\partial \tau} + \gamma w \, \text{grad} \, J$$

$$= \text{div} \left(\frac{\lambda}{c_p} \, \text{grad} \, J + k_T D \, \frac{c_p \gamma}{q} \, dh \right) + Q(J, h) \tag{6-22}$$

and

$$\gamma \frac{dh}{d\tau} = \gamma \frac{\partial h}{\partial \tau} + \gamma w \, \text{grad} \, h$$

$$= \text{div} \left(D \gamma \, \text{grad} \, h + k_T D \gamma \frac{h}{J} \, \text{grad} \, J \right) - Q(J, h) \tag{6-23}$$

---

[7] For example, if we write the equality of the elementary quantity of heat being liberated during the reaction to the increment in the heat content as $-q \, dc = c_1 \gamma \, dT = c_p (P/R) \cdot dT/T$ then, despite the irreproachability of this expression from dimensional aspects, the result of integration $T_m = T_0 e^{qc_0/c_p T_0}$ can differ very radically from the correct result in the general case $-q \, dc' = -q \gamma \, dc = c_p \gamma \, dc$, i.e., $-q \, dc = c_p \, dT$, $T_m = T_0 (1 + qc_0/c_p T_0)$.

Let us be limited in the sequel to the case $\mu_1 \approx \mu_2$; $k_T = 0$ and $\lambda/c_p = D\gamma$ ($\alpha = D$). Instead (6-22) and (6-23) can be written

$$\gamma \frac{dJ}{d\tau} = \gamma \frac{\partial J}{\partial \tau} + \gamma w \text{ grad } J = \text{div} \left(\frac{\lambda}{c_p} \text{ grad } J \right) + Q(J, h) \quad (6\text{-}24)$$

$$\gamma \frac{dh}{d\tau} = \gamma \frac{\partial h}{\partial \tau} + \gamma w \text{ grad } h = \text{div} \left(D\gamma \text{ grad } h \right) - Q(J, h) \quad (6\text{-}25)$$

Let us add the last two equations term by term by denoting the total enthalpy of the mixture units, i.e., the sum of the heat content and the chemical enthalpy, by the symbol

$$H = J + h \quad (6\text{-}26)$$

The equation for the quantity H, the total enthalpy obtained by adding (6-24) and (6-25), is

$$\gamma \frac{dH}{d\tau} = \gamma \frac{\partial H}{\partial \tau} + \gamma w \text{ grad } H = \text{div} \left(\frac{\lambda}{c_p} \text{ grad } H \right) \quad (6\text{-}27)$$

i.e., does not contain the expression for the reaction rate $W(J, h)$.

In order to integrate (6-27), it is necessary to have the boundary and initial conditions assigned. Let us assume that there is no reaction at the initial instant

$$J = J_0, \quad h = h_0 \qquad \text{for } \tau = 0$$

$$H = J + h = J_0 + h_0 \qquad (\text{for } T = T_0, c = c_0)$$

and also, that the surfaces being bounded by the system are impervious to heat and matter, i.e., the values of the diffusion or thermal flow at the surface which are expressed in terms of the appropriate derivatives along the normal to the surface F, are identically zero

$$\left. \frac{\partial H}{\partial n} \right)_F = \left. \frac{\partial h}{\partial n} \right)_F = \left. \frac{\partial J}{\partial n} \right)_F = 0$$

Under this assumption, the system under consideration is completely isolated in thermal and diffusion respects from the ambient medium, therefore, the quantity of total enthalpy contained therein at the initial instant is retained without change. In a particular case, the original fresh mixture ($J = J_0$; $h = h_0$; $H = J_m$) or the products of complete combustion ($J = J_m$; $h = 0$; $H = J_m$) can be found on the boundaries of the system.

Equation (6-27) under such boundary conditions has the simple integral

$$H = J + h = J_m = \text{const} \quad (6\text{-}28)$$

i.e., the total enthalpy of 1 kg of gas is identical at all points of the field during the whole course of the process (18).[8]

It is not difficult to see that condition (6-28) means similarity of the physical and chemical enthalpy fields J and h since the latter are related by a linear relation.

For example, if, as before, the coefficient of completeness of combustion φ were to be introduced according to the expression

$$\varphi = 1 - \frac{c}{c_0} = 1 - \frac{h}{h_0}$$

then from (6-28), taking into account the obvious equalities

$$J_m - J_0 = h_0; \quad J - J_0 = h_0 - h$$

it would follow that

$$\varphi = 1 - \frac{h}{h_0} = \frac{J - J_0}{J_m - J_0} \tag{6-29}$$

The last equality denotes similarity of the $J-$ and $h-$ fields. It is a generalization of the similarity of the temperature and concentration fields to the case of variable specific heat since $c_p \neq$ const and, by the way, $a = D$ (6-29).

Formula (6-29) agrees with (2-16) obtained in Chapter 2 for adiabatic combustion in the absence of transport processes and with (3-16) of Chapter 3, also for the case $a = D$.

It should be emphasized that the constancy of the total enthalpy in the whole space (and time) H = const, just as the similarity of the fields J and h resulting therefrom, is not a trivial result. In particular, it is not observed in the adiabatic process if $a \neq D$. In the case considered below, a local redistribution of the energy between the individual gas layers is observed within the flame front, and the quantity H varies; there is no similarity in the distributions of J and h (or T and c for c_p = const).

Mathematically, the presence of the similarity of the J and h fields is also seen from the two Eqs. (6-24) and (6-25) becoming identical when $a = D$. If a transformation is made from the variable J (or h) to the quantity φ in any of these equations according to (6-29), then we obtain after simple manipulation

[8] Giving the conditions $\dfrac{\partial H}{\partial n}\Big)_F = 0$ or $H = J_m$ = const on the system boundaries is essential in this result, in addition to the form of (6-27). For example, if we were to speak of the progress of the reaction in a tube in the presence of heat loss through the walls, then although (6-27) retains the same form, i.e., the magnitude of the total enthalpy H enters only under the differential, the expression H = const (6-28) will no longer be an integral; the fields J and h will not be similar.

$$\gamma \frac{d\varphi}{d\tau} = \gamma \frac{\partial \varphi}{\partial \tau} + \gamma w \text{ grad } \varphi = \text{div}\left(\frac{\lambda}{c_p} \text{ grad } \varphi\right) + \frac{Q(\varphi)}{h_0} \quad (6\text{-}30)$$

An investigation of this equation, required to find the flame propagation rate, will be made in the next section; later (section 6-4) the question of the relation between J and h (T and c) and the character of the change in the total enthalpy H for $a \neq D$ will be analyzed qualitatively also.

6-3. THEORY OF IA. B. ZEL' DOVICH ON NORMAL FLAME PROPAGATION

Following Ia. B. Zel' dovich (18), let us analyze the one-dimensional stationary flame propagation in the flow of a burning gas mixture moving to a fixed flame front at velocity w_0 in the region of fresh (cold) mixture.

For the $a = D$ case, to which we shall be limited here, the system of fundamental differential equations of heat conduction and diffusion (6-16) and (6-17) can be represented for the one-dimensional stationary process as

$$\frac{\partial}{\partial \tau} = 0; \quad \frac{\partial}{\partial x} = \frac{d}{dx}; \quad \frac{\partial}{\partial y} = \frac{\partial}{\partial z} = 0$$

$$\gamma w \frac{dJ}{dx} = \frac{d}{dx}\left(\frac{\lambda}{c_p} \frac{dJ}{dx}\right) + Q(J, h) \quad (6\text{-}31)$$

and

$$\gamma w \frac{dh}{dx} = \frac{d}{dx}\left(D\gamma \frac{dh}{dx}\right) - Q(J, h) \quad (6\text{-}32)$$

The boundary conditions for these equations will be written in conformance with the diagram on Figure 6-5 as

$$\left.\begin{array}{l} \text{for } x = -\infty; \quad J = J_0, h = h_0 \\ \text{for } x = +\infty; \quad J = J_m, h = 0 \end{array}\right\} \quad \frac{dJ}{dx} = \frac{dh}{dx} = 0 \quad (6\text{-}33)$$

Fig. 6-5. Diagram of a flame front.

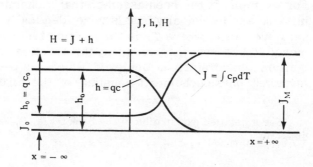

Since the integral (6-28), $H = J + h$ = const satisfies (6-31) and (6-32) and the boundary conditions (6-33) for $a = D$ (i.e., the fields J and h are similar), a transformation, analogous to the preceding, can be made from the two equations (6-31) and (6-32) to the single equation (6-30) for the coefficient of completeness of combustion φ, defined by (6-29).

Let us represent this equation as

$$\gamma w \frac{d\varphi}{dx} = \frac{d}{dx}\left(\frac{\lambda}{c_p}\frac{d\varphi}{dx}\right) + \frac{Q(\varphi)}{h_0} \tag{6-34}$$

The boundary conditions for (6-34) will be the following in correspondence with (6-33)

$$\text{for } x = -\infty, \quad \varphi = 0, \qquad \frac{d\varphi}{dx} = 0$$
$$\tag{6-35}$$
$$\text{for } x = +\infty, \quad \varphi = 1.0, \qquad \frac{d\varphi}{dx} = 0$$

From the continuity equation for motion in a pipe of constant cross section (or an elementary gas stream line), there follows

$$w\gamma = w_0\gamma_0 = \text{const} \tag{6-36}$$

i.e., the gas flow density $(w\gamma)$ in (6-34) is constant, from which

$$w_0 = \frac{w\gamma}{\gamma_0} = \frac{\text{const}}{\gamma_0}$$

The problem is to find such a (constant) value of w and, therefore, of w_0, which would satisfy the nonlinear differential Eq. (6-34) and the boundary conditions (6-35).

The fundamental complexity here is related to the presence of nonlinear function, $Q = W(\varphi)q$, dependent exponentially on the temperature, in (6-34), i.e., on the variable φ in the long run.

Let us note that the first attempts to determine the quantity $w_{fl} = w_0$ analytically, which are principally of historical interest,[9] were related to an incorrect representation of the physical nature of ignition and the temperature dependence of the reaction rate. For example, it has been assumed that a chemical reaction is missing and its velocity equals zero identically in the $T < T_i$ temperature range, where T_i is the ignition temperature. Furthermore, it has been assumed that the reaction starts again as the ignition temperature is achieved which has been considered an invariant physicochemical constant of the mixture (and is not

---

[9] See a detailed explanation in the book by Ia. B. Zel'dovich (13a) and also (50).

a characteristic of the process) and it proceeds with a constant, temperature-independent rate, or occurs instantaneously in the course of a certain period of induction, characteristic for a given mixture, which is also temperature-independent. These naïve conceptions of the kinetics of the combustion reaction contradict not only the nature of the process but also basic laws of dialectics; the preflame period of a slow development of the reaction related to accumulation of heat or active centers, and the possibility of specifying a further sharp increase in its rate is neglected therein and the ignition temperature is treated without connection with the relation between the quantity of heat being liberated and eliminated, which plays, as has been shown in detail above, a fundamental part in the dynamics of the process. In the exact theory of Ia. B. Zel'dovich being considered here (18), the exponential temperature dependence of the reaction rate and the correct concept of the ignition temperature resulting from the work of N. N. Semenov (44, 45), have been taken into account. Hence, as will be seen later, there arises, however, a mathematical contradiction in the very formulation of the problem of stationary combustion propagation. The substance of the question reduces to the following:

Let us visualize, for example, a pipe length filled with a combustible mixture at a comparatively low initial temperature. If the mixture were to be kindled at any point then the combustion would be propagated over the fresh mixture and would be displaced further from the kindling point as it is burned up. The flame will traverse the whole tube after a certain time. However, according to the exponential temperature dependence of the reaction rate $W \sim e^{-E/RT}$ the reaction rate becomes exactly zero at a temperature equal to absolute zero (it follows from elementary considerations of molecular-kinetic theory that a certain number of collisions between molecules, part of which, for active molecules, lead to a reaction, occur for any value of the temperature $T > 0°K$). This means that a reaction will occur simultaneously with flame propagation and independently in the whole volume of the combustible mixture. No matter how small the reaction rate at low temperatures (see Table 1-1), the mixture composition and temperature will vary continuously. At a certain large distance from the flame source, total burn-up of the mixture can, in principle, always occur before the flame reaches this place. Hence, a correct representation of the temperature dependence of the reaction rate leads to the impossibility of a strictly stationary flame propagation process.

It is clear that we speak of the mathematical and not of the physical exactness, or rather, not of the practical contradiction between the formulation of the problem and the experimental observations. Actually, the exceptionally sharp exponential temperature dependence of the reaction rate leads to there being practically no reaction in the comparatively low temperature range. For example, the characteristic reaction time at $T = 300°K$ and $E = 30,000$ cal/mol is of the order of magnitude $\tau'_K = e^{E/RT}/k_0 = 5 \times 10^{21}/10^{10} \approx 5 \times 10^{11}$ sec for a value $k_0 \sim 10^{10}$ (1/sec) (number of collisions), which corresponds approximately to 20,000 years. This graphic example shows the complete validity of neglecting the mixture reaction rate in the low-temperature region. In order to avoid the mathematical contradiction in the Zel'dovich theory (see below), it is assumed that the reaction rate equals zero at a certain temperature $T_1 > T_0$, where T_0 is the initial temperature of the combustible mixture, i.e., for a certain value of $\varphi = \varphi_1 \geq 0$. Hence, a concrete value of T_1 is not determined in the solution of the problem.[10]

The introduction of a finite temperature interval $T_1 \geq T \geq T_0$, in which the reaction rate equals zero instead, apparently, of the simple condition of its being equal to zero only at the temperature T_0, is easily explained from stability considerations. If it is assumed that $W = 0$ at $T = T_0$, $\varphi = 0$, and $W > 0$ for any value as close as desired to $T = T_0$ in order to solve the stationary problem, then any infinitesimal rise in the temperature leads to the progress of the chemical reaction in the whole mixture volume independently of the flame propagation; i.e., to the previous contradiction to the stationary problem. Such an infinitesimal perturbation is naturally always possible and even inevitable. As Frank-Kamenetskii (50) shows, it can also be visualized as an infinitesimal ignition pulse being propagated at some required rate; mathematically, the condition $W = 0$ only for $T = T_0$ yields a continuous spectrum of solutions instead of a single one; i.e., an innumerable set of values of the flame rate satisfying (6-34) and the boundary conditions (6-35). The condition that a reaction be absent in the cold mixture in a certain finite range of temperature values near T_0 or the quantity φ: $0 < \varphi < \varphi_1$ is, consequently, a reasonable mathematical approximation of the actual conditions of the progress of the reaction,[11] which guarantees uniqueness of the solution. Understandably it has nothing in common with the arbitrary introduction of a constant ignition temperature in old theories of flame propagation.

Hence, we as yet assume only two conditions for the function $Q(\varphi)$: $Q(\varphi)$ is positive and finite in the whole range of the process

[10] This value is assigned in numerical computations but has almost no effect on their result.

[11] In particular, if it is recalled that the influence of heat loss is not taken into account in this theory.

$0 < \varphi < 1$ and $Q(\varphi) = 0$ for $\varphi = 1$ in the total combustion region in connection with the consumption of the initial mixture. An additional condition for the $0 < \varphi < \varphi_1$ range will be introduced below. Returning to an investigation of (6-34), let us transform to the independent variable φ instead of x

$$\frac{d}{dx} = \frac{d}{d\varphi}\frac{d\varphi}{dx} = t\frac{d}{dx}; \quad \frac{d}{dx}\left(\frac{\lambda}{c_p}\frac{d\varphi}{dx}\right) = t\frac{d}{d\varphi}\left(\frac{\lambda}{c_p}t\right)$$

where $l = d\varphi/dx$.

Let us transform to nondimensional variables in the first-order equation obtained.

$$t\frac{d}{d\varphi}\left(\frac{\lambda}{c_p}t\right) - w\gamma t + \frac{Q}{h_0} = 0 \tag{6-34'}$$

To do this, let us multiply (6-34') by the quantity $(\lambda/c_p)(h_0/q) = \lambda/c_p c_0$ and let us select a constant value consisting of any arbitrarily chosen values of the quantities λ_*, c_{p*}, and W_*, for example:

$$\lambda_* = \lambda\,(\varphi = 0;\ T = T_0); \quad c_{p*} = c_p(\varphi = 0;\ T = T_0);$$

$$W_* = W(\varphi = 0;\ T = T_m)$$

as the scale for the last term $(\lambda Q)/(c_p q\gamma) = (\lambda/c_p)W$. Naturally, the concrete choice of the constant values λ_*, c_{p*}, W_* is not felt therein.

Such a transformation of Eq.[12] (6-34') permits the following nondimensional variables, convenient for the subsequent investigation, to be introduced

$$\psi = \frac{\dfrac{\lambda}{c_p}\dfrac{d\varphi}{dx}}{\sqrt{\dfrac{1}{c_0}\left(\dfrac{\lambda}{c_p}W\right)_*}}; \qquad \eta = \frac{w\gamma}{\sqrt{\dfrac{1}{c_0}\left(\dfrac{\lambda}{c_p}W\right)_*}};$$

[12] Let us, for clarity, write it thus:

$$\frac{\dfrac{\lambda}{c_p}t}{\sqrt{\dfrac{1}{c_0}\left(\dfrac{\lambda}{c_p}W\right)_*}}\frac{d}{d\varphi}\left[\frac{\dfrac{\lambda}{c_p}t}{\sqrt{\dfrac{1}{c_0}\left(\dfrac{\lambda}{c_p}W\right)_*}}\right] - \frac{w\gamma}{\sqrt{\dfrac{1}{c_0}\left(\dfrac{\lambda}{c_p}W\right)_*}}$$

$$\times \frac{\dfrac{\lambda}{c_p}t}{\sqrt{\dfrac{1}{c_0}\left(\dfrac{\lambda}{c_p}W\right)_*}} + \frac{\dfrac{\gamma}{c_p}W}{\left(\dfrac{\lambda}{c_p}W\right)_*} = 0$$

$$\Phi(\varphi) = \frac{\dfrac{\lambda}{c_p} W}{\left(\dfrac{\lambda}{c_p} W\right)_*} \; ; \qquad \varphi = \frac{J - J_0}{h_0} \tag{6-37}$$

Physically, the quantity ψ corresponds to the gradient of the completeness of combustion along the length, consequently $\psi > 0$; η is the nondimensional combustion propagation rate; its value $\eta = \eta_0 = $ const is sought in the whole investigation; $\Phi(\varphi)$ is the reaction rate. As has been mentioned, the function $\Phi(\varphi)$ is positive, finite, and becomes zero at $\varphi = 1$.

Equation (6-34) in the variables of (6-37) becomes

$$\psi \frac{d\psi}{d\varphi} - \eta\psi + \Phi(\varphi) = 0 \tag{6-38}$$

and the boundary conditions (6-35), respectively, are

$$\psi = 0 \begin{cases} \text{for } \varphi = 0 \\[2mm] \text{for } \varphi = 1 \end{cases} \tag{6-39}$$

It is required to find the constant value η_0 satisfying (6-38) and (6-39).

Let us first establish the existence condition for the solution. To do this, let us draw an isocline (line of equal slope) in the ψ-φ plane (Figure 6-6) for Eq. (6-38) $\psi_0 = \Phi(\varphi)/\eta$, for which $d\psi/d\varphi = 0.$[13] The curve $\psi_0(\varphi)$, which issues from the point $\psi = 0$, $\varphi = 1$, separates the ψ-φ plane into two regions according to the conditions (6-39) and the equality $\Phi(\varphi = 1) = 0$: the derivative $d\psi/d\varphi > 0$ above the curve and $d\psi/d\varphi < 0$ below (i.e., $d\varphi < 0$, $d\psi > 0$ as the origin is approached).

Therefore, none of the integral curves of (6-38) issuing from the point $\psi = 0$, $\varphi = 1$, nor for any value of η can pass through the origin for $\Phi(\varphi) > 0$ in the whole interval $0 < \varphi < 1$. In order for the solution to exist, it is evidently necessary that the function $\Phi(\varphi)$ become zero for $\varphi > 0$.

The physical meaning of this result, indicating the mathematical impossibility of stationary flame propagation in the case of a finite, nonzero value of the reaction rate at $\varphi = 0$ ($T = T_0$) has been explained above.

In order to clarify the uniqueness of the solution, let us consider the case when $\Phi(\varphi) = 0$ in a finite interval of values of φ; $0 < \varphi < \varphi_1 < 1$ and $\Phi(\varphi) > 0$ for $1 > \varphi > \varphi_1$ (Figure 6-7).

---

[13] The integral curves of (6-38) pass through a maximum on the line $\psi_0(\varphi)$.

Let us consider the family of functions $\psi(\varphi, \eta)$ of the two variables φ and η, which satisfy the differential Eq. (6-38) and one of the boundary conditions for the complete combustion region for any value η = const for

$$\varphi = 1; \quad \psi(\varphi = 1; \eta) = 0$$

In order to investigate the behavior of the curves $\psi(\varphi, \eta)$ at the second boundary point $\varphi = 0$ as the parameter η varies, let us consider the equation for the partial derivative $\psi' = \partial\psi/\partial\eta$. We obtain this equation from (6-38) by dividing it by ψ and differentiating with respect to η

$$\frac{d\psi'_\eta}{d\varphi} - \frac{\Phi(\varphi)}{\psi^2(\varphi, \eta)} \psi = 1; \quad \text{for } \varphi = 1, \ \psi'_\eta = 0$$

Let us note that the function ψ' is negative in the interval of values $\varphi_1 < \varphi < 1$. Let us prove this, for example, by investigating the values of $d\psi'_\eta/d\varphi$ in the neighborhood of the point $\varphi = 1$. Let us represent all the terms of the differential equation for ψ' near $\varphi = 1$ for a small (negative) increment in the argument $\delta\varphi$ as

$$\frac{d\psi'_\eta}{d\varphi} \approx \left(\frac{d\psi'_\eta}{d\varphi}\right)_{\varphi=1} + \left(\frac{d^2\psi'_\eta}{d\varphi^2}\right)_{\phi=1} \delta\varphi;$$

$$\Phi(\varphi) \approx \left[\frac{d\Phi(\varphi)}{d\varphi}\right]_{\varphi=1} \cdot \delta\varphi;$$

$$\psi(\varphi, \eta) \approx \left(\frac{d\psi}{d\varphi}\right)_{\varphi=1} \cdot \delta\varphi; \quad \psi^2(\varphi, \eta) \approx \left(\frac{d\psi}{d\varphi}\right)^2_{\varphi=1} \delta^2\varphi;$$

$$\psi'_\eta \approx \left(\frac{d\psi'_\eta}{d\varphi}\right)_{\varphi=1} \delta\varphi;$$

$$(\Phi(\varphi)_{\varphi=1} = \psi_{\varphi=1} = \psi'_\eta, _{\varphi=1} = 0)$$

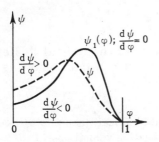

Fig. 6-6

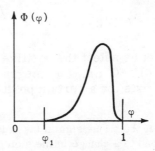

Fig. 6-7

Substituting these expressions in the equation for ψ' and discarding terms of third and higher orders, we obtain after simple manipulations

$$\left(\frac{d\psi'_\eta}{d\varphi}\right)_{\varphi=1} \approx \frac{\left(\dfrac{d\psi}{d\varphi}\right)^2_{\varphi=1}}{\left(\dfrac{d\psi}{d\varphi}\right)^2_{\varphi=1} - \left[\dfrac{d\Phi(\varphi)}{d\varphi}\right]_{\varphi=1}}$$

Since $d\Phi/d\varphi < 0$ in the $\varphi_1 < \varphi < 1$ range, the derivative $[d\psi'/d\varphi]_{\varphi=1}$ is positive and less than unity. This latter means that the slope of the curves $\psi(\varphi, \eta)$ at the point $\varphi = 1$, $\psi = 0$ decreases as the parameter η increases (the curves corresponding to large values of η are located close to the horizontal axis; $d\psi/d\varphi < 0$ and $(\partial/\partial\eta)(d\psi/d\varphi > 0)$. From the condition $0 < (d\psi'_\eta/d\varphi)_{\varphi=1} < 1$ and the equation for ψ, it follows that the function ψ'_η near $\varphi = 1$ (for $\varphi = 1 - \delta\varphi$) is negative and since the integral curves of (6-38) never intersect (there are no singular points for $\varphi_1 < \varphi < 1$), then the condition $\psi'_\eta = (\partial\psi/\partial\eta) < 0$ is retained in the whole interval.

The function $\Phi(\varphi) = 0$ in the $0 < \varphi < \varphi_1$ range and, therefore, $d\psi'_\eta/d\varphi = 1$. Let us integrate this equation between $\varphi = 0$ and $\varphi = \varphi_1$ limits

$$\psi'_\eta(\varphi_1; \eta) - \psi'_\eta(0; \eta) = \varphi_1; \quad \psi'_\eta(0, \eta) = -\varphi_1 + \psi'_\eta(\varphi_1; \eta) < 0$$

since according to what has been proved $\psi'_\eta(\varphi_1; \eta) < 0$.

Hence, the function ψ'_η is always negative for $\varphi = 0$ and is larger than a definite finite quantity φ_1 in absolute value.

Let us solve (6-38) for $\eta = 0$ for the condition $\psi(\varphi = 1; \eta = 0) = 0$

$$\psi \frac{d\psi}{d\varphi} = \frac{d}{d\varphi}\left(\frac{\psi^2}{2}\right) = -\Phi(\varphi); \quad \left|\frac{\psi^2}{2}\right|^\varphi_1 = \int_\varphi^1 \Phi(\varphi)\,d\varphi;$$

$$\psi = \pm \sqrt{2 \int_\varphi^1 \Phi(\varphi)\,d\varphi}$$

for $\varphi = 0$

$$\psi(\varphi = 0; \eta = 0) = \pm \sqrt{\int_0^1 \Phi(\varphi)\,d\varphi}$$

Let us select the positive sign in front of the radical.[14] Hence $\psi(0,0) > 0$ i.e., the integral curve $\psi(\varphi, \eta = 0)$ intersects the vertical axis for a certain positive value of ψ.

---

[14] If the minus sign is taken in front of the radical, then this will correspond to a change in the sign of the propagation velocity η_{01}, i.e., to the flame-front motion in the opposite direction.

As the parameter η increases, the value of $\psi(\varphi = 0, \eta)$ decreases monotonically, the derivative $\partial\psi/\partial\eta$ here is always larger than zero (in absolute value) for $\varphi = 0$. Therefore one, and only one value of η_0 exists, which satisfies the equality $\psi(\varphi = 0; \eta_0) = 0$.

Hence the existence and uniqueness of the solution have been proved. The desired value of w_0 is determined from (6-37) for the magnitude of η in terms of the η_0 found.

In practice, the calculation of η_0 according to Zel' dovich consists in successively assigning a number of values η_i and looking for the points of intersection of the appropriate integral curves $\psi(\varphi_1; \eta_i)$ with the vertical axis on Figure 6-7 by numerical integration. The desired value of η_0 is found by interpolation on the auxiliary graphs of the dependence of $\psi(0, \eta_i)$ on η_i.

The final formula to compute the flame-propagation rate, as follows from (6-37), is for $\eta = \eta_0$:

$$w_0 = \frac{\eta_0}{\gamma_0} \sqrt{\frac{1}{c_0}\left(\frac{\lambda}{c_p} W\right)}_* \tag{6-40}$$

here η_0 is a number determined by the numerical integration of (6-38) for a given concrete form of the function $\Phi(\varphi)$, i.e., the temperature and concentration dependences of the reaction rate W and of the physical constants λ and c_p as well.

After the value η_0 satisfying (6-38) and both boundary conditions (6-39) has been determined, as has the integral curve $\psi_0 = \psi(\varphi, \eta)$ also, the change in all the variables (J, h, T, and c) as a function of the coordinate x can be calculated by numerical integration. It follows from the first formula that

$$dx = \frac{\dfrac{\lambda}{c_p} d\varphi}{\psi(\varphi_1, \eta_0) \sqrt{\dfrac{1}{c_0}\left(\dfrac{c_p}{\lambda} W\right)}_*}$$

or

$$x = \sqrt{\frac{c_0 \lambda_*}{c_{p_*} W_*}} \int_0^\varphi \frac{\lambda}{\lambda_*} \cdot \frac{c_{p_*}}{c_p} \frac{d\varphi}{\psi(\varphi_1, \eta_0)} \tag{6-41}$$

For $\varphi = 0$ $\varphi(0; \eta_0) = 0$ and $x = -\infty$
for $\varphi = 1$ $\psi(1; \eta_0) = 0$ and $x = +\infty$

Hence, both boundary conditions (6-34) are satisfied. The value $\varphi = 1$, $T = T_m$ is actually attained theoretically at infinity.

As Zel' dovich mentions, $\psi(\varphi) = \eta\varphi$ can be assumed near $\varphi = 0$, from which after substitution of the value η_0 from (6-35) into the integral of (6-36), the following expression is obtained

$$T - T_0 = \text{const } e^{w_0 x/a}$$

which is similar to the known formula of V. A. Mikhel' son, first computed for the preheating of a gas in the preflame zone (32).

Shown on Figure 6-8, schematically, are the curves $\Phi(\varphi)$ and $\psi(\varphi_1; \eta_0)$ as a function of φ. Shown by dashes on Figure 6-8 are the integral curves $\psi(\varphi, \eta)$ for $\eta = \eta_0$ and, therefore, not satisfying the boundary condition $\psi = 0$ for $\varphi = 0$; also shown is the conditional curve for $\eta = 0$ and the direction of growth of the parameter η.

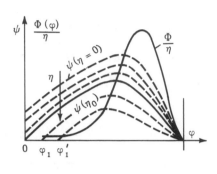

Fig. 6-8

In order to obtain a unique solution in conformance with an investigation of (6-38) and the above-mentioned physical considerations, $\Phi(\varphi) = 0$ should be taken at a certain finite value $\varphi = \varphi_1 > 0$. Results of numerical computations depend very slightly on the specific value of φ_1, as is seen, for example, on Figure 6-8 for two values of φ_1. This means that in practice the known arbitrariness in the selection of φ_1 is not felt in the final results of the computations.

Let us note than an investigation of (6-38) shows that it has an innumerable set of solutions for $\Phi(\varphi) > 0$ for any value of $\varphi > 0$ as small as desired, and $\Phi(\varphi) = 0$ just at $\varphi = 0$; the integral curves $\psi(\varphi, \eta)$ for any value of η (starting from a certain minimum value $\eta_{min} = \eta_0$, which agrees with the exact solution of the equation) pass through the point $\varphi = 0$; $\psi = 0$. We shall not present the proof,[15] since the physical meaning of introducing the finite segment $0 < \varphi < \varphi_1$ on which the reaction rate is $\Phi(\varphi) = 0$ was discussed in detail above, and the uniqueness of the solution for $\Phi(\varphi) = 0$ in the interval $0 < \varphi < \varphi_1$ was proven rigorously.

Zel' dovich in (18) considers a similar equation for the propagation of an isothermal chain reaction whose rate is proportional to the quantity of final product being formed during the process, and he also discusses the solution of the thermal problem in the absence of similarity between the J and h fields ($a \neq D$ case) as well as discussing the progress of several reactions, in parallel or successively, under the condition that the concentrations of the

---

[15] See Kolmogorov, Petrovskii, and Piskunov (26) for an exact mathematical investigation of (6-38) for different kinds of functions $\Phi(\varphi)$.

different substances are not related by algebraic relations. These questions, just as a number of mathematical details related to the above-mentioned investigation of (6-38), will not be considered here.

In this same (18), Zel' dovich presents an approximate formula for the flame propagation rate for the most interesting practical case of a strong exothermal reaction for which the function $\Phi(\varphi)$ has a comparatively sharp maximum near $\varphi = 1$ and, therefore, the basic quantity of substance reacts near the maximum temperature

$$\eta_0 = \sqrt{2 \int_0^1 \Phi(\varphi) \, d\varphi}$$

which agrees with earlier approximate formulas (16). The expression (6-40) for a power-concentration dependence of the reaction rate can be transformed by using a series expansion of the exponential (see section 3-3) near the maximum temperature

$$w_0 \approx \sqrt{\frac{a}{\tau_K'}} \approx \text{const} \sqrt{\frac{a}{\tau_K}} \, e^{-E/RT_m}$$

i.e., into formula (6-6).

Let us present some brief conclusions.

Normal flame propagation occurs because of heat transmission by heat conduction from the burning gas to the fresh mixture. Stationary combustion for given mixture characteristics occurs for just one value of the flame propagation rate. In the $a = D$ case, i.e., for identical values of the thermal-diffusion and molecular-diffusion coefficients, the temperature (for variable specific heat-heat content) and concentration fields are similar; the total gas enthalpy remains constant along the whole extent of the flame front in the absence of losses. An analytic solution of the stationary problem of flame propagation in the $a = D$ case is possible in closed form, in the course of which it is necessary to consider the reaction rate (absent, in practice, in the region of low values of the temperature) identically zero in a certain temperature range near the initial value. The specific magnitude of this interval affects the results of the computation slightly; according to the physical content of the operation, the cutoff of the low-temperature region does not mean a return to the old theory based on a constant ignition temperature independent of the physical arrangement of the process. The most general expression for the flame propagation rate is

$$w_{fl} \approx \sqrt{\frac{a}{\tau_K'}}$$

The investigation of the one-dimensional normal combustion equation explained in this paragraph is of great theoretical as well as practical value, in connection with the experimental investigations of the behavior of various combustible mixtures. It shows the difficulties with which an analytic solution of apparently even the simplest problems of thermal combustion theory is related. Its rigor (taking into account the temperature dependence of the physical constants, etc.) corresponds to comparatively high accuracy of the experimental method of measuring the normal combustion rate. Moreover, the problem considered is also of interest because it shows the suitability of simpler, approximate methods of investigation in order to estimate the behavior of phenomena and the fundamental characteristic quantities.

When heat emission (through the walls of the tube) is taken into account, as Zel'dovich showed (13a), the limits of flame propagation in narrow tubes, which are substantially the appropriate extinction phenomena, are successfully determined. The temperature in the flame for the extinction region drops by the order of magnitude $\theta_m - \theta_e \approx \theta_m^2$ (section 3-3). Taking radiation into account is essential for concentration limits of propagation.

The basic result of these investigations reduces to the flame being propagated along the combustible mixture not being able to be cooled strongly by means of heat elimination; weak heat elimination leads to a certain reduction in the combustion temperature; strong enough heat elimination leads to extinction—its abrupt collapse.

Hence, the picture of the phenomenon is in complete agreement with the peculiarities of the thermal region of strongly exothermal reactions considered above.

6-4. ON LOCAL REDISTRIBUTION OF THE TOTAL ENERGY IN THE FLAME ZONE

In Chapter 3, in the consideration of the thermal region of heterogeneous combustion, and in section 6-2 in connection with the basic equations of heat conduction and diffusion, the case was considered when the coefficients of molecular heat and matter transport were interrelated by the relation (6-19) $a = D$.

Now let us analyze qualitatively certain peculiarities of the thermal process when the temperature-conduction and diffusion coefficients are unequal.

Let us start with the heterogeneous process (11, 50) and let us be limited only to the question of the maximum combustion temperature, i.e., to the temperature of the reaction surface of the solid phase for $a = D$.

The expression (3-11) obtained in section 3-2 relates the coefficient of the completeness of gas combustion φ to the temperature in the form

$$\varphi = \frac{\alpha}{\alpha_D \, q c_0} \, (T - T_0)$$

where q and c_p (see below) are the heat productivity and specific heat per cubic meter of gas.

As has been shown there (see section 3-2), the ratio of the heat-transfer coefficient α to the gas-transfer coefficient α_D can be expressed by (3-13) according to empirical data on convective heat transfer and diffusion (33, 41)

$$\frac{\alpha}{\alpha_D} = c_p \left(\frac{a}{D} \right)^{1-m}$$

From this formula, there follows for $a = D$

$$\varphi = \frac{c_p}{q c_0} \, (T - T_0), \quad \varphi = \frac{T - T_0}{T_m - T_0}$$

$$T_m = T_0 + q \, \frac{c_0}{c_p}$$

and, therefore, the temperature and concentration fields are similar.

Denoting $(D/a)^{1-m} = \mu$ as before in the $a \neq D$ case, we obtain

$$\varphi = \mu \, \frac{c_p}{q c_0} \, (T - T_0)$$

or

$$T_m = T_0 + \mu \, \varphi \, \frac{q c_0}{c_p} ; \quad T_{\varphi = 1} = T_0 + \mu \, \frac{q c_0}{c_p}$$

In the limiting case of complete burn-up of the reacting gas at $\varphi = 1$ (i.e., in the diffusion combustion region when $c = 0$, $\varphi = 1$ on the surface of the solid phase), the maximum combustion temperature $T_{\varphi = 1}$, which equals in the adiabatic process the temperature of the solid-phase surface, appears to be not equal to the quantity $T_m = T_0 + (q c_0 / c_p)$ (called the theoretical combustion temperature in thermal engineering).

In particular, in the case $a > D$ (the temperature-conduction coefficient is larger than the diffusion coefficient)

$$T_{\varphi = 1} < T_m$$

the maximum combustion temperature is less than the theoretical; for $a < D$, correspondingly

$$T_{\varphi = 1} > T_m$$

the maximum combustion temperature is higher than the theoretical; finally, in the $a = D$ case only will

$$T_{\varphi=1} = T_m$$

the maximum and theoretical values of the temperature agree.

The physical explanation of the inequality in the values of $T_{\varphi=1}$ and T_m in the $a \neq D$ case is the following: A reaction occurs on the surface of the solid phase in the scheme of the heterogeneous process used.[16] Because of the reaction proceeding on the surface and the disappearance of the initial material, a concentration distribution is built up in the boundary layer (a drop in c in a direction toward the surface for the initial material, and a rise for a finite reaction product). Simultaneously, because of heat liberation on the surface, there is also established a counter temperature distribution (with respect to the reacting gas) which drops with distance from the surface. For $a \neq D$ (or $\alpha \neq \alpha_D c_p$), the possible heat and material transports for identical values of the temperature and concentration gradients are not mutually equal, consequently, the temperature and concentration fields must be dissimilar; the difference in the local values of the gradients of T and c seems to compensate the difference in the values of a and D. This same result can be represented approximately as the difference in the conditional thicknesses of the thermal and diffusion boundary layers. In the $a > D$ case, the conditional thickness of the first (thermal), i.e., the region of notable change in the temperature, is larger than in the diffusion, i.e., the region of notable change in concentration. The reciprocal relation is established in the $a < D$ case (for example, for catalytic heterogeneous combustion of lean hydrogen mixtures on platinum (5, 6)). Finally, for $a = D$ the thicknesses of thermal and diffusion layers agree. These representations of the effective thickness of the boundary layer are approximate since, actually, the distribution curves are asymptotic.

The change in the heat content $J = \int c\, dT$ (for the $c \neq$ const case) and in the chemical enthalpy $h = qc$ is shown schematically on Figure 6-9 for three cases, $a > D$; $a = D$; and $a < D$.

In connection with the absence of similarity in the J and h fields for $a \neq D$ fields, the total mixture enthalpy $H = J + h$ in the boundary layer near the surface does not remain constant. Far from the surface for all the cases $(a \lessgtr D)$

$$J = J_0; \quad h = h_0; \quad \text{and} \quad H = h_0 + J_0 = H_0$$

[16] It is understood that we speak of the physical and not the mathematical surface, i.e., of a thin surface layer. The thickness of this surface for coal and other porous bodies increases as the temperature drops and as the reaction rate drops in connection with the penetration of the reacting gas in coal pores (20, 34).

In the $a > D$ case, in connection with the earlier beginning of the temperature rise rather than with the drop in the concentration as the surface is approached, the quantity H passes through a maximum at the external boundary of a boundary layer and a minimum on the surface. The surface temperature is less than T_m. For $a < D$, the total enthalpy at the boundary of the layer is a minimum; the temperature of the latter $T_{\varphi = 1}$ is larger than the value $T_m = T_0 + (qc_0/c_p)$. Only in the $a = D$ case where there is compliance in the whole layer with the equality

$$H = J + h = H_0 = \text{const}$$

does the surface temperature $T_{\varphi = 1}$ agree with the quantity T_m.

Simplifying the phenomenon, it can be explained as follows: In the $a > D$ case, when the possible heat-elimination rate is greater than the possible rate of supplying the active gas for identical gradients of T and c, the stationary drop in the temperature between the surface of the solid phase and the gas far from it is reduced somewhat in comparison with the $a = D$ case, and for $a < D$ (i.e., for a possible heat-elimination rate less than the gas supply) it is

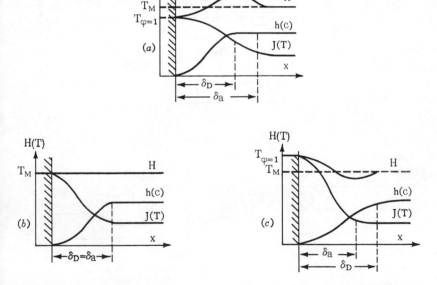

Fig. 6-9. Diagram of the temperature (heat content), concentration (chemical enthalpy), and total enthalpy of the reacting gas distributions on the surface of the solid phase. (a) $a > D$ case; (b) $a = D$; (c) $a < D$ case; δ_D —conditional thickness of the diffusion boundary layer; δ_a —conditional thickness of the heat-transfer boundary layer.

raised somewhat; in all cases, naturally, the law of energy conservation is retained both in the whole (integrally) and also in any element of the boundary layer.

Similar relations also occur in the flame front during the combustion of a well-mixed mixture (11, 13a, 14). This follows mathematically from the system of heat-conduction and -diffusion differential Eqs. (6-21) and (6-22) not reducing to a single equation for $a = D$. The quantity $H_0 = J_0 + h_0 = $ const is no longer an integral of the system; the condition $H_0 = $ const is observed far from the flame front in the region of a cold gas and in the region of the products of complete combustion, and is violated within the flame front. The appropriate curves of the changes in H, J, and h are shown schematically on Figure 6-10 for the cases $a > D$, $a = D$, $a < D$. In the first, when $a > D$ (Figure 6-10a), the total enthalpy of the mixture H passes through a maximum in the region of the cold gas and through a minimum near complete combustion. In the second case, for $a = D$ (Figure 6-10b), as follows from the exact solution (section 6-2, formula (6-28)), $H = H_0 = $ const in the whole front; the curves J and H are similar. Finally, in the $a < D$ case (Figure 6-10c), the total enthalpy H is a minimum in the region of

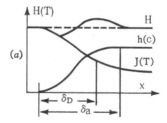

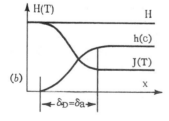
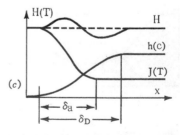

Fig. 6-10. Diagram of the temperature (heat content), concentration (chemical enthalpy) and total enthalpy distribution in a flame front. (a) $a > D$ case; (b) $a = D$ case; (c) $a < D$ case; δ_a —conditional thickness of the thermal front; δ_D —conditional thickness of the diffusion front.

the cold gas and a maximum near completed combustion.[17] Just as in the previous case, the extremal form of the total enthalpy curve $H = H(x)$ is related to the inequality in the rates of heat and mass transport; because of this inequality the conditional thicknesses of the thermal and diffusion boundary layers (δ_a and δ_D on Figures 6-9 and 6-10) are also different.

Ia. B. Zel' dovich (14) indicated the error made by Lewis and Elbe (30), who assumed that the condition H = const, the equality of the total enthalpy in all the gas layers in the flame front, is a consequence of the energy-conservation law (and to its being related to the diffusion of active centers from the flame zone into the fresh mixture). As has been shown above, H = const in the flame front for $a = D$; the equality H = const is a result of a definite kinetic transport mechanism ($a = D$) and similarity of the boundary conditions. As regards the conservation of the law of the conservation of energy then, it is guaranteed (both integrally and also for any layer of the flame front) by the initial differential equations which are none other than one of the forms of writing the energy-conservation law applied to the process under consideration. Moreover, postulating H = const, Lewis and Elbe enter the $a \neq D$ case precisely in contradiction to the energy-conservation law, since the quantity of thermal and chemical enthalpy transported through every gas layer in opposite directions in this case (chemical enthalpy to the front and thermal enthalpy against the front), when the J and h fields are similar and $a \neq D$, should not be equal.

Without going into the details of the question, let us also note that, as Zel' dovich mentioned (13a, 14), the great difference between the molecular weights of the mixture components also affects the dependence of the flame propagation limit on the place where the mixture kindles (above or below) during combustion in vertical pipes. The concentration limit in lean hydrogen mixtures is broader for flame propagation upward when the predominance of D over a is expressed (see section 3-21). Apparently (13a) the flame is not propagated along a continuous front in this case, but by individual spheres on the surface of which the combustion proceeds according to a diffusion mechanism. For a clearer comprehension of the substance of the local redistribution of the local enthalpy which arises for $a \neq D$, it is interesting to note the physical analogy of the process considered here to the phenomenon

[17] On Fig. 6-10, in contrast to the curves presented by Zel' dovich (13a, 14) two extrema (maximum and minimum) of the total enthalpy are shown in both cases ($a = D$). The first extremum, at the beginning of the combustion zone where there is practically no reaction, is of substantial value; the second, near the maximum temperature, is not if it is much extended.

encountered in rapidly flowing gas streams (11). Briefly, we speak of the following: When an adiabatically insulated body is introduced in a gas flow, near the surface of a body a boundary layer forms in which the value of the velocity drops to zero. This deceleration is related to viscous (and turbulent) friction and is accompanied by the transformation of the kinetic energy into heat. The heat liberated in the boundary layer is eliminated therefrom by molecular conduction and by turbulent heat transfer. Hence, we also speak here of two kinetic processes—momentum transport and heat transport. The ratio of the rates of these processes, as in the combustion case, can be expressed by the ratio of the coefficients of temperature conduction a and kinematic viscosity ν (for molecular transport and the appropriate effective values a_{turb} and ν_{turb} for turbulent transport). The total enthalpy H is composed in this case of the heat content J and the kinetic energy $E_k = A(w^2/2gc_p)$

$$H = J + E_k$$

(the total temperature[18]

$$T_* = T + Aw^2/2gc_p = T + \Delta T_w$$

where ΔT_w, the increment in the temperature caused by the deceleration, is usually introduced into the consideration for the c_p = const case).

Shown schematically on Figure 6-11 are various cases of distributions of H, J, and E_k in the boundary layer at the surface of the body (11). In complete analogy with heterogeneous combustion, the case $a > \nu$ corresponds to a temperature, reduced in comparison to the total flow temperature, of an adiabatically insulated body. This case ($\nu < a$, for example, air) is typical for the measurement of the temperature at high air speeds when the meter (the thermocouple, etc.), indicates a temperature which is the average between the actual T and the total T_* (11, 29). In principle a reciprocal relation, the meter temperature higher than the total gas temperature, should be observed for $a > \nu$. Finally the body temperature for $a = D$ agrees with the gas stagnation temperature. As in the combustion case, similar relations also occur in the gas flow far from the body surface, in the region of a sharp velocity gradient and (in connection with the transformation of the kinetic energy into heat) a temperature gradient.[19]

---

[18] The so-called stagnation temperature rise (see (10) and also section 7-3).

[19] For example, shown on Fig. 6-11d is a distribution of H, J, and E_k in laminar or turbulent free compressible jets for $\nu < a$ (air, free turbulence in gases). As is seen from the graph, more rapid air jets seem to exhaust the energy of the less rapid.

It is understood that the local energy-redistribution phenomenon (more exactly, enthalpy) observed in the gas flow between separate jets also does not in the least contradict the energy-conservation law, which is here observed: the total enthalpy of the flow remains constant both integrally and also differentially for any gas element.

In all cases (Figures 6-8, 6-11), a local redistribution of the complete enthalpy is outwardly expressed as if in the "entrainment" of the excess energy by the flow, corresponding to a larger transport rate for equal gradients. Consequently a minimum in the complete enthalpy H is established in the region of the complete process, and a maximum in the region of its start if the possible heat-elimination rate is larger than the material transport rate $(a > D)$ or the momentum transport rate $(a > \nu)$. When the heat supply "lags" in comparison with the diffusion $(a < D)$ or viscosity $(a < \nu)$, the extrema of the complete enthalpy exchange places (the minimum of H is established at the start of the process, the maximum near completion). The complete enthalpy is constant in the whole region only for $a = D$ (or $a = \nu$); the fields of the heat content and the chemical (or kinetic) energy are similar.

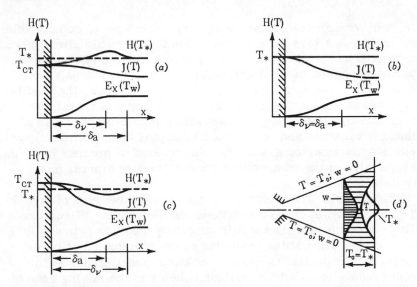

Fig. 6-11. Diagram of the distribution of heat content (temperature), kinetic energy, and total heat content (stagnation temperature) in a compressible gas flow. Boundary layer of an adiabatically insulated body. (a) $a > \nu$; (b) $a = \nu$; (c) $a < \nu$; δ_a—thermal boundary layer; δ_ν—dynamic boundary layer; (d) $\nu < a$ for a free jet of a compressible gas (flow from a reservoir in which the temperature equals the temperature of the surrounding medium).

As already remarked in section 3-2 (and as is seen from the above-mentioned references to experiments with lean hydrogen-air mixtures), the inequality in the coefficients $a \neq D$ is expressed especially clearly near the critical ignition and extinction conditions, in particular, near the limits of the flame propagation (13a, 50). Let us note that this same phenomenon can be one of the reasons for the difference in the combustion process of lean and rich mixtures of identical heat productivity. Evidently, the inversion in the sign of the inequality $a \neq D$ will correspond to such mixtures for a transition from lean to rich, in one case (for example, in a lean mixture) the effective value of the mixture heat productivity $\vartheta_{eff} = \mu\vartheta$ will be larger than the real, in the other (corresponding to a rich mixture) it will be less. The effect under consideration can hardly be of substantial value for combustion in technical apparatus; in particular, for the turbulent combustion of a well-mixed mixture, since the effective values of the turbulent diffusion and turbulent temperature conduction coefficients agree in practice $a_{turb} = D_{turb}$ (see section 7-2).

6-5. LAMINAR COMBUSTION OF UNMIXED GASES

A laminar diffusion flame, occurring when a jet of combustible gas, flowing at a very slow speed, is kindled in an air atmosphere, can be used as an elementary example of a furnace process with separated supplies of the combustible mixture components, fuel and oxidizer. The simplest match and candle flames; the kindling of a gas in actual heating instruments or furnace burners; the combustion of wood, shale, or coal with a high content of volatile elements; all these and many other examples of the combustion of preliminarily unmixed gases refer to one kind of process in which the formation of the combustible mixture occurs simultaneously with its combustion.

Mixing occurs in real combustion chambers because of turbulent diffusion; analysis of the phenomenon is also made difficult essentially by a complex and as a rule generally unknown primary fuel and air distribution at the beginning of the chamber.[20] Consequently, it is expedient to explain the basic peculiarities of the process by a simplified combustion scheme in the mixing zone of two laminar gas flows (fuel and air) when the heat and material (diffusion) transport is accomplished by a molecular mechanism.

The presence in the furnace space of separate regions, with a predominant content of one of the gases and the practical absence

---

[20] In particular during the kindling of liquid fuel (25).

of the others, is typical for combustion of unmixed gases. These regions are mutually separated by a narrow flame zone in which both mixture components coexist and burn and to which the diffusion flows of the original substances are directed. The heat and combustion products are propagated from the flame zone into the unmixed gas region. In the limit, for very rapid combustion, i.e., for high reaction rate, the flame zone is such a very thin layer that it can be considered as a mathematical surface in the solution of the problem. This limiting case, to which zero values of the reacting gas concentrations on the surface of separation correspond, is naturally called "diffusion combustion."

Let us note that the representation of the diffusion flame front as a surface on which a stoichiometric mixture ($a = 1$) burns instantaneously is quite reasonable. Actually, if it is assumed that the concentration of one of the reacting gases does not become zero on the combustion surface, then a combustible mixture will be formed on each side of the front, in which the second component (19, 41) would be burned up under high-temperature conditions without reaching the flame front. Hence, the front would be shifted to a single stable position for which the reacting gas concentrations are zero, and the flows of both components diffusing to the front are found to be in a stoichiometric relation. The width of the combustion zone becomes finite for comparatively slow combustion; the values of the concentrations of the reacting gases never become zero simultaneously.

Relations between the temperature and concentration will be analyzed below for the combustion of unmixed gases, in most detail for the diffusion combustion case. For the latter, it is not difficult also to find the equation of the interface (the diffusion flame front) for the simplest problems.

In conclusion, certain of the simplest considerations on the thermal combustion region and the inherent critical conditions will be explained. Since the peculiarities of the process and the description of the equations for the case of variable constants (c_p, D, etc.) were analyzed in detail in sections 6-2 and 6-3, let us be limited here to the simplest case of constant physical gas properties (the extension of the results to the c_p = const case, etc., is not difficult).

Let us analyze the simplest diagram of a diffusion gas burner (Figure 6-12), consisting of a cylindrical chamber to which the combustible gases are supplied by two coaxial tubes. Let us assume that the gas "T" (conditionally, the fuel) is presented to the burner along the inner tube of radius r and the gas "O" (conditionally the oxidizer) along the external pipe of radius R. Let us

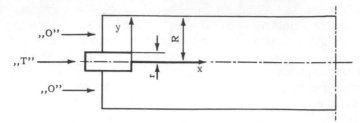

Fig. 6-12. Diagram of a diffusion burner.

assume the initial concentrations of both gases to be c_{T_0} and c_{O_0}, respectively; similarly, the initial temperatures to be T_{T_0} and T_{O_0}; we assume the velocities of both flows to be identical and equal to w. Let us also assume that the thermal diffusion constant $k_T = 0$ for both gases and the values of all the mutual diffusion coefficients (the combustible gases in each other, in the combustion products or inert gases) are identical and equal to the temperature-conduction coefficient $D_1 = D_2 = D = a$.

Let us consider the process stationary ($\partial/\partial\tau = 0$).

Under these assumptions, let us write the diffusion equation for each of the gases as[21]

$$w \frac{\partial c_T}{\partial x} = D \left[\frac{\partial^2 c_T}{\partial x^2} + \frac{1}{y} \frac{\partial}{\partial y} \left(y \frac{\partial c_T}{\partial y} \right) \right] - W_T \qquad (6\text{-}42)$$

for the gas "T"; similarly

$$\frac{w \, \partial c_O}{\partial x} = D \left[\frac{\partial^2 c_O}{\partial x^2} + \frac{1}{y} \frac{\partial}{\partial y} \left(y \frac{\partial c_O}{\partial y} \right) \right] - W_O \qquad (6\text{-}43)$$

for the gas "O" and the heat-conduction equation

$$w \frac{\partial T}{\partial x} = \alpha \left[\frac{\partial^2 T}{\partial x^2} + \frac{1}{y} \frac{\partial}{\partial y} \left(y \frac{\partial T}{\partial y} \right) \right] + W \frac{q_0}{c_p} \qquad (6\text{-}44)$$

where q_0 is the heat productivity of 1 kg of a stoichiometric mixture ($\alpha = 1$) of the gases "T" and "O."

Let us write the boundary conditions for all three equations together. In the initial section

[21] Equations (6-42) to (6-44) are written in a cylindrical coordinate system for the axisymmetric problem; for the plane problem (i.e., for channels very extended in a direction normal to the plane of the sketch on Fig. 6-12), $\partial^2/\partial y^2$ appears in the right side of the equation instead of

$$\frac{1}{y} \frac{\partial}{\partial y} \left(y \frac{\partial}{\partial y} \right) = \frac{\partial^2}{\partial y^2} + \frac{1}{y} \frac{\partial}{\partial y}$$

Boundary conditions (6-45) to (6-47) are identical for both problems.

$$0 \leqslant y \leqslant r; \quad c_T = c_{T_0}; \quad c_0 = 0; \quad T = T_{T_0} \Big\}$$
$$r \leqslant y \leqslant R; \quad c_T = 0; \quad c_0 = c_{O_0}; \quad T = T_{O_0} \Big\} \text{ for } x = 0 \tag{6-45}$$

From symmetry conditions on the axis

$$\frac{\partial c_T}{\partial y} = 0 = \frac{\partial c_O}{\partial y} = \frac{\partial T}{\partial y} \quad \text{for } y = 0 \tag{6-46}$$

Finally, from the condition of the impermeability of the outer surface to matter and heat (adiabatic gas-impermeable shell) we have on this surface

$$\frac{\partial c_T}{\partial y} = \frac{\partial c_O}{\partial y} = \frac{\partial T}{\partial y} = 0 \quad \text{for } y = R \tag{6-47}$$

As before, let us introduce the stoichiometric characteristic of the reaction χ_O, whose value is the number of kilograms of gas "O" reacting with 1 kg of gas "T." Using χ_O, let us interrelate all the values of the reaction rate in (6-42) to (6-44), namely: W_T is the reaction rate of the gas "T"; W_O of the gas "O," and W is the total quantity of the stoichiometric mixture reacting in unit time in unit space. Evidently

$$W = W_T + W_O = W_T(1 + \chi_O) - W_O \frac{1 + \chi_O}{\chi_O};$$

$$W_T = \frac{W_O}{\chi_O} \tag{6-48}$$

In order to find the distribution of all the values of the concentrations of both reacting gases c_T and c_O (as well as of the combustion products) and of the temperature, the three nonlinear Eqs. (6-42) to (6-44) should be integrated for the appropriate boundary conditions (6-45) to (6-47). The identity of these equations permits us, however, to be limited to the integration of just one of them, and of one linear equation without a term dependent on the reaction rate.

Let us first reduce the three Eqs. (6-42) to (6-44) to one general equation corresponding, substantially, to the condition of conserving the total mixture enthalpy. For this purpose, let us introduce the new variable z as a linear combination of the quantities c_T, c_O, and T selected so that the equation obtained would not contain the reaction rate.

It is evident from (6-48) that the expression

$$\zeta W_T + (1 - \zeta) \frac{W_O}{\chi_O} - \frac{W}{1 + \chi_O} \equiv 0$$

is identically zero for any value of the constant ζ. In conformance with this the choice of the new variable z as

$$z = \zeta c_T + (1 - \zeta) \frac{c_O}{\chi_O} + \frac{c_p T}{q_0 (1 + \chi_O)} \tag{6-49}$$

for any value of ζ permits[22] the following new linear equation to be obtained for z after multiplying (6-42) by ζ, (6-43) by $(1 - \zeta)/\chi_O$, and (6-44) by $c_p/[q_0(1 + \chi_O)]$

$$w \frac{dz}{dx} = D \left[\frac{\partial^2 z}{\partial x^2} + \frac{1}{y} \frac{\partial}{\partial y} \left(y \frac{dx}{dy} \right) \right] \tag{6-50}$$

which does not contain a term with the expression for the reaction rate.

Let us impose an additional condition on the constant ζ in the form of the values of z at the input to the chamber being equal

$$z = z_0 \, (0 \leqslant y \leqslant r) \equiv z_0 \, (r \leqslant y \leqslant R) \quad \text{for } x = 0$$

Taking (6-45) into account, this means

$$z = z_0 = \zeta c_{T0} + \frac{c_p T_{T0}}{q_0 (1 + \chi_O)} = (1 - \zeta) \frac{c_{O0}}{\chi_O} + \frac{c_p T_{O0}}{q_0 (1 + \chi_O)}$$

from which

$$\zeta = \frac{\dfrac{c_{O0}}{\chi_O} + \dfrac{c_p (T_{O0} - T_{T0})}{q_0 (1 + \chi_O)}}{\chi_O c_{T0} + c_{O0}} \tag{6-51}$$

Therefore, the new variable z is defined uniquely by means of the old variables c_T, c_O, and T and their boundary values.

The boundary conditions for (6-50) will be written as

$$z = z_0 \qquad \text{for } x = 0$$

$$\frac{\partial z}{\partial y} = 0 \qquad \text{for } y = 0 \text{ and } y = R \tag{6-52}$$

Equation (6-50) and boundary conditions (6-52) are satisfied by the simple integral

---

[22] The values $\zeta = 0$ and $\zeta = 1$ should be discarded in the general case since one of the Eqs. (6-42) or (6-43) drops out with them. In the expression for z, the sign before the last term is changed in comparison with the identity $\zeta W_T + (1 - \zeta)(W_O/\chi_O) - W/(1 + \chi_O)$ since the quantity $Q = Wq_0$, the rate of heat liberation, enters in the heat-conduction Eq. (6-44) with a sign opposite to the sign of W_T and W_O (rate of gas consumption) in the diffusion equations (see (19) also).

$$z = z_0 = \text{const}; \qquad \frac{z}{z_0} = 1 \qquad (6\text{-}53)$$

Actually, the quantity z is distributed uniformly in the flow in the initial section of the channel, sources and sinks of magnitude z are absent in the whole space and on its boundaries, the system is isolated from the surrounding medium, and the reaction occurring leads to a mutual redistribution of the physical and chemical enthalpy but does not alter their total.

Let us use the result obtained in a more simple case when both the "T" and the "O" gases at the chamber input have the same temperature

$$T_{T0} = T_{O0} = T_0$$

In this case, it is possible to write instead of (6-53)

$$T = T_0 + \frac{c_{O0} c_{T0}}{\chi_O c_{T0} + c_{O0}} \cdot \frac{q_0 (1 + \chi_O)}{c_p} \left[1 - \left(\frac{c_T}{c_{T0}} + \frac{c_O}{c_{O0}} \right) \right] \qquad (6\text{-}54)$$

or

$$\frac{T - T_0}{T_m - T_0} = 1 - \left(\frac{c_T}{c_{T0}} + \frac{c_O}{c_{O0}} \right) \qquad (6\text{-}54')$$

We used the following notation in the last expression

$$T_m - T_0 = \frac{c_{T0} \cdot c_{O0}}{\chi_O c_{T0} + c_{O0}} \frac{q_0}{c_p} (1 + \chi_O) \qquad (6\text{-}55)$$

It is not difficult to show that the factor in front of the square brackets in the right side of (6-54) is actually the maximum preheating of the gases for total combustion of a stoichiometric mixture. For example, let us assume that the combustion occurred of 1 kg of "O" gas with which $1/\chi_O$ kg of "T" gas entered into reaction. As a result $1 + (1/\chi_O) = (1 + \chi_O)/\chi_O$ of the stoichiometric mixture of the pure "T" and "O" substances took part in the reaction and, correspondingly, $q_0 [(1 + \chi_O)/\chi_O]$ kcal of heat was liberated. This quantity of heat is expended in heating $1/c_{O0}$ (original gas "O") and $1/\chi_O c_{T0}$ ("O" gas) of gas, i.e., $(1/c_{O0}) + (1/\chi_O c_{T0})$ kg of combustion products. The temperature rise under these conditions will equal the ratio $q_0 [(1 + \chi_O)/\chi_O] : c_p [(1/c_{O0}) + (1/\chi_O c_{T0})]$, i.e., the expression (6-55).

Hence, the combustion temperature on the flame surface agrees with the maximum combustion temperature of a well-mixed stoichiometric mixture for $c_T = c_O = 0$ during the rapid combustion of unmixed gases.

Equation (6-54') relates the temperature distribution in the whole field to the concentration distribution c_T and c_O of both reacting gases. The relation between the latter can be obtained if the expression of the reaction rate is eliminated by an analogous transformation from the diffusion Eqs. (6-42) and (6-43). Intending to do this later, let us introduce the new variable c as[23]

$$c = c_T - \frac{c_O}{\chi_O} \qquad (6\text{-}56)$$

When (6-43) is multiplied by $1/\chi_O$ and then subtracted term by term from (6-42), we obtain a linear equation for the variable c

$$w \frac{\partial c}{\partial x} = D \left[\frac{\partial^2 c}{\partial x^2} + \frac{1}{y} \frac{\partial}{\partial y} \left(y \frac{\partial c}{\partial y} \right) \right] \qquad (6\text{-}57)$$

with the boundary condition

$$\left. \begin{array}{ll} 0 \leqslant y \leqslant r; \quad c = c_T \\ r \leqslant y \leqslant R; \quad c = c_O/\chi_O \end{array} \right\} \text{ for } x = 0 \\ \frac{\partial c}{\partial y} = 0 \qquad\qquad \text{ for } y = 0 \text{ and } y = R \right\} \qquad (6\text{-}58)$$

The integral of this equation (see below) gives the relation between the variables c_T and c_O in the whole field. Finally, if one of the nonlinear Eqs. (6-42) to (6-44) is integrated for a specific form of the reaction rate expression as a function of the temperature and concentration, then the values of all the variables c_T, c_O, and T will be determined for any point of space.

---

[23] The method used in the well-known solution of Burke and Shuman (30) for the problem of diffusion combustion. These authors substantiate it (the substitution $c = c_T - c_O/\chi_O$) by the fact that the fuel can be considered as "negative oxygen." Such an explanation only obscures the substance of the question. The reaction rate is lacking for diffusion combustion in (6-24) and (6-43), consequently, any variable in the form of a linear combination of the quantities c_T and c_O reduces them to one equation. For example, introducing the variable $\bar{c} = c_{T/c_{To}} + c_{O/c_{Oo}}$, an equation identical with (6-57) can be obtained with simple and identical boundary conditions for both gases: $\bar{c} = 1$ for $x = 0$.

Use of the variable c from (6-56) in the case of a finite reaction rate and correspondingly, of finite width of the combustion zone, permits two nonlinear equations of diffusion to be replaced by one linear equation and to interrelate the values of c_T and c_O at any point of space.

See (19, 30, 42, 50) also on the relation between the concentration and temperature fields.

The problem is simplified substantially in the case of diffusion combustion when the chamber is divided into two regions by the flame-front surface ($c_T = 0$; $c_O = 0$; $T = T_m$), in one of which the gas "T" is lacking ($c_T = 0$) and the gas "O" in the other ($c_O = 0$).

For this case (for $T_{T_0} = T_{O_0} = T_0$),[24] we first obtain from (6-54')

$$\frac{T - T_O}{T_m - T_0} = \frac{c_T}{c_{T_0}} \quad \text{or} \quad \frac{T - T_O}{T_m - T_0} = \frac{c_O}{c_{O_0}}$$

respectively, for each of the two regions in which just the gas "T" or the gas "O" exists.

The temperature and concentration fields of each of the gases are similar. In order to find the distribution of each variable separately, in this case it is sufficient to integrate just one linear equation, for example (6-57). Substituting the value $c = 0$ ($c_T = c_O = 0$) in the solution obtained, the equation of the combustion surface can be obtained therefrom.

A number of conclusions about the latter can also be obtained, however, without this (13b, 50).

Let us neglect diffusion transport in the flow direction in (6-57) in comparison with its transverse transport, i.e., we assume

$$\frac{\partial^2 c}{\partial x^2} \ll \frac{\partial^2 c}{\partial y^2} + \frac{1}{y} \frac{\partial c}{\partial y}$$

in the axisymmetric problem or

$$\frac{\partial^2 c}{\partial x^2} \ll \frac{\partial^2 c}{\partial y^2}$$

in the plane problem. Such an assumption is sufficiently strict for not-too-short channels. Let us introduce the nondimensional coordinates

$$\bar{x} = \frac{Dx}{wR^2} \quad \text{and} \quad \bar{y} = \frac{y}{R}$$

after which (6-57) becomes

$$\frac{\partial c}{\partial x} = \frac{1}{\bar{y}} \frac{\partial}{\partial \bar{y}} \left(\bar{y} \frac{\partial c}{\partial \bar{y}} \right) \tag{6-59}$$

Let us rewrite the boundary conditions, respectively, as

---

[24] The case of different initial gas temperatures ($T_{T_0} \neq T_{O_0}$) is also investigated easily by using the above-mentioned formulas.

$$\left.\begin{array}{ll} 0 \leqslant \bar{y} \leqslant \dfrac{r}{R}; & c = c_{T_0} \\[2ex] \dfrac{r}{R} \leqslant \bar{y} \leqslant 1; & c = -\dfrac{c_{O_0}}{\chi_O} \end{array}\right\} \quad \text{for } \bar{x} = 0 \qquad (6\text{-}60)$$

$$\frac{\partial c}{\partial \bar{y}} = 0 \qquad\qquad \text{for } \bar{y} = 0 \text{ and } \bar{y} = 1$$

The integral of (6-59), taking (6-60) into account, can be written as the functional dependence

$$c = c\left(\bar{x}, \bar{y}, \frac{r}{R}\right)$$

For a given value of the parameter r/R, the geometric burner characteristic, a relation between the ordinate of the flame front $\bar{y}_f = y_{fl}/R$ and the reduced length $\bar{x}_f = \bar{x}_{fl}/R$, i.e., a dependence such as

$$\bar{y}_{fl} = \bar{y}(\bar{x}_{fl}) \quad \text{or} \quad \bar{x}_{fl} = \bar{x}(\bar{y}_{fl})$$

evidently corresponds to the condition $c = 0$ $(c_T = c_O = 0)$; here $\bar{x}_f$ and $\bar{y}_f$ are nondimensional coordinates of points of the combustion surface.

Let us determine the flame length as a function of the burner radius from this expression to the accuracy of a constant factor dependent on the parameter r/R and the initial gas concentrations. We shall understand the distance $x = x_0$ from the chamber mouth $(x = 0)$ to that point of the flame front where combustion is completed to be the flame length. Let us note that two kinds of flame-front shapes are possible under the conditions of the diffusion process for an initial surplus of the gas "O" or its inadequacy with respect to the stoichiometric relation. In the first case, the flame front for a lean mixture is enfolded within the region of the gas "T" and will terminate on the burner axis (Figure 6-13a); in the second case, for a rich mixture, the flame front will be inclined to the periphery and will terminate on the outer wall (Figure 6-13b). Consequently, either the equality $\bar{y}_{fl} = 0$, i.e., $y_{fl}(x_0) = 0$ or $\bar{y}_{fl} = 1$, i.e., $y_{fl}(x_0) = R$, corresponds to the end of the flame. In both cases, there follows for the end of the flame from the dependence $\bar{x}_f = \bar{x}(\bar{y}_f)$

$$\bar{x}_0 = \text{const}; \qquad \frac{Dx_0}{wR^2} = \text{const}$$

and therefore

$$\bar{x}_0 \sim \frac{wR}{D} \qquad\qquad\qquad (6\text{-}61)$$

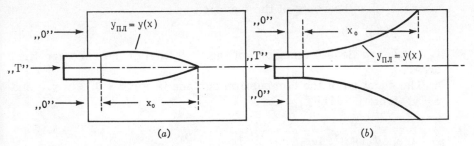

Fig. 6-13. Diffusion flame front. (a) Excess oxygen; (b) inadequate oxygen.

i.e., the flame length is directly proportional to the gas rate and to the square of the burner dimension (for r/R = const) and inversely proportional to the diffusion coefficient; the nondimensional flame length x/R proportional to the number $R = wd/\nu$ (assuming $\nu \approx D$).

Let us note that the condition $\bar{x}_0 = (D/wR)(x_0/R)$ = const (usual for laminar problems) (33, 42) refers to both the axisymmetric and the plane problems. The difference between them becomes noticeable if a dependence of the flame length on the burner dimension for a constant gas discharge per second is obtained from this condition. The gas discharge for a circular burner is $v \approx wR^2$ and for a plane is $v \approx wR$. Correspondingly, for a circular burner, the flame length

$$x_0 \approx \frac{v}{D} \tag{6-62}$$

for the constant discharge, v = const, is independent of the dimension and for a plane burner

$$x_0 \approx \frac{vR}{D} \tag{6-63}$$

the flame length for v = const is proportional to the burner dimension. The value of the constant factors in these equalities is determined from the solution of (6-59). According to Burke and Schuman (30), the latter can be represented as follows:

The distribution of the concentration c is expressed for a circular burner by the formula

$$\frac{\chi_0 c + c_{O_0}}{\chi_0 c_{T_0} + c_{O_0}} = \frac{r^2}{R^2}\left[1 + 2\frac{R}{r}\sum_{i=1}^{\infty}\frac{J_1\left(\mu_i\frac{r}{R}\right)J_0\left(\mu_i\frac{y}{R}\right)}{\mu_i J_0^2(\mu_i)}e^{-\mu_1^2 Dx/wR^2}\right] \tag{6-64}$$

where μ_i are the roots of the equation

$$J_1(\mu_i) = 0$$

J_0 and J_1 are Bessel functions of the first kind of the zero and first order.

The equation of the combustion surface is for $c = 0$, $x = x_{fl}$, and $y = y_{fl}$ from (6-64)

$$\sum_{i=1}^{\infty} \frac{J_1\left(\mu_i \frac{r}{R}\right) J_0\left(\mu_i \frac{y_{fl}}{R}\right)}{\mu_i J_0^2(\mu_i)} e^{-\mu_i^2 \frac{Dx_{fl}}{wR^2}}$$

$$= \frac{R}{2r}\left(\frac{c_{Oo}}{\chi_O c_{To} + c_{Oo}} - \frac{r}{R^2}\right) \tag{6-65}$$

For the plane problem, the concentration distribution c is expressed in terms of trigonometric functions

$$\frac{\chi_O c + c_{Oo}}{\chi_O c_{To} + c_{Oo}}$$

$$= \frac{r}{R} + \frac{2}{\pi} \sum_{n=1}^{\infty} \frac{1}{n} \sin\left(n\pi \frac{r}{R}\right) \cos\left(n\pi \frac{y}{R}\right) e^{-n^2\pi^2 \frac{Dx}{wR^2}} \tag{6-64'}$$

from which the equation of the flame surface for $c = 0$, $x = x_{fl}$, and $y = y_{fl}$ is

$$\sum_{n=1}^{\infty} \frac{1}{n} \sin\left(n\pi \frac{r}{R}\right) \cos\left(n\pi \frac{y_{fl}}{R}\right) e^{-\frac{n^2\pi^2 Dx_{fl}}{wR^2}}$$

$$= \frac{\pi}{2}\left(\frac{c_{Oo}}{\chi_O c_{To} - c_{Oo}} - \frac{r}{R}\right) \tag{6-65'}$$

All the basic conclusions, obtained from the solution of the problem (the dependence of the flame length on the parameters, the flame shape for a lean and rich mixture, etc.), are found in a qualitative and satisfactory quantitative correspondence with experiment (30). This circumstance is of considerable interest, since it confirms the negligibility of the part of the chemical kinetics in diffusion combustion conditions when the process is determined practically completely by mixing conditions.

In particular, it is obvious that the fields of the concentration distributions of both gases in the chamber should be noticeably different during combustion and in the case of simple mixing (without a reaction). Here Eq. (6-59) and its solution remain the same; however, the surface $c = 0$, determined by Eqs. (6-65) and (6-65'), will correspond to a stoichiometric mixture $\alpha = 1$; $c_O/c_{To} = \chi_O$.

Hence, the diffusion flame surface approximately agrees with the surface $\alpha = 1$ for cold mixing (in connection with neglecting the change in the constant during combustion).[25]

As regards the distributions of the concentrations c_T and c_O for isothermal mixing, it is determined completely by the cited solution of (6-59) with the boundary conditions (6-60). It also follows from (6-54) for this case

$$\frac{c_O}{c_{O_0}} = 1 - \frac{c_T}{c_{T_0}}$$

that the concentration fields of both gases are similar. Combining this equation with expressions (6-64) or (6-64'), similar concentration fields can be constructed in the mixing chamber. The character of the curves c_T and c_O are shown schematically on Figure 6-14 for both cases (with and without combustion).

Shown on Figure 6-15 is the schematic temperature and concentration distribution for the combustion of unmixed gases. The curves 1-1 refer to diffusion combustion, the dashes to isothermal mixing, the rest of the lines to the intermediate cases of finite combustion zones. According to (6-65) or (6-65'), the relation of the values of the concentrations of both gases on the surface $c = 0$ corresponds to the equality $\alpha = (c_O/\chi_O c_T) = 1$ in all cases under the assumptions made (the constant being constant, etc.).

As the reaction rate decreases, the combustion zone broadens continuously, and the maximum temperature drops therein. In order to obtain an exact picture of the process, an investigation of the linear equations with the reaction rate eliminated is inadequate, and it is necessary, as mentioned above, to integrate one of the equations containing the reaction rate.

An approximate analysis of the question of the critical conditions of the existence of a diffusion flame has been presented by Zel'dovich (19).

His results show that the extinction condition of the flame zone for unmixed gases is similar to the extinction condition presented in Chapter 3 for the heterogeneous process. Extinction occurs as the temperature is reduced in the combustion zone by a quantity on the order of

$$\theta_m - \theta_e \approx \theta_m^2; \quad T_m - T_e \approx \frac{RT_m^2}{E} \tag{3-35}$$

The substance of the phenomenon reduces approximately to the following:

[25] It should also be kept in mind that changes in velocity and gas density are not taken into account in the approximate solution under consideration.

As the combustion rate is reduced, the flame zone is propagated in a certain finite gas layer within whose limits the temperature becomes lower than in the diffusion front ($T = T_m$) and the concentrations of both reacting gases differ from zero.

Intensifying the mixing, i.e., by increasing the presentation of gases to the flame zone, it is always possible to arrive at a limit such that the reaction rate starts to lag behind the mixture supply; combustion is disrupted because of cooling and extinction. The latter is related to the predominance of the cooling effect (temperature reduction, exponential temperature dependence of the reaction rate, etc.) over the influence of the increase in the concentration of the combustible mixture within the flame zone.

If the flame zone is considered as a kind of combustion chamber, then the picture of extinction therein will be completely analogous to the phenomenon considered in Chapter 2 for the well-mixed mixture and in Chapter 3 for the heterogeneous process. The similarity to the latter is especially great according to the dependence on the concentration. In both cases a zero-reacting gas concentration on the combustion surface in the heterogeneous process,

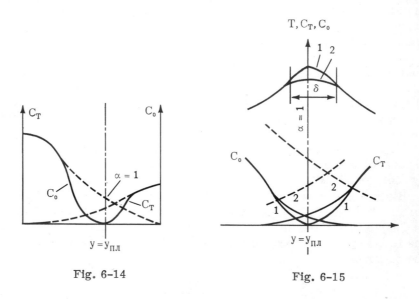

Fig. 6-14   Fig. 6-15

Fig. 6-14. Distribution of the concentrations of the reacting gases for diffusion combustion. Solid line, combustion; dashed line, mixing.
Fig. 6-15. Temperature and concentration distribution during combustion of unmixed gases. 1-1—Diffusion combustion; 2-2—combustion with a finite flame zone δ; solid line, combustion; dashed line, mixing; dotted and dashed line, flame-front coordinate.

and in both components during the combustion of unmixed gases, corresponds to the diffusion-controlled process. As the concentration increases in the region where the reaction is proceeding, a critical temperature drop, i.e., extinction, occurs gradually at the beginning in both cases and then abruptly.

Along with the adiabatic critical phenomena during the combustion of unmixed gases, heat exchange, primarily radiant heat exchange, is also possible. The occurrence of high heat loss calls for, in particular, the presence of a second, lower boundary of stable combustion for very small gas supply to the reaction zone, in complete analogy to the picture of the progress of the process considered in detail in Chapters 3 and 4. Hence the thermal region of the process, even in the case of the combustion of unmixed gases, is characterized, for a strongly exothermal reaction, by the presence of critical ignition and extinction phenomena, etc. These phenomena can be absent in a process of weak intensity for very low-caloric gases, just as an intense progress of the reaction— combustion—is also absent in this case, in practice. Let us note as a detail of the phenomenon that "passage" of the initial products through the flame zone corresponds to a deflection of the process from the purely diffusion process (finite flame zone, reacting gas concentrations nowhere become zero), since the region of active combustion is limited by temperature (and concentration) limits (Figure 6-15).

Finally, let us note that it would be possible to investigate the case of a "double" flame front, corresponding for example to the supply of a rich mixture of fuel and air instead of the gas "T," by a similar means also (Figure 6-16). In this process, which is not considered in detail here (see the work of Schwab (42)), a normal flame front is formed in the burner mouth, in which a stoichiometric mixture, in the gas composition "T," burns, and the rest of the fuel, being mixed with the surrounding air, burns in the diffusion front just as occurs in the combustion of pure unmixed gases. As in many other cases, a rise in the gas temperature related to partial combustion in the primary (normal) front, is here felt more strongly than contamination of the mixture by inert reaction products. In order to estimate the influence of preheating, the formulas presented above could be used for the case $T_{T_0} = T_{O_0}$. However, a detailed investigation of the question requires integration of one of the nonlinear diffusion equations, taking into account the dependence of the reaction rate on the temperature and concentration.

The brief considerations presented illustrate one of the important conclusions of a general character formulated in the introduction. If the subject of the investigation is the stationary progress

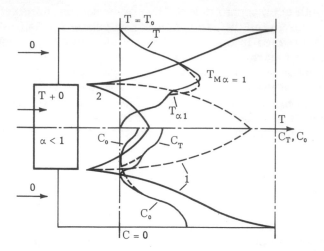

Fig. 6-16. Diagram of a "double" flame front. 1—Diffusion flame front; solid line, $\alpha_{total} < 1$; dashed line, $\alpha_{total} > 1$; 2—normal flame front.

of the combustion, and the process is known to be stable, then practically all the interesting relations and dependences can be obtained by assuming the reaction rate to be infinitely high and by neglecting the thickness of the combustion zone. Hence the problem is reduced, substantially, to the computation of the transport process. However, any judgment on the stability of the process, the ignition or collapse (extinction) conditions, which are always related to a finite reaction rate, is impossible for such a formulation of the question.

In conclusion, let us recall that the conclusions obtained in this section refer to the case of equality of the diffusion and temperature-conduction coefficients. Similarity of the fields T and c is disturbed for $a \neq D_1 \neq D_2$. For the solution of the problem, all three nonlinear equations should be integrated and not just one, as is possible for $a = D$. The general considerations on the influence of the inequality $a \neq D$, obtained in the preceding section (local energy redistribution, rise in the flame temperature over the value T_m for diffusion combustion, $a < D$ and, conversely, the inequality $T < T_m$ on the combustion surface for $a > D$, the widening of the concentration limits of stability of combustion in the first case, and the reduction in the second, etc.), remain valid for the combustion of unmixed gases also. The case $a = D$ considered and the general results obtained therefor are important in practice because they correspond to the conditions of progress of the combustion process for turbulent flow, although the values of the transport coefficients a_{turb} and D_{turb} in this case have substantially another meaning than in molecular heat conduction and diffusion (see section 7-2).

Chapter 7

Elements of Combustion Gas Dynamics

7-1. THE L. D. LANDAU THEORY OF FLAME SELF-TURBULIZATION

The combustion process is always accompanied by gas motion. Even in the simplest case of flame propagation in an initially motionless gas, the expansion of the combustion products causes gas motion which, in turn, substantially affects the character of the combustion. The presence of a velocity profile in the stream leads to the flame being transported not with the average rate of motion but with the most rapid jet (from which it is propagated not only downstream but also across the flow (17)). The flame-front curvature in conjunction with the flow conditions leads to an increase in the combustion rate over that of the plane flame front. The turbulent motion typical of practical systems sharply accelerates the heat exchange between the combustion products and the fresh mixture and, correspondingly, the flame propagation. The flow conditions in the combustion of unmixed gases determine the mixing and the total combustion rate in the range of high temperatures. Shockwaves occurring during combustion lead under specific conditions to detonation whose propagation is determined completely by gas-dynamic relations.

In addition, a far from complete list of examples of the influence of gas motion on the progress of combustion can be indicated: flame stabilization beyond a poorly streamlined body or vortex generator, the introduction of "sharp" jets of secondary air, the increase of the mixture stay time in vortical and cyclone furnaces (25), etc. Finally, the gas dynamics substantially affects the operation of the combustion process, predetermines the mixture consumption in forced-flow installations, or affects the heat supply for a given consumption and chamber dimensions, sharply affects the mixture formation conditions, the combustion stability and occurrence of pulsations, the uniformity of the exhaust temperature and concentration fields, the conditions for cooling the chamber walls, etc.

As has already been mentioned in the introduction, the creation of a complex theory of combustion (and furnace processes) which correctly combines all aspects of the phenomenon—gas dynamics, heat-exchange, and reaction rate—is a problem of the future to a considerable degree, and is related, moreover, to many-sided experimental investigations. The first research in this direction, performed by Soviet scientists, shows its fruitfulness and prospects.

The preceding chapters of this book were devoted principally to the thermal side of the combustion process; the flow velocity was considered given and its influence was considered only in general respects. In this chapter, certain of the simplest information from combustion gas dynamics, related basically to two groups of questions, will be explained. In the first group is the problem of normal combustion instability (flame self-turbulization) and elementary considerations of turbulent combustion. In the second group are the gas-dynamic relations for a process with heat supply, in particular, the propagation of detonation.

Let us start with the first group of questions. L. D. Landau did valuable research on the question of the instability of a plane flame front under normal combustion (27, 28).

Before presenting the mathematical solution of the problem, let us briefly explain the substance of the question. The possibility of the practical realization of a plane flame front can be clarified by investigating its stability with respect to small perturbations. If the perturbations which occur for a small deviation from the equilibrium state (plane front) decrease with time, the front will be stable; if they increase without limit, the front will be unstable and therefore not realizable in practice.

The flame front thickness in the work of L. D. Landau (27) is taken to be small in comparison with the scale of the perturbations, the "wavelength" (equal to the tube diameter in order of magnitude); also the absence of viscosity is assumed, the equality of the pressure on both sides of the front (the case of velocities which are small in comparison with the sound speed) and for the same reason, the constancy of the density (incompressibility) of both the cold and the hot gas, individually (ρ_1 = const; ρ_2 = const; but it is understood that $\rho_2 \neq \rho_1$). In addition, it is assumed in the work cited that the normal flame propagation rate is identical in all points of the plane and deformed front. The method of investigation reduces to the imposition of small perturbations, periodic in time, on the basic motion on both sides of the front. The results of the solution show that the basic motion is unstable in the case of a density drop behind the front ($\rho_2 < \rho_1$), which is typical for combustion, since there are always such perturbation "frequencies" for which the initial displacements of the surface elements with time increase without limit.

A more detailed discussion of this result will be presented below after a brief explanation of the solution (27, 28); the reader not interested in the mathematics of the question can omit the derivation and turn to the physical interpretation of the problem presented at the end of the section.

Let us investigate[1] the gas motion near a certain surface element of the flame front, considered as a surface of discontinuity, on which (according to the "refraction" conditions, see section 6-1) the parameters of the state of the gas vary: the density and temperature and the normal velocity component vary but not the tangential velocity component. Let us assume that the pressure and total enthalpy ($H = h + J$) of the gas do not vary when passing through the front for low values of the motion rate. Let us select an n, t coordinate system related to the flame-front element toward the motion and the t-axis tangentially to the front surface. In order to differentiate the cold and hot states of the gas, let us introduce the subscripts 1 (up to the front $n < 0$) and 2 (beyond the front; $n > 0$). Let us consider the unperturbed gas motion to be stationary and directed along the n axis. Let us consider the values of the gas density ρ_1 and ρ_2 as well as the values of the pressure $p_1 = p_2$ as constant (Figure 7-1). Let us superpose the small perturbations $w'_1 = w(n, t, \tau)$ and $w'_2 = w(n, t, \tau)$ on the basic unperturbed motion with the velocities w_1 and w_2 and also let us superpose $p' = p(n, t, \tau)$, where we will consider it to be periodic in time and along the coordinate t.

$$w' \sim p' \sim e^{ikt - i\omega t} \tag{7-1}$$

Let us substitute new values of the velocity $w_n + w'_n$; $w_t + w'_t$ and also the pressure $p + p'$ into the Euler equations for plane motion (29)

[1] Let us recall the mathematical scheme of the investigation of the stability of fluid motion with respect to infinitely small perturbations (28). If the stability of a certain stationary state is investigated [this can be represented as the dependence of the velocity vector on the coordinate $w_0 = w(x, y, z)$] then a nonstationary, small perturbation $w' = w'(x, y, z, t)$ selected so that the total motion $w = w_0 + w'$ would satisfy the motion equations and the boundary conditions, is superposed on the stationary state. After the substitution of w' in the motion equations, a system of linear differential equations is obtained for the perturbing motion with coefficients which are functions of the coordinates but not of the time. The general solution of such a system of equations can be represented as the sum of particular solutions in which the time-dependence of w' is expressed by a factor such as $e^{-i\omega t}$ The values of the perturbation frequencies ω are determined from the solutions of the equations. Generally speaking they are complex. If there are encountered among the frequencies some for which the imaginary part is positive, then using $\omega = \omega_1 + i\omega_2$ after substitution in $e^{-i\omega t}$, we obtain a factor such as $e^{+\omega_2 \tau}$ which increases without limit with time. In this case, the motion under investigation is unstable.

$$\frac{\partial w_n}{\partial \tau} + w_n \frac{\partial w_n}{\partial x} + w_t \frac{\partial w_n}{\partial y} = -\frac{1}{\rho} \frac{\partial p}{\partial n}$$

$$\frac{\partial w_t}{\partial \tau} + w_n \frac{\partial w_t}{\partial x} + w_t \frac{\partial w_t}{\partial y} = -\frac{1}{\rho} \frac{\partial p}{\partial t}$$

and in the continuity equation

$$\frac{\partial w_n}{\partial n} + \frac{\partial w_t}{\partial t} = 0$$

keeping in mind that in the basic motion

$$\frac{\partial w}{\partial \tau} = 0; \quad w_n = w = \text{const}; \quad w_t = 0; \quad p = \text{const}$$

Neglecting second-order infinitesimals ($(w')(\partial w')/\partial n$ and $w'(\partial w')/\partial t$) we obtain

$$\frac{\partial w'_n}{\partial \tau} + w \frac{\partial w'_n}{\partial n} = -\frac{1}{\rho} \frac{\partial p'}{\partial n} \qquad\qquad (7\text{-}2)$$

$$\frac{\partial w'_t}{\partial \tau} + w \frac{\partial w'_t}{\partial t} = -\frac{1}{\rho} \frac{\partial p'}{\partial t}$$

$$\frac{\partial w'_n}{\partial n} + \frac{\partial w'_t}{\partial t} = 0$$

These equations refer to the cold gas for $w = w_1$, $\rho = \rho_1$, $p = p_1$, and to the hot gas for $w = w_2$, $\rho = \rho_2$, and $p = p_2$. If the first of the motion equations is differentiated with respect to n and the second with respect to t and they are then added, the following equality is obtained:

$$\frac{\partial}{\partial \tau} \left(\frac{\partial w'_n}{\partial n} + \frac{\partial w'_t}{\partial t} \right)$$

$$+ w \left(\frac{\partial^2 w'_n}{\partial n^2} + \frac{\partial^2 w'_t}{\partial t^2} \right).$$

$$= -\frac{1}{\rho} \left(\frac{\partial^2 p'}{\partial n^2} + \frac{\partial^2 p'}{\partial t^2} \right)$$

in which the left side is zero from the condition of the continuity and potentiality of the motion. Consequently

$$\frac{\partial^2 p'}{\partial n^2} + \frac{\partial^2 p'}{\partial t^2} = 0 \qquad\qquad (7\text{-}3)$$

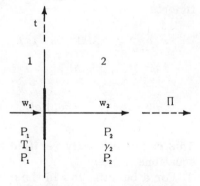

Fig. 7-1. Diagram for the computation of the instability of a plane flame front. 1—Cold gas region; 2—hot gas region.

Let us determine the boundary conditions on the flame-front surface. The condition of a constant tangential component of the velocity $w_{t_1} = w_{t_2}$ will be written by introducing a small displacement of the surface points in the direction of the $n - \nu (t, \tau)$ axis as

$$\text{for } n = 0, \quad w'_{1,t} + w_1 \frac{\partial \nu}{\partial t} = w'_{2,t} + w_2 \frac{\partial \nu}{\partial t} \tag{7-4}$$

Assuming the flame propagation rate to be constant and independent of the perturbations and, therefore, the relative velocity of the gas and the flame front to be zero ($w'_n = \partial \nu / \partial \tau$), we obtain the second condition

$$w'_{1,n} = w'_{2,n} = \frac{\partial \nu}{\partial t}, \quad \text{for } n = 0 \tag{7-5}$$

Finally, we have from the pressure being equal on both sides of the front

$$p'_1 = p'_2 \qquad \text{for } n = 0 \tag{7-6}$$

Let us write the solution of (7-3) for the pressure perturbations in the cold gas region ($n < 0$) according to (7-1) as

$$p' = \text{const } e^{ikt + kn - i\omega t}$$

If the expressions for w'_t and w'_n are written in the same form, then (7-2) for a cold gas can be satisfied by selecting the coefficients

$$w'_{1,n} = A\, e^{ikt + kn - i\omega t}$$

$$w'_{1,t} = iA\, e^{ikt + kn - i\omega t} \tag{7-7}$$

$$p'_1 = A_{\rho_1} \left(\frac{i\omega}{k} - w_1 \right) e^{ikt + kn - i\omega t}$$

This result is easily verified by substituting (7-7) in the original equations.

For a burning gas in the $n > 0$ range, in addition to the analogous solution of the form $\text{const } e^{ikt - kn - i\omega t}$, as L. D. Landau mentions, a particular solution, which is obtained if $p' = 0$ is assumed in the Euler equations (7-2), should be taken into account. In this case the homogeneous equations

$$\frac{\partial w'_{2,n}}{\partial \tau} + w_2 \frac{\partial w'_{2,n}}{\partial n} = 0$$

and

$$\frac{\partial w'_{2,t}}{\partial \tau} + w_2 \frac{\partial w'_{2,t}}{\partial t} = 0$$

have solutions such as $\mathrm{const} \exp\left[ikt + (i\omega/w_2)n - i\omega t\right]$.

Collecting coefficients, as in the previous case, let us represent the solution for the hot gas $(n > 0)$ as

$$w'_{2,n} = B\, e^{ikt - kn - i\omega t} + C\, e^{ikt + i\frac{\omega}{w_2} n - i\omega t}$$

$$w'_{2,t} = -iB\, e^{ikt - kn - i\omega t} - \frac{\omega}{kw_2} C\, e^{ikt + i\frac{\omega}{w_2} n - i\omega t} \qquad (7\text{-}8)$$

$$p'_2 = -Bp_2\left(w_2 + \frac{i\omega}{k}\right) e^{ikt - kn - i\omega t}$$

The fact that the additional particular solution at $p' = 0$ has been taken into account only in the hot gas region, and not for the cold gas, is explained by the factor $e^{i\omega n/w}$ increasing without limit in absolute value as n increases for frequencies ω with positive imaginary part (which is the reason for the instability of the basic motion).

Let us also assume from the displacement of the particles of the front

$$v = D\, e^{ikt - i\omega t} \qquad (7\text{-}9)$$

Substitution of all the solutions (7-7) to (7-9) into the boundary conditions (7-4) to (7-6) leads to a system of four homogeneous equations in the constants $A, B, C,$ and D. The compatibility condition for these equations can be written as the following equality:

$$\Omega^2 (w_1 + w_2) + 2\Omega kw_1 w_2 + k^2 w_1 w_2 (w_1 - w_2) = 0 \qquad (7\text{-}10)$$

The following notation is used in the last equation for convenience of operation with the actual coefficients:

$$\Omega = -i\omega, \qquad (\Omega^2 = -\omega^2)$$

There follows from (7-10)

$$\Omega = -k\frac{w_1 w_2}{w_1 + w_2} \pm \sqrt{\frac{k^2 w_1^2 w_2^2}{(w_1^2 + w_2^2)}\left(1 - \frac{w_1}{w_2} + \frac{w_2}{w_1}\right)} \qquad (7\text{-}11)$$

Evidently, both roots of the last equation are real and different in sign for $w_1 < w_2$, i.e., $\rho_2 < \rho_1$. This means that there are such values of Ω among the perturbation frequencies, for which the real part is positive or, respectively, the imaginary part of ω is negative.

Hence there are always such values in the spectrum of perturbation frequencies ω, which lead to an unlimited increase in the deviation with time. Therefore the basic motion is unstable.

In order to represent graphically the physical picture of the loss of flow stability, let us first consider the scheme of the generation of turbulence used in hydrodynamics. Let us assume that the line separating two stream jets of fluid is twisted just as is shown on Figure 7-2. According to the Bernoulli equation (we

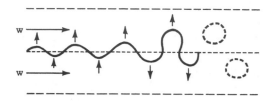

Fig. 7-2. Diagram of the development of perturbations on the boundary of two jets. (Arrows show the direction the pressure acts on the surface of separation.)

speak of motions at low speeds) the pressure rises at the places where the jet is expanded, and it is reduced at the places where it is contracted. Such a pressure distribution will lead to a further increase in the curvature of the separating line and, in the long run, will lead to the transition of the particles from one fluid jet to the other; the jet (laminar) motion will be violated, with turbulence resulting instead. Hence, the surfaces of separation tangent to the direction of the velocity are unstable. It is also known that turbulent motion does not occur in all cases but begins with certain minimum critical Reynolds numbers $Re = wd/\nu$, characterizing the ratio of the inertial to the viscous forces.

It is proved in hydrodynamics that so-called tangential discontinuities, i.e., surfaces of separation, on each side of which the velocity component tangent to the surface is different, are unstable (28). Shown on Figure 7-3a, for example, is the practically impossible motion of parallel fluid flows, because of the instability of the surfaces of separation (tangential discontinuity), which have different velocities; the real motion, a turbulent free boundary layer, is shown on Figure 7-3b.

Now, let us attempt to use similar reasoning in the problem of the stability of a plane flame front.

As the gas passes through an unperturbed normal flame front (Figure 7-4a), the stream lines will not be bent, since only the normal velocity components will change, but the tangential components will remain unchanged, i.e., will equal zero on both sides of the front.

Now, let us assume that the flame front is deformed under the influence of some kind of perturbations and becomes "wavy" (Figure 7-4b). In this case, in conformance with the "refraction" conditions considered in section 6-1 (see Figure 6-3), the stream lines intersecting the front will be curved just as is shown on Figure 7-4b; they will diverge on passing over a convexity and converge when passing over a concavity (actually, a certain curvature of the streamline will occur in a subsonic flow not only in a hot but also in a cold region ahead of the flame front, since the pressure-wave disturbances being propagated upstream from the flame front at sonic speed will lead to reconstruction of the whole flow).

In connection with the gas streamlines diverging in the convex sections of the front toward the hot gas, the velocity drops, and the pressure rises at the gas jets intersecting these sections. On the other hand, the pressure drops in the troughs as the streamlines compress, i.e., the motion accelerates. Such a pressure field, which occurs in the cold and hot regions of the flow, inevitably leads to the subsequent broadening of the convex sections of the

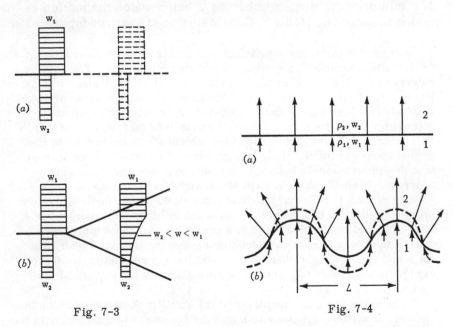

Fig. 7-3   Fig. 7-4

Fig. 7-3. Instability of a tangential discontinuity. (a) Unstable motion (not realizable); (b) turbulent boundary layer.
Fig. 7-4. Diagram of the development of shallow perturbations in a flat flame front. (a) Unperturbed motion; (b) perturbed motion; 1—region of cold gas; 2—region of burning gas.

front and to the contraction of the troughs, hence sections of the interphase surface parallel to the direction of the basic motion arise during further deformation of the flame front, i.e., unstable tangential discontinuities occur, which lead, as has been shown above, to turbulization of the motion.

The mechanism of the instability, self-turbulization of the motion for a plane flame front, therefore consists in the growth of the disturbances, the origin of tangential discontinuities and, consequently, leads to a discontinuity of the flame front itself. In the turbulent motion which thereby arises, heating of the fresh gas will be accomplished not primarily by molecular heat conduction but by the considerably more intense turbulent mixing, the flame front begins to spread, and its width increases. This case (turbulent combustion) will be discussed in somewhat more detail below.[2]

The role of the gas viscosity (this means we speak of significant numbers $Re = wd/\nu$) is not taken into account in the theory of L. D. Landau, as are not certain other factors which stabilize the flame front. Taking viscosity into account, as is always done in a discussion of the question of flow stability, leads to the establishment of a minimum (critical) number Re_{cr}, below which the motion remains laminar and stable.[3] Consideration of heat conduction also

---

[2] Let us note the error sometimes encountered (for example (13b), p. 91) in attempts to explain flame-front instability qualitatively. The authors, referred to by Shchelkin, write, ". . . such a picture is obtained that the jets diverge from the convexities of the flame so that a reduced pressure is created at these places and an elevated pressure must result at the concavities where the jets converge," and they furthermore state that ". . . such a pressure distribution inevitably leads to the strongest increase in the curvature," i.e., to a growth of the disturbances. However, if such a pressure distribution, impossible in a subsonic flow, were to occur then it would not violate but would stabilize the motion.

It is curious to note that the divergence of the jets actually leads to a pressure reduction in a supersonic flow according to the "reciprocity effect" (10), and contraction leads to a pressure rise. Such a pressure distribution for a supersonic discontinuity (for the velocity higher than the sound speed on both sides of the front, for a condensation shock, for example) must apparently guarantee the stability of the surface of discontinuity.

[3] It is known from investigations of the stability of laminar motion in channels of variable cross section that the presence of an inflection in the velocity profile as a rule yields instability for Re numbers considerably less than in a right cylindrical pipe (29). The formation of such inflections apparently is inevitable in the deformation of a plane front, since the velocity profile at the output of a wavy front also becomes wavy, where to the troughs, i.e., the sections formed by convexities at the cold gas, will

leads to a similar result. It is assumed in the Landau theory that the rate of flame propagation at all points of the front is constant. Actually, since the flame is propagated normally to the surface, the preheating will occur more intensely for a curved front at the convex sections (toward the hot gas) than at the concave sections; it is natural that the flame propagation should be more intense for converging vectors w_{fl} than for diverging vectors. This circumstance leads to flattening of the front. A quantitative estimate (13b) again leads to the critical number Re_{cr}. Actually, the characteristic time of the growth of the disturbances is of the order $\tau_1 = L/w_{fl}$ according to Landau (27, 28), where L is the wavelength of the critical disturbance (a quantity of the order of the tube diameter), w_{fl} is the normal combustion rate, τ_1 is the time during which the disturbances increase by e times.

From (6-4), the characteristic time for the flame propagation process is of the order of $\tau_2 \sim \tau_{K'} \approx a_2/w_{fl}$. The critical condition corresponds to the equality $\tau_1/\tau_2 = \text{const}$, that is, $w_{fl}L/a = \text{const}$; we obtain a certain value $Re_{cr} = wL/\nu$ defined in terms of the flame-propagation rate, for $\nu \approx a$.

The stabilizing role of gravity (13b) should also be taken into account for flame propagation in vertical pipes. Here, as is always the case with gravitational effects, the characteristic time can be taken as $\tau_3 \approx \sqrt{L/g}$. From the equality $\tau_3/\tau_1 = \text{const}$, we obtain a certain critical value of the criterion $w^2/gL = \text{const}$, just as in the problem, for example, of the wave drag of a ship. Of the other factors not taken into account can be mentioned the ratio D/a. The stability of a plane flame front rises for $D/a < 1$ and decreases for $D/a > 1$.

The first of the above-mentioned motion-stabilizing mechanisms, the heat conduction, limits the instability of the surface of separation to perturbations of very low wavelength, commensurable with the flame front thickness. Characteristic therefore for $L \sim d$ (pipe diameter) and $\nu/a \approx 1$ is a certain critical number

$$Re_{cr} = \frac{w_{fl}d}{\nu} = \text{const} \tag{7-12}$$

calculated, as mentioned above, in terms of the flame propagation rate. A plane flame front will be unstable for $Re > Re_{cr}$; stable for $Re < Re_{cr}$. Hence it is seen, in particular, that the probability of realizing a plane flame front in narrow pipes (small values of Re) is larger than in wide pipes (if the influence of the velocity profile and the heat transfer to the pipe walls is neglected).

---

correspond maximum values of the velocity, and to the sections whose convexity is turned toward the hot gases will correspond minimum velocities.

According to the numerical estimate of Zel'dovich and Frank-Kamenetskii (13b), the critical rate of normal flame propagation is of the order of 1.0 m/sec.; flame self-turbulization occurs for large values of w_{fl}, the motion becomes unstable and turbulent.

The L. D. Landau theory has received its first experimental confirmation, comparatively recently, in the laboratory experiments of Zel'dovich and Rozlovskii (13b) and Shchelkin, et al. (38), where the loss in stability of normal combustion was observed under conditions when the stabilizing effect of the wall had been eliminated (for spherical flame propagation). As the number $Re = w_{fl}d/\nu$ increased, a sharp acceleration in the flame was observed in certain cases, and its transformation into detonation in others.

The value of the L. D. Landau theory explained here is particularly important, not for laboratory conditions of the progress of combustion, but for the process in technical apparatus.[4] Precisely here at high pressures and large volumes the normal combustion is apparently always unstable and turbulent, where the turbulence being generated by the flame itself can also play a large part in addition to the usual stream turbulence.

7-2. TURBULENT MOTION AND GAS COMBUSTION

Before analyzing the very scarce and, moreover, purely qualitative representations of turbulent combustion, let us recall certain of the simplest information on turbulent motion.

As is known (28, 29), turbulent motion can be visualized as a nonstationary flow arising as a result of the superposition of different perturbations (with a practically continuous frequency spectrum) on a laminar flow unstable for large enough numbers $Re = wd/\nu$.

Characteristic for turbulent motion is the noncoincidence of the instantaneous values of the velocity, temperature, etc., and the average values of these quantities taken over a sufficiently long time interval. These latter are time invariant for a steady (on the average) flow. If some kind of inertial instrument (pitot tube, thermocouple, etc.) is inserted into a stationary turbulent flow, then it will show a certain quantity constant with time. In contradistinction

---

[4] The following selection from the second part of the *Course on Combustion Theory*, edited by Ia. B. Zel'dovich and cited here repeatedly, is not without interest in this connection: "The result is that the whole normal combustion with a plane front and with a definite normal rate is the exception. We studied it only under laboratory conditions and the phenomena which occur under practical conditions are of an entirely different character" (see 13b).

to this, a practically inertialess instrument (the filament of a hot-
wire anemometer, for example) records the continuous time change
of the quantity being measured, the complex and, at first glance,
completely disordered fluctuations of the instantaneous values
around the average. These fluctuations of all the quantities characteristic to the flow, the velocity vector primarily, indicate the
complex picture of the motion in which the actual gas-particle
trajectories diverge from the average and are independent of the
shape of the walls bounding the flow. Continuous and very intense
mixing occurs in the flow. The usual representation of the velocity
w as the sum of two values, the average value of the velocity $\overline{w}$ and
the deviation therefrom w' (the so-called velocity pulsation) is used
to describe the phenomenon quantitatively

$$w = \overline{w} + w' \tag{7-13}$$

and similarly for the temperature, concentration, etc.:

$$T = \overline{T} + T' ; \quad c = \overline{c} + c' \tag{7-13'}$$

The quantities with the bar are the average (if, as is usual, we
speak of the time average) and are determined from the expression

$$\overline{w} = \frac{1}{\tau_0} \int_0^{\tau_0} w(\tau) d\tau \tag{7-14}$$

and similarly for $\overline{T}, \overline{c}$, et al. The time interval τ_0 over which the
average is taken must satisfy the condition that $\overline{w}$ is invariant to
repeated averaging, i.e., the equality

$$\overline{\overline{w}} = \int_0^{\tau_0} \overline{w}(\tau) d\tau = \overline{w}$$

Hence it follows that the average value of the pulsating velocity w'
is zero,

$$\overline{w'} = 0 \tag{7-15}$$

since we obtain from the equality $w = \overline{w} + \overline{w}'$ upon averaging: $\overline{w} =$
$\overline{w} + \overline{w}'$; $\overline{w}' = 0$. In order to estimate the intensity of the pulsations,
a mean-square quantity is introduced just as in kinetic theory; in
particular, the root-mean-square value of the pulsating velocity
$\sqrt{(\overline{w'})^2}$ as well as $\sqrt{(\overline{T'})^2}$; $\sqrt{(\overline{c'})^2}$, etc. (or the nondimensional characteristics of the form $\sqrt{(\overline{w'})^2}/\overline{w}$; $\sqrt{(\overline{T'})^2}/\overline{T}$, etc.). These values
are measured directly in experiment, for example, by connecting
some kind of thermal instrument to the ends of the wire of a ther-
moanemometer balanced at the average value of the velocity or
temperature (29). The mean-square value of the pulsation is one

of the fundamental characteristics of a turbulent flow. In the sequel, as has been done earlier in Chapter 3, we shall denote it for one of the flow-velocity components by the symbol

$$u' \equiv \sqrt{(\overline{w'})^2} \tag{17-16}$$

The second characteristic quantity for a turbulent flow is the mean scale of turbulence. The concept of the scale of turbulence is also explained by starting from experimental observations. Let us visualize the following comparatively simple experiment (29). The average magnitude of the product of the pulsations of any variable (the longitudinal velocity components w_1', w_2', say) is measured at two points of the flow as the distance ξ between them increases successively (starting from $\xi = 0$, i.e., from the superposition of the two points).

Evidently, $w_1' w_2' = \sqrt{(\overline{w_1'})^2} \cdot \sqrt{(\overline{w_2'})^2} = (\overline{w_1'})^2$ at $\xi = 0$ or the non-dimensional quantity $K = \overline{w_1'} \cdot \overline{w_2'} / \sqrt{(w_1')^2} \sqrt{(w_2')^2} = 1$ at $\xi = 0$.

As the distance ξ increases, the value of K (the so-called correlation coefficient) will diminish and become zero at a certain $\xi = \xi_2$. Actually, although ξ is very small, it can be assumed that the fluid particles near the points selected participate in the common motion; as the points are separated the relation between the elementary fluid jets will be weaker, although it does not completely vanish. This latter corresponds to the independence of the instantaneous values w'_1 and w'_2 and, therefore, of the equality $\overline{w_1' w_2'} = \overline{w_1'} \, \overline{w_2'} = 0$, $K = 0$.

The quantity l defined by the equality

$$l = \int_0^{\xi_0} K(\xi) d\xi \quad \text{(meters)} \tag{7-17}$$

is treated as the average weighted length within which a connection between two points appears in the turbulent flow; it is customarily called the scale of turbulence.

Both the characteristics u' and l of the turbulent motion are, generally speaking, functions of the coordinates, the velocity, its derivatives, etc.

If the sums $w + w'$, $T + T'$, etc., are substituted in the motion, heat-transport, etc., equations instead of the average values of the variables w, T; then after averaging and transforming to the average quantities in the equations, additional terms of the form $\overline{w'_x w'_y}$, $\overline{w'_x T'_y}$, etc., appear which owe their occurrence to the quadratic terms in the original equations. Evidently these quantities reflect additional turbulent transport; for example, the instantaneous displacement of fluid particles with the excess velocity

w', temperature T', or concentration c', across a flow with velocity w'_y, corresponds to the momentum transport $\rho w'_x w'_y$; the quantity of heat $\gamma c_p w'_y T'$, and of material $w'c'$. Correspondingly, we obtain for the average values of the specific flows, $\overline{\rho w'_x w'_y}$, $\gamma c_p \overline{w'T'}$, and $\overline{w'c'}$. Assuming, in a first approximation, that the difference in the values of the average quantities, say $\overline{w}_x$ in two layers of fluid separated by the distance l, is proportional to the gradient of the average $\partial \overline{w}_x / \partial y$ (for a plane flow in which $\overline{w} = \overline{w}_x(y)$; $\overline{w}_y = 0$), we obtain $\overline{w}_x(y + l) - \overline{w}_x(y) \approx w'_x \sim l\,(dw_x/dy)$ and also $T' \sim dT/dy$, etc. Finally, if the expressions are written for the momentum (the apparent stress friction), heat, and material flows as

$$\frac{\tau}{\rho} = \nu_{\text{turb}} \frac{d\overline{w}}{dy} = \overline{w'_x w'_y} \approx l^2 \left(\frac{d\overline{w}}{dy}\right)^2 \left(\frac{\tau}{\rho} = \nu \frac{dw}{dy}\right) \qquad (7\text{-}18)$$

$$\frac{q}{c_p \gamma} = a_{\text{turb}} \frac{d\overline{T}}{dy} = \overline{T'w'y} \approx l^2 \frac{d\overline{w}}{dy} \frac{d\overline{T}}{dy} \left(q = \lambda \frac{dT}{dy}\right) \qquad (7\text{-}19)$$

$$j = D_{\text{turb}} \frac{d\overline{c}}{dy} = \overline{w'_y c'} \approx l^2 \frac{d\overline{w}}{dy} \frac{d\overline{c}}{dy} \left(j = D \frac{dc}{dy}\right) \qquad (7\text{-}20)$$

then it follows from their comparison with the formulas written to the right (in the parentheses) for the molecular transport that

$$\nu_{\text{turb}} \approx a_{\text{turb}} \approx D_{\text{turb}} \sim l^2 \frac{d\overline{w}}{dy} \approx lu' \qquad (7\text{-}21)$$

It is also assumed here that $w'_x \approx w'_y$.

Experiment shows that the effective turbulent coefficients of viscosity, heat conduction, and diffusion are considerably larger (hundreds and thousands of times for $Re > Re_{cr}$) than the corresponding molecular-flow coefficients, just exactly as the friction, heat transport, and diffusion observed in a turbulent flow are many times more intense than the molecular values (despite the more equalized mean values of $\overline{w}_1 \overline{T}$ and $\overline{c}$ because of the intense mixing of the profile). Consequently, the latter (the molecular flows) are usually neglected in comparison with the turbulent (far from solid walls).

Experience shows that the mean and local values of a_{turb} and D_{turb} are identical in the same flow but the values of ν_{turb} differ noticeably from those in free turbulent flows (jets, wakes behind bodies, etc.), but are comparatively close to those in motions in channels or the boundary layer near a body surface. This relationship results from the similarity of the T and c fields in all cases, the absence of similarity of the w and T (or c) fields in free turbulent flows, and the approximate similarity of w and T fields in the turbulent boundary layer near a solid wall.[5]

The introduction of the quantity l permits good agreement to be obtained in semiempirical turbulence theories (29) between computations and experiment by introducing one experimental constant; such solutions are especially effective in those comparatively simple cases where the form of the dependence of l on the coordinates can be predicted from dimensionality considerations (for example, the proportionality of l to the x coordinate in free jets, or to the coordinate y in the boundary layer on a plate, etc.; the value of the proportionality coefficient is taken from experiment).

In recent years the statistical theory of turbulence, including as yet mainly the simplest case of isotropic (independent of the coordinates) turbulence, has received considerable development, along with the semiempirical theories, in the research of Soviet scientists such as A. N. Kolmogorov and his colleagues, L. D. Landau, and others. Let us also note that the introduction of the quantity l is usually based on the formal analogy with molecular motion [the theory of "mixing length," etc., see (29)]. The exact equations of turbulent motion (in the form of a closed system of equations which is integrable, in principle) are still lacking, as are also clear, physical representations of its mechanism.

There is particularly little information in the literature on the character of turbulence in compressible gas flows with significant temperature drops and also high values of the velocity. Finally, the question of turbulence in a burning flow has not been investigated at all.

Certainly, the brief amount of information presented does not exhaust the whole complexity of the problem to even a slight degree. However, it is sufficient to clarify existing attempts to explain the mechanism of turbulent combustion.

In substance, the latter reduces to operating with the effective values of the quantities u', the average velocity pulsation l, the average scale of turbulence, or the coefficient of turbulent transport

$$a_{\text{turb}} \approx lu'$$

Let us turn first to the combustion of a well-mixed mixture.

Significant intensification of the heat exchange in the flow leads to a sharp increase in the heat transmission from the burning gas to the fresh mixture, and therefore, to an increase in the flame

---

[5] This also means that in the general case there is a difference between the dynamic (velocity) scale of turbulence l and the analogous heat and diffusion characteristics and the agreement between the latter two:
$$l_w \neq l_T = l_c.$$

propagation rate. In particular, K. I. Shchelkin first indicated that gas turbulization (set in motion because of rarefaction during flame propagation in the initially fixed burning mixture) is one of the reasons for the transformation of normal combustion into detonation (56, 57).

Evidently the simplest manner to take into account the influence of turbulence on the flame propagation rate (13b, 57) is to replace the coefficient of molecular heat conduction a by a_{turb} in (6-4) $w_f \approx \sqrt{a_{turb}/\tau_K'}$. In this case, we obtain[6]

$$w_{turb} \approx \sqrt{\frac{a_{turb}}{K}} = \sqrt{\frac{u'}{\tau_K'}} \tag{7-22}$$

the turbulent flame rate is proportional to the square root of the average velocity pulsation. If we also put $u'/w = $ const, then $w_{turb} \approx \sqrt{\overline{w}}$ where $\overline{w}$ is the average value of the flow velocity.

Along with the increase in the flame propagation rate in a turbulent flow, the depth of the flame zone is also increased (36):

$$\delta_{turb} \approx \frac{a_{turb}}{w_{turb}} \approx \sqrt{lu'} \tag{7-23}$$

or

$$\frac{\delta_{turb}}{\delta_{norm}} \approx \sqrt{\frac{a_{turb}}{a}} \approx \sqrt{\frac{lu'}{a}} \tag{7-23'}$$

since the reaction time remains invariant $\tau_K' = (e/K_0)^{-1/\theta_m}$. The increase in the combustion zone depth is also a reason for an increase in the flame rate in turbulent flow.

Let us note that an increase in the flame rate because of the growth of the reaction rate, other conditions being equal, results, in contrast, to a decrease in the flame zone depth at $a = $ const

$$\delta \approx w_{fl}\tau_K' \sim \sqrt{\tau_K'} \tag{7-24}$$

(as the reaction rate W grows, the reaction time $\tau_K' \approx 1/W$ drops). The reasoning developed refers just to the case of the so-called "fine-scale" turbulence (13b, 57), i.e., to such a ratio between the characteristic length l and δ_{turb} that $l \ll \delta_{turb}$; turbulent transport occurs within the flame front.

[6] More exactly

$$w_{turb} \approx \sqrt{\frac{a + a_{turb}}{\tau_K'}} \sim w_{fl}\sqrt{1 + \frac{a_{turb}}{a}} \quad ; \text{ since}$$

$$a \ll a_{turb} \qquad \frac{w_{turb}}{w_{fl}} \approx \sqrt{\frac{a_{turb}}{a}}$$

In the opposite case of "large-scale" turbulence (13b, 57), another mechanism of the influence of turbulence is usually proposed for $l \gg \delta$. This latter mechanism is related to the wrinkling of the combustion surface under the influence of the turbulent pulsations and the "relay-race" transport of the combustion by individual gas particles ("moles"), performing pulsating motion and transporting elements of burning gas (as if they were elements of the flame front) into the fresh mixture. In this case, from dimensionality considerations we can put

$$w_{turb} \approx u' \qquad\qquad (7-25)$$

or what is substantially the same (57), we can replace the quantity τ_K in the formula $w_{turb} \approx \sqrt{lu'/\tau'_K}$ by the time of turbulent transport $\tau \approx l/u'$, from which we again obtain $w_{turb} \sim u'$. In a more general form, the dependence of w_{turb} on u' is represented by the following relation if the influence of the normal rate w_{fl} is taken into account (13b, 57)

$$w_{turb} = u'f\left(\frac{u'}{w_{fl}}\right) \approx (u')^\alpha (w_{fl})^\beta ; \qquad \alpha + \beta = 1.0 \qquad (7-26)$$

As K. I. Shchelkin (57) indicates, the function $f(u'/w_{fl})$ must approach unity for $u' \gg w_{fl}$; this same author, estimating the values of the exponents α and β in the latter formula, considers α to be almost unity and β to be correspondingly small. It is considered that these considerations of Shchelkin are verified by experiments on combustion in a piston engine, from which it has been established that the combustion rate is proportional, in a first approximation, to the rate of engine revolutions (57). The latter quantity is proportional to the rate of air motion during the intake, along with which the intensity of the turbulence also increases. Without entering into the substance of the questions related to the combustion process in piston engines here (they are not under consideration in this book), let us note that the experimental proof of the mechanism of "large-scale" turbulent flame propagation ($w_{turb} \approx u'$) is apparently still lacking in every case of turbulent combustion in a stationary flow.

Moreover, the above conceptions of the role of turbulence as a whole cannot be considered final, graphic as they are, nor can they serve as a serious foundation for any kind of substantial conclusions.

It should first be noted that operating with the average values of l and u' corresponds only slightly to the nature of the phenomenon. These values vary sharply and continuously from place to place (especially u') in real flows in combustion chambers as contrasted with the general picture of the motion (the average velocity distribution.

etc.). It is also very difficult to separate the influence of turbulence on flame propagation from the influence of the velocity profile (13b, 17). Finally, in the light of the phenomenon of flame self-turbulization considered here, it is difficult to establish a unique relation between the characteristics of "cold" turbulence and the process of combustion propagation. In addition to these basically hydrodynamic considerations, it should also be taken into account that a plane flame front, normal to the flow direction, is never observed in real flows. Its actual position is determined by the presence of stable "incendiary" points in which mixture ignition occurs (within known limits of the velocity and of other parameters) unlimitedly, and from which the flame is propagated over the rest of the mixture as an oblique (plane or curvilinear) front.

As has been shown in section 6-1 (Figure 6-4), the slope of the flame front relative to the flow is determined by the following condition only at a known distance from the incendiary points:

$$\cos \alpha = \frac{w_{fl}}{w} = \frac{w_{turb}}{w} \tag{6-7}$$

where w_{turb} is the rate of turbulent flame propagation which, in contrast to the normal flame rate w_{fl}, is not a fixed physicochemistry constant of the mixture; w is the average flow speed.

Consequently, in order to estimate the flame propagation rate in a turbulent flow, a detailed experimental investigation should be made with a sufficiently extended flame front in a uniform stream with isotropic turbulence. Apparently, such experiments are lacking at the present time, but they could aid in the development of more complete and distinct concepts. On the whole, the theory of turbulent combustion must be closely connected to an investigation of the flow structure and its local, not average, characteristics. Sufficiently detailed, primarily experimental, data on this question have apparently not yet been obtained.

It should also be noted that the above-mentioned conceptions of turbulent flame propagation do not adequately consider the part of factors related to the thermal aspect of the process. In substance, primarily the mixture of hot gases, the combustion products, and the fresh mixture, occurs in turbulent combustion. It can be assumed that intensification of the preheating of the fresh mixture plays a substantial part in all cases of turbulent combustion. As is known, this preheating is never proportional to the velocity, and consequently the direct dependence $w_{turb} \sim \overline{w}$ is of low probability.

Even if an approximation to such a dependence were possible (let us recall that in the empirical expression for heat exchange $\alpha \approx w^n$ the power n has the value 0.8 - 0.82) it cannot be general if it is to be extended over a wide range of values of the mixture heat productivity, the excess-air coefficient, the initial temperature, etc.

The initial ignition conditions are determined by the conditions near the incendiary points and, therefore, the limits of the stability of the process as a whole with respect to the change of different parameters are always related to the progress of the reaction in the kinetic region, i.e., to the final value of the reaction rate or time.

In any case, the turbulent combustion of a well-mixed mixture requires further study. It is possible that the dependence of the rate of turbulent flame propagation on the various parameters will be obtained only in the final stage of the investigation, after a detailed study of the flow structure and the influence of the reaction rate. It is also very probable that this dependence will not be universal, since the very properties of turbulent motion themselves depend greatly on the hydrodynamic arrangement of the process.

Let us now turn to turbulent diffusion combustion. Just as in the laminar combustion of unmixed gases (section 6-5), the diffusion flame front reduces, in practice, to a surface separating the region of the primary fuel and air (oxidizer) content from a mixture with the combustion products. Here, as also for the flame front in the turbulent flow of a well-mixed mixture, we speak of the average position of the combustion surface, which is obtained as a result of averaging, with respect to time, the values of the coordinates of each flame-front element, which oscillate continuously because of the turbulent pulsations. The effective values of the temperature-conductivity and diffusion coefficients for a turbulent flow, a_{turb} and D_{turb}, are identical, as has already been mentioned. Consequently, the general results obtained in section 6-5 for the case $a = D$, in particular the similarity of the T and c fields, are completely applicable to the turbulent combustion of unmixed gases. The combustion temperature on the combustion surface equals the quantity T_m, the maximum combustion temperature of a well-mixed stoichiometric mixture ($\alpha = 1$) in the absence of losses; the flame-front surface agrees approximately with the stoichiometric surface during cold mixing,[7] etc.

A computation of the temperature and concentration distributions for turbulent diffusion combustion can be performed, in principle, exactly as is done for laminar flow if, for example, the equations of turbulent heat and mass transport are taken for the mixing

---

[7] If the change in the physical constants and the influence of the combustion on the velocity is neglected and, therefore, the mixing of the reacting gases is too.

process in regions separated by combustion surface. Such a problem can be solved both for the process in mixed flows with identical velocities (similar to the problem of Burke and Schuman, section 6-5), and for the practically more interesting case of different values of the initial velocities of both gases. The temperature and concentration fields in the latter problem are determined by the velocity distribution which, in turn, influences the character of the motion. Hence, the problem reduces to the joint simultaneous solution of the system of motion, continuity, heat-propagation, and diffusion equations. The interrelation of these equations (in addition to the fact that the velocity enters into the heat-conduction and -diffusion equations) depends, first of all, on the change in the density because of initial heating. Simplified solutions, interesting mainly methodologically, can be based on the approximate independent determination of the velocity field (for example, from the problem of an incompressible fluid, etc.) and its subsequent assignment for the integration of the turbulent heat-transport and -diffusion equations. The solution is simplified for laminar problems in the $\nu = a$ case when the velocity and temperature fields are similar. As already mentioned, $\nu_{turb} \neq a_{turb}$ for turbulent flows; the relation between these quantities depends on the character of the flow and has been studied insufficiently. Despite this, even rough attempts at such solutions, in particular in connection with experiments, are of considerable interest and indisputably lead to valuable practical conclusions. Thus, in 1940, V. A. Shvab (42) performed a theoretical investigation of a turbulent diffusion torch (a free jet) according to this plan. Despite a number of deficiencies, this work contains the correct general formulation of the problem and, consequently, can be the starting point for perfected investigations.

Its value lies in the determination of the location of the flame front,[8] the agreement of problems with the theory and experiments on free turbulent jets, the determination of the maximum temperature on the combustion surface, the analysis of a "double" flame front scheme (Figure 6-16), etc.

Of the inadequacies of the work cited (42), the initial hypotheses on the similarity of the velocity and temperature distributions in a free turbulent jet should be noted (actually, as has already been remarked, by its lack) and the incorrect image of the temperature and concentration curves in the combustion zone. In particular, the the author assumes that the values of the fuel and air concentrations on the combustion surface are not zero and correspond

[8] From the conditions of the stoichiometric relations of the flow components.

approximately to isothermal mixing at $\alpha = 1$, and also he incorrectly assumes the temperature in the final flame zone to equal the maximum combustion temperature for $\alpha = 1$, i.e., $T = T_m =$ const and the same, as in the previous case (in diffusion combustion), for the concentration field. The correct temperature and concentration distribution in the combustion zone of unmixed gases was shown above (see Figures 6-14 and 6-15; and (19) also).

As the reaction rate decreases or the turbulent mixing is intensified, the flame zone is broadened and becomes finite (not only for the pulsating quantities but also for the average quantities). In this case, the combustion temperature is reduced and after a certain drop, extinction occurs. Hence turbulent mixing, which determines the combustion mechanism, leads in the limit to "exhaustion" of the reaction rate, to transition of the combustion into the intermediate and kinetic regions, and to collapse (extinction). The latter is also inevitable for weak intensity of the mixing in connection with strong heat emission. A qualitative explanation of these phenomena has been given in Chapter 3.

The analytical representation of such a process (with a finite flame zone) makes the question of the selection of the temperature values in the reaction-rate formula particularly difficult.

In general, the average value $\overline{\exp(-E/RT)} \neq \exp(-E/RT)$. The difference between these quantities can be very significant in regions of large pulsations ($T' \approx \overline{T}$): in the turbulent wake near the body, on the edge of a jet, etc. For small pulsations ($T' \ll T$), substituting the sum $\overline{T} + T'$ instead of the actual values of the temperature T in the exponential, we obtain

$$e^{-E/RT} = e^{-E/R(\overline{T}+T')} \approx e^{-E/R\overline{T}(1 - T'/\overline{T})}$$
$$= e^{-E/R\overline{T}} \cdot e^{E/R\overline{T} \cdot T'/T'} \tag{7-27}$$

After averaging in the time interval τ_0, we will have

$$\overline{e^{-E/RT}} \approx e^{-E/R\overline{T}} \cdot 1/\tau_0 \int_0^{\tau_0} e^{E/R\overline{T}^2} T'(\tau) d\tau$$
$$= \zeta e^{-E/R\overline{T}} \tag{7-28}$$

The value of the function ζ and the character of the dependence of this quantity on the flow parameters are unknown at present; apparently an approximate estimate is possible from experiment. This remark, it is understood, also refers to the turbulent combustion of a well-mixed mixture. It can be substantial in investigations related to the stability of combustion, and to the critical ignition and extinction phenomena, since the problem for investigations of the stationary process of high-speed combustion of a well-mixed mixture or unmixed gases reduces to the integration of the transport equations which do not contain the reaction rate, and the region of combustion progress can be reduced approximately to the bounding surface, the flame front.

In addition to the elementary schemes of the turbulent combustion of unmixed gases (free jets with a simple spatial distribution of the fuel and air regions), the case of preliminary separation and primary mixing of the fuel and air flows, which is widespread in practice, is of great value. In such a process, called "microdiffusion" (31, 50) by Frank-Kamenetskii, the separate fuel and oxidizer "islets" are distributed in a complex manner in the general flow of the burning mixture.[9]

In this case, the combustion process proceeds in the developed and multiform flame zones separating the individual small volumes with the predominating fuel and air content, and for the high-speed combustion of the combustion surface visualized in practice. Different conditions for the progress of the process are here accumulated at different locations of the furnace chamber. Apparently, the formation of sections of well-mixed mixture whose combustion results in a significant temperature rise predominates in the low-temperature range. This rise, in turn, guarantees the conditions requisite for the burnout of the remaining mixture in the primarily diffusional process on the interfaces of the individual concentration zones. Just as for the simple diffusion flame, intensification of mixing (or, conversely, its strong lag) is continuously related to the increase in the heat elimination and leads to extinction in the limit. The presence of different conditions for the progress of the combustion process in the individual sections of the combustion chamber makes the role of the individual parameters (for example, the average velocity, etc.), and their influence on the total, final characteristics of the process especially complex.

Meanwhile, all possible combinations of fuel and air distributions are encountered in the combustion chamber, including those most favorable for the progress of combustion. These latter are incendiary points of a kind which increase the total stability of the combustion process. Indeed, stable combustion of completely unmixed gases occurs over considerably wider limits (for example, over the average excess air, its average velocity, etc.) than does the combustion of the well-mixed mixture.

Precisely this complexity of the process, related primarily to division of the whole furnace space into a larger number of miniature "combustion chambers" distributed in the total flow in a

[9] Formed, for example, in the evaporation of drops of liquid fuel injected into air (25, 31).

complex and time-varying manner, necessitates reliance on the
introduction of total quantities and approximate estimates (for example, the introduction of the "turbulent time" τ_D, the addition of
τ_D and τ'_K, etc., see section 3-4) in order to explain even the
basic, elementary, and qualitative laws.

The conclusions thus obtained were presented in Chapter 3; they
reduce to the predominance of kinetic combustion in the range of
low values of the temperature, and of turbulent diffusion combustion in the range of high values of the temperature. Just as in the
rest of the cases of turbulent combustion, the theory of the thermal
region gives only a general physical picture of the phenomenon
here, which is necessary to the comprehension of the relations observed in the actual process; specific conclusions must be based
on experimental data.

7-3. GAS MOTION WITH HEAT SUPPLY

It has been assumed up to now that gas combustion occurs for
velocities which are small in comparison with the speed of sound.
This assumption permitted changes in pressure during combustion
in the flow to be left out of the considerations, and the kinetic energy to be neglected in comparison with the heat content. Now let
us consider peculiarities of gas motion with heat supply, without
limiting the possible values of the velocity. Briefly, these peculiarities reduce to the following (1, 10): In the general case, the
heat supplied to the gas is expended not only in the change in its
heat content but also, partially, in the change of the directed trans-
lational kinetic energy; the importance of the latter increases as
the velocity increases. It is also obvious that the heat supply influences the parameters of a gas flow moving at sub- or supersonic speed in an opposite manner; for example, the velocity increases in the first case and decreases in the second, etc.[10]

Let us be limited to the simplest case of stationary, one-dimensional gas motion in which the sections to which heat is supplied
(1-2 on Figure 7-5) will be considered to be very short, in which
connection we shall assume that the cross-sectional areas F_1 and
F_2 are equal and we shall also neglect friction and heat losses.
This assumption corresponds to a straight flame front normal to
the flow (Figure 7-5 b) or to a comparatively short cylindrical
combustion chamber (Figure 7-5 a); finally, the results presented
below also refer to an oblique flame front, if the normal component
of the gas velocity w_n, perpendicular to the front (Figure 7-5 c) is

---

[10] The "reverse-effects" law in gas flows, see (10).

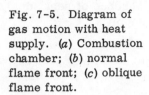

Fig. 7-5. Diagram of
gas motion with heat
supply. (a) Combustion
chamber; (b) normal
flame front; (c) oblique
flame front.

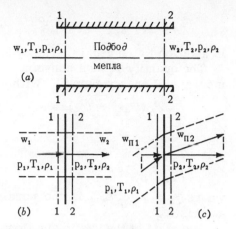

substituted in all the relations instead of the velocity. For simplicity, let us speak below of flow in a cylindrical chamber.

If the velocity at the chamber input is less than the local sonic
velocity, then heat supply leads to an increase in the absolute velocity and in its ratio to the sonic velocity (the number $M = W/a$,
where $a = \sqrt{kgRT}$ is the speed of sound). The gas pressure and
density therefore drop; the gas temperature rises, but its growth
is limited. The maximum gas heating occurs at $M = 1/\sqrt{k}$, where
k, equal to c_p/c_v, is the isentropic index (10). The gas temperature drops with the further supply of heat and increase in the velocity; its quantitative drop is a very insignificant part of the maximum value, on the order of 1 to 2 per cent, at $M = 1/\sqrt{k}$. In turn,
an increase in the gas velocity with heat supply is also limited by
the attainment of a velocity equal to the sonic velocity [$M_2 = 1$ (10)],
at the chamber exit. This means the occurrence of a limiting,
maximum value of the number M_1 at the chamber inlet for a given
mixture heat productivity, i.e., a limitation in the mixture discharge through a unit cross section or, on the other hand, a limitation of the quantity of heat which can be supplied to 1 kg of gas
at a given M_1 number.[11]

For a quantitative computation of the relations connected to the
heat supply, it is convenient to express the change in the velocity
and in the state parameters as a function of the nondimensional
characteristics, the number $M = w/a = w/\sqrt{kp/\rho}$, and the reduced
velocity $\lambda = w/a_{cr}$, where a_{cr} is the so-called critical velocity
(the value of the velocity at $M = 1$, see below). It is also expedient
to introduce the flow stagnation temperature T_* for $c_p =$ const according to the equality

[11] The "thermal crisis" phenomenon first mentioned by G. N.
Abramovich (1).

$$T_* = T + \frac{Aw^2}{2_g c_\rho} \qquad \text{(for } w = 0, \ T = T_*) \qquad (7\text{-}29)$$

in addition to the usual thermodynamic temperature.

The quantity T_* is a constant in the absence of heat supply (and mechanical energy supply). With heat supply

$$q = c_p \left(T_{*2} - T_{*1} \right) \qquad (7\text{-}30)$$

or

$$\frac{T_{*2}}{T_{*1}} = 1 + \overline{q}_*$$

where $\overline{q}_* = q/(c_p T_{*1})$ is the nondimensional preheating characteristic.

The state of the gas in any flow cross section in which the stagnation temperature equals $T_* = T + A \left[w^2/(2_y c_p) \right]$ can be characterized by the value of the critical speed a_{cr} which would occur if the actual speed became equal to the local speed of sound in an energetically insulated process, i.e., for the same value of T_*. Keeping in mind the usual thermodynamic formula $c_p = ARk/(k-1)$ for the specific heat of an ideal gas at constant pressure, the expression (7-29) for the stagnation temperature can be rewritten as

$$T_* = T \left(1 + \frac{Aw^2}{2_g c_p T} \right) = T \left(1 + \frac{k-1}{2} M^2 \right)$$

$$= \frac{(k-1)w^2}{2 \, \text{kg} R} \left(1 + \frac{2}{(k-1)M^2} \right) \qquad (7\text{-}31)$$

We have $w = a_{cr}$ for $M = 1$, where

$$a_{cr} = \sqrt{\frac{2gk}{k+1}} \, RT_* = a \, \sqrt{\frac{2}{k+1}} \, \sqrt{1 + \frac{k-1}{2} M^2} \qquad (7\text{-}32)$$

is the critical velocity. In conformance with this, the reduced velocity $\lambda = w/a_{cr}$ and $M = w/a$ are interrelated by means of

$$\lambda^2 = \frac{\dfrac{k+1}{2} M^2}{1 + \dfrac{k-1}{2} M^2} \ ; \qquad M^2 = \frac{\dfrac{2}{k+1} \lambda^2}{1 + \dfrac{k-1}{k+1} \lambda^2} \qquad (7\text{-}33)$$

($\lambda = 0$ for $M = 0$; $\lambda = 1$ for $M = 1$; $\lambda = \lambda_{max} = \sqrt{\dfrac{k+1}{k-1}}$ for $M = \infty$).

The expression for the stagnation temperature (7-31) can also be written as

$$T_* = \frac{T}{1 - \dfrac{k-1}{k+1} \lambda^2}$$

Now, let us derive the most important relations for a flow with heat supply.

From the continuity equation

$$\rho_2 w_2 = \rho_1 w_1 \qquad (7\text{-}34)$$

and the momentum equation

$$p_2 + \rho_2 w_2^2 = p_1 + \rho_1 w_1^2 = \text{const} \qquad (7\text{-}35)$$

there follows

$$\frac{w_2}{w_1} = \frac{\rho_1}{\rho_2} \qquad (7\text{-}36)$$

and

$$\frac{p_2}{p_1} = 1 - \frac{\rho_1 w_1^2}{p_1}\left(\frac{w_2}{w_1} - 1\right) = 1 - kM_1^2\left(\frac{w_2}{w_1} - 1\right)$$

$$= \frac{1 + k_1 M_1^2}{1 + k_2 M_2^2} \qquad (7\text{-}37)$$

The latter, in particular, means that the process of rarefaction of a gas moving in a cylindrical combustion chamber is mapped by a straight line in the pv diagram since $w_2/w_1 = v_2/v_1 = \rho_1/\rho_2$, where $v = 1/\rho$ is the specific volume (Figure 7-6 a).

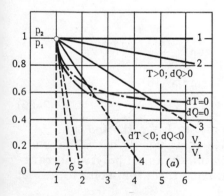
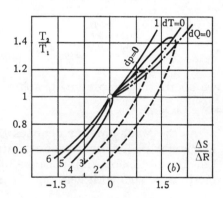

Fig. 7-6. Rarefaction of a gas moving in a cylindrical pipe (for $k = 1.4$).
(a) Change in the state of a gas in the pv plane (pressure–specific volume).
$1—M = 0$; $2—M_1 = 0.15$; $3—M_1 = 0.3$; $4—M_1 = 0.45$; $5—M_1 = 1/\sqrt{k}$;
$6—M_1 = 1$; $7—M_1 = \infty$.
(b) Change in the state of a gas in the temperature–entropy plane;
$1—M_1 = 0$; $2—M_1 = 0.45$; $3—M_1 = 0.55$; $4—M_1 = 1/\sqrt{k}$; $5—M_1 = 1$;
$6—M_1 = \infty$.
Solid line, heat supply; dashed and dotted line, maximum stagnation temperature ($dQ = 0$); dashed line, heat elimination; dashed and double-dotted line, maximum thermodynamic temperature ($dT = 0$).

Substituting in (7-37)

$$\frac{p_2}{p_1} = \frac{\rho_2 T_2}{\rho_1 T_1}$$

we also obtain an expression relating the temperature and the velocity

$$\frac{T_2}{T_1} = \frac{w_2}{w_1}\left[1 - kM_1^2\left(\frac{w_2}{w_1} - 1\right)\right] \qquad (7\text{-}38)$$

The expression obtained relates the change in all the state parameters to the velocity. Let us note that the last equation shows that the gas temperature passes through an extremum (maximum) for a continuous increase in the speed.[12]

The physical meaning of this phenomenon is that the gas rarefaction for significant values of velocity (in the range $1/\sqrt{k} \leqslant M \leqslant 1$) occurs so intensely that part of the internal gas energy is expended in addition to the heat supplied to increase the kinetic energy. This can be shown graphically if the local variable polytropic index is introduced according to the equation

$$\frac{dp}{p} = n\,\frac{d\rho}{\rho}$$

Comparing this equality with (7-35) in differential form

$$dp + \rho\,w\,dw = 0;$$

$$\frac{dp}{p} = -\frac{\rho w^2}{p}\frac{dw}{w} = kM^2\frac{d\rho}{\rho}\ \left(\rho w = \mathrm{const}\ \frac{d\rho}{\rho} = -\frac{dw}{w}\right)$$

we obtain the simple and graphical formula (10)

$$n = kM^2 \qquad (7\text{-}39)$$

As the Mach number changes from 0 to $1/\sqrt{k}$, the index of the elementary polytropic process varies continuously between 0 and 1, i.e., the continuous interchange of infinitely small polytropic rarefactions occurs with heat supply, starting from the isobaric ($n = 0$;

---

[12] From (7-38) it follows that

$$\frac{d(T_2/T_1)}{d(w_2/w_1)} = 1 + kM_1^2 - 2kM_1^2\,\frac{w_2}{w_1} = 0;$$

$$\frac{d^2(T_2/T_1)}{d(w_2/w_1)^2} = -2kM_1^2 < 0;$$

$$\frac{T_2}{T_1} = \frac{T_{max}}{T_1} = \frac{(1 + kM_1^2)^2}{4kM_1^2}\ \text{ for }\ \frac{w_2}{w_1} = \frac{1 + k_1M_1^2}{2kM_1^2}$$

$dp = 0$) to the isothermal ($n = 1$; $dT = 0$). A further increase in M in the subsonic range corresponds to the change in n from 1 to $n = k$, i.e., to a change in the process from isothermal ($n = 1$; $M = 1/\sqrt{k}$) to isentropic ($n = k$; $dS = 0$; $M = 1$). Within this range, heat is supplied for gas rarefaction but the temperature drops. Finally, $k = n = \infty$ will correspond to $1 \leqslant M \leqslant \infty$ in the supersonic range, an increase in M is possible with heat elimination and a further drop in the temperature; the thermodynamic process changes from isentropic ($M = 1$) to isochoric ($M \rightarrow \infty$; $dp = 0$).

Now, let us express the values of w_2/w_1 and T_{*2}/T_{*1} as functions of λ_1 and λ_2, keeping in mind (7-37)

$$\frac{p_2}{p_1} = \frac{1 + kM_1^2}{1 + kM_2^2}$$

The Mach number ratio in two cross sections of the flow for a cylindrical pipe ($\rho w = $ const) can be represented as

$$\frac{M_2^2}{M_1^2} = \frac{w_2^2}{w_1^2}\frac{T_1}{T_2} = \frac{w_2^2}{w_1^2}\frac{p_1}{p_2}\frac{\rho_2}{\rho_1} = \frac{w_2}{w_1}\frac{p_1}{p_2} = \frac{w_2}{w_1}\frac{1 + kM_2^2}{1 + kM_1^2}$$

Hence, taking into account the relation (7-33) between M and λ, there follows:

$$\frac{w_2}{w_1} = \frac{\lambda_2^2}{\lambda_1^2}\frac{1 + \lambda_1^2}{1 + \lambda_2^2} \tag{7-40}$$

and also taking (7-31′) into account

$$\frac{T_{*2}}{T_{*1}} = \frac{T_2}{T_1}\frac{1 - \dfrac{k-1}{k+1}\lambda_1^2}{1 + \dfrac{k-1}{k+1}\lambda_2^2} = \frac{w_1}{w_2}\frac{1 + kM_1^2}{1 + kM_2^2}\frac{1 - \dfrac{k-1}{k+1}\lambda_1^2}{1 - \dfrac{k-1}{k+1}\lambda_2^2}$$

or, finally, after simple manipulations

$$\frac{T_{*2}}{T_{*1}} = \frac{\lambda_2^2}{\lambda_1^2}\left(\frac{1 + \lambda_1^2}{1 + \lambda_2^2}\right)^2 \tag{7-41}$$

Let us consider the gas parameters given at the input to the chamber. Then, it follows from formula (7-40) that the velocity will increase continuously as λ_2 increases from a certain number $\lambda_1 < 1$ to $\lambda_{2\,max}$. In opposition to this continuous increase in λ_2, there corresponds the limited growth of T_{*2} to the value $\lambda_2 = 1$ after which T_{*2} drops.

Actually, from the equality

$$\frac{d\left(\dfrac{T_{*2}}{T_{*1}}\right)}{d\lambda_2^2} = \frac{(1 + \lambda_1^2)^2}{\lambda_1^2}\frac{d}{d\lambda_2^2}\left[\frac{\lambda_2^2}{(1 + \lambda_2^2)^2}\right] = 0$$

there follows

$$(1 + \lambda_2)^2 - 2\lambda_2^2 (1 + \lambda_2^2) = 0$$

or finally

$$\lambda_2^2 = 1$$

In correspondence with the thermodynamic explanation presented above, this means that the reduced velocity λ_2 and, according to (7-40), the absolute motion velocity w_2 will increase, for a supply of heat and an increase in the stagnation temperature $T_{*2} = T_{*1} + q/c_p$, just to the establishment of a value of the velocity equal to the sonic velocity in section 2 at the exit from the chamber (or beyond the flame front):[13]

$$\lambda_2 = M_2 = 1; \qquad w_2 = a_2 = a_{cr\ 2}$$

The region at which $M_2 = 1$ is evidently limiting. From the formulas presented above, it follows that the greatest possible pressure drop corresponds thereto (for infinitely high initial heating)

$$\frac{P_2}{P_1} = \frac{p_{min}}{p_1} = \frac{1}{1+k} \qquad \text{for } M_1 \approx 0; \ M_2 = 1; \ q_* \rightarrow \infty$$

$$\text{for } k = 1.4, \qquad \frac{\Delta p_{max}}{p_1} = \frac{k}{1+k} \approx 60 \text{ per cent}$$

For a finite, nonzero value of M_1, the limiting ratio of the pressure for $M_2 = 1$ equals

$$\frac{p_2}{p_1} = \frac{1 + kM_1^2}{1+k}$$

and the maximum increase in the velocity, in turn, equals

$$\frac{w_2}{w_1} = \frac{a_{cr\ 2}}{w_1} = \frac{1 + \lambda_1^2}{2\lambda_1^2} = \frac{1 + kM_1^2}{(1+k)M_1^2}$$

From a comparison of the last formulas with the expression for w_2/w_1 at $T_2 = T_{max}$ (see previous footnote on page 272) it follows that the ratio of the value of the critical speed $a_{cr\ 2}$ at $M_2 = 1$ to the value of the velocity at which the gas temperature is a maximum, equals

$$\frac{a_{cr\ 2}}{w_{T_m}} = \frac{2k}{k+1} = \frac{T_{*max}}{T}$$

---

[13] A further increase in the values of λ_2 and w_2 is possible upon a transition to heat elimination in supersonic flow (a thermal nozzle, see (10)).

(where $T_{*\,max}$ and T_{max} are, respectively, the maximum value of the stagnation temperature at $M_2 = 1$ and of the thermodynamic temperature at $M_2 = 1/\sqrt{k}$ for the same value of the number M_1). Finally, the ratio of the values of the limiting temperature at the output at $M_2 = 1$ and the maximum temperature at $M_2 = 1/\sqrt{k}$ equals from (7-38)

$$\frac{T_{M=1}}{T_{max}} = \frac{4k}{(1+k)^2} < 1$$

The character of the variation of all the gas parameters with heat supplied to a subsonic flow is illustrated on Figure 7-7.

Let us dwell in rather more detail on the questions related to heat supply.

From Eq. (7-41) $M_2 = \lambda_2 = 1$, we obtain a relation between the characteristic of heat supply and the initial value of the reduced velocity

$$\frac{T_{*\,max}}{T_{*1}} = \left(\frac{1+\lambda_1^2}{2\lambda_1}\right)^2; \quad \bar{q}_{*\,max} = \frac{T_{*\,max}}{T_{*1}} - 1 = \left(\frac{1-\lambda_1^2}{2\lambda_1}\right)^2 \qquad (7\text{-}42)$$

For $\lambda_1 = 1$, evidently $T_{*\,max}/T_{*1} = 1$; $\bar{q}_* = 0$, the heat supply is zero.

Shown on Figure 7-8a is a curve of the reduced velocity λ_1 at the chamber input as a function of the quantity $\bar{q}_{*\,max}$ for the $\lambda_2 = 1$ case and presented on Figure 7-8b is a series of curves of λ_2 as a function of λ_1 with the parameter $\bar{q}_*$ for a subsonic flow. These graphs illustrate the above-mentioned relationships.

More graphic results can be obtained if the quantity $\bar{q}_* = q/c_p T_{*1}$ is replaced by a similar nondimensional characteristic of gas heating, referred to the initial heat content: $\bar{q} = q/c_p T_1$. The relation between $\bar{q}_*$ and $\bar{q}$ is evident:

$$\bar{q} = \bar{q}_* \frac{T_*}{T_1} = \bar{q}_* \left(1 - \frac{k-1}{k+1}\lambda_1^2\right)$$

Let us rewrite Eq. (7-42) thus

$$\bar{q}\left(1 - \frac{k-1}{k+1}\lambda_1^2\right) = \left(\frac{\lambda_1^2 - 1}{2\lambda_1}\right)^2 \qquad (7\text{-}43)$$

or after manipulation

$$\lambda_1^4 - 2\,\frac{1 + 2\bar{q}}{1 + 4\dfrac{k-1}{k+1}\bar{q}}\,\lambda_1^2 + 1 = 0$$

Let us find, hence, the value of the reduced velocity $\lambda_1 M$ for $\lambda_2 = 1$

$$\lambda_{1M}{}^2 = \frac{1 + 2\overline{q}}{1 + 4\dfrac{k-1}{k+1}\overline{q}} \left[1 \pm \sqrt{1 - \frac{1 + 4\dfrac{k-1}{k+1}\overline{q}}{1 + 2\overline{q}}} \right] \qquad (7\text{-}44)$$

The positive sign in front of the radical corresponds to the value $\lambda_{1M} > 1$, supersonic flow velocity, the negative sign to $\lambda_{1M} < 1$, subsonic velocity. As will be shown in the next section, the first case corresponds to detonation, the second to maximum gas velocity at the chamber inlet (or to the greatest possible sub-

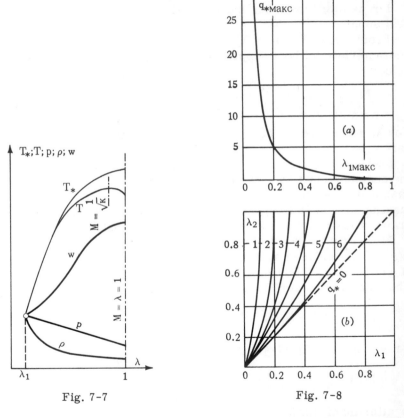

Fig. 7-7

Fig. 7-8

Fig. 7-7. Change in the parameters of the state of a gas moving in a cylindrical pipe with heat supply.

Fig. 7-8. Dependence of the reduced velocity λ on the heat-supply characteristic ($\overline{q}_* = q/c_p T_{*1}$). (a) Relation between the maximum values of the heat-supply characteristics and the reduced velocity at the chamber input (for $\lambda_2 = 1$); (b) dependence of the reduced velocity at the chamber exit on its inlet value and the heating characteristics.

sonic rate of propagation of a normal plane flame front) as the gas accelerates to $\lambda_2 = 1$ during the combustion process.

Equation (7-44) can be replaced (2) for the latter case for $\bar{q} > 1$ with an accuracy of the order of 2 per cent by

$$\lambda_1^2{}_{max} \approx \frac{1}{2 + 4\bar{q}} \tag{7-45}$$

Let us turn to a numerical example. Let us assume that we speak of the ignition of a hot mixture with a heat productivity $q = 600$ kcal/kg. Let us assume the initial gas temperature to be $300°K$ and the average specific heat of the combustion products to be $c_p = 0.33$ kcal/kg deg. Hence, the quantity $\bar{q} = 6$. We find from (7-45) that the greatest possible value of the reduced velocity at the chamber input is

$$\lambda_{1\ max} \approx \sqrt{\frac{1}{26}} = 0.195; \quad T_{*_1} = T_1 \left(1 - \frac{k-1}{k+1} \lambda_1{}^2\right)^{-1}$$

$$\approx 303°K \approx T_1, \text{ (for } k = 1.3\text{)}$$

$$a_{cr\ 1} \approx 335 \text{ m/sec}$$

The maximum gas velocity at the input is

$$w_{1\ max} = \lambda_1 a_{cr\ 1} = 0.195 \times 335 \approx 65 \text{ m/sec}$$

Let us also determine the parameters at the exit. From the formulas presented above there follows:

$$\frac{T_2}{T_1} \approx 5.85; \quad T_2 \approx 1750°K : \frac{w_2}{w_1} \approx 13.5; \quad w_2 \approx 870 \text{ m/sec};$$

$$\frac{p_2}{p_1} \approx 0.44$$

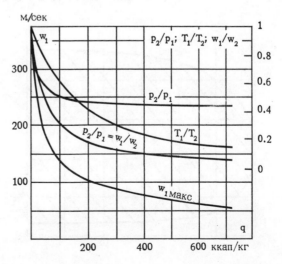

Fig. 7-9. Example of computing the chamber parameters for limiting heating. ($M_2 = 1$, $T_1 = 300°$ K; $c_p = 0.33$ kcal/kg deg.)

Presented on Figure 7-9 are the results of a computation for the same values $T_1 = 300°K$ and a variable value of the mixture heat productivity from $q = 0$ to $q \approx 750$ kcal/kg.

All these results refer to the $M_2 = 1$ case. For $M_2 < 1$, the computation should be made according to the relations presented above in which the sequence is determined by assigning the conditions at the chamber inlet or exit.

Hence, it is not difficult to determine limiting relations for flame propagation which will correspond to the greatest possible acceleration of the combustion products at the output from the flame front. In conformance with this, the quantity $\lambda_{1\ max}$ from (7-44) is the maximum reduced rate of combustion propagation, the actual value λ_1 (within the limits from $\lambda_1 = 0$ to $\lambda_1 = \lambda_{1\ max}$) cannot be determined from just one of the equations of gas dynamics; its determination is possible when the kinetic mechanism of the reaction rate and the processes of heat and concentration transport are considered, as has already been shown in Chapter 6.

Let us again return to (7-44). Both its roots correspond to real physical phenomena (2-10). The approximate expression, analogous to (7-45), for supersonic flow at $\lambda_{1M} > 1$ is (2)

$$\lambda_{1\ min} = \frac{2 + 4\overline{q}}{1 + 4\dfrac{k-1}{k+1}\overline{q}} \tag{7-46}$$

The dependence of λ_{1M} from (7-44) on the characteristic q is given on Figure 7-10. The lower branch of the curve refers to combustion in a subsonic flow, the region below it corresponds to an infinite set of possible values of the flame propagation rate

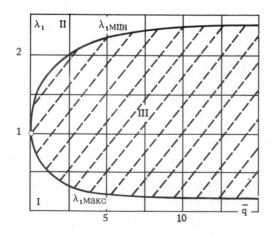

Fig. 7-10. The reduced combustion propagation rate as a function of the nondimensional caloricity. $\lambda_{1\ max}$—Maximum value for subsonic flow; $\lambda_{1\ min}$—minimum value for supersonic flow; I—region of slow combustion; II—region of nonstationary detonation; III—region in which stationary combustion is not possible.

(from 0 to $\lambda_{1\,max}$), the upper branch of the curve and the region above it correspond, respectively, to the minimum value of the stationary combustion propagation rate in a supersonic flow $\lambda_{1\,min}$ and the infinite set of theoretically possible values of the propagation rate from $\lambda_{1\,min}$ to $\lambda_{1\,max} = \sqrt{(k + 1)/(k - 1)}$.

The crosshatched region (within the curve $\lambda_{1M} = \lambda\,(q)$) corresponds to stationarily impossible regions; here λ_{1M} becomes imaginary.

It will be shown in the next section that a single-valued dependence $\lambda_{1\,min} = \lambda(\bar{q})$ according to (7-44) or approximately (7-46), i.e., the upper branch on Figure 7-10, corresponds to stationary flame propagation in a supersonic flow (detonation) for the natural development of the process (i.e., without forced ignition).

As regards the computation of the changes in the state parameters as a supersonic flow passes through a flame front, all the above-mentioned quantitative relations remain valid if it is assumed therein that $\lambda_1 > 1$ or $M_1 > 1$.

As has already been remarked, the physical picture of the influence of heat supply in a supersonic flow will be similar to a mirror image of the dependence for subsonic flow. Heat supply at $M_1 > 1$ leads to a drop in the absolute and relative (M, λ) velocity and to the growth of the temperature, density, and pressure.

The "thermal crisis" phenomenon limits the drop in the velocity up to the limiting value $M_2 = 1$ (if the heat supply is not accompanied by an adiabatic shock which transforms the flow into subsonic). The thermal crisis phenomenon limits the minimum value $\lambda_{1\,min}$ ahead of a detonation wave front for a given value of mixture heat productivity (see section 7-4).

7-4. STATIONARY PROPAGATION OF DETONATION

As has been mentioned by V. A. Mikhel' son (32), the incendiary mechanism of a hot mixture during detonation combustion consists in shock compression of the gas into an adiabatic compression shock. The mixture is preheated to a very high temperature of the order of 2000 to 3000°K and higher because of the compression. The reaction rate is exceptionally high at such temperatures and in this connection, self-ignition of the mixture occurs. The liberation of energy in the combustion zone of a detonation wave guarantees its continuous propagation with an undamped velocity, in contrast to a shockwave being propagated in an inert gas. As is known, the latter is continuously retarded because of energy dissipation in the shock, and it degenerates into an acoustic sound wave at a known distance from the location of the explosion.

A detonation wave can be visualized as the combination of two successive shocks, an adiabatic shockwave and a flame front (2, 10, 14). The extent of the first layer, the compression shock, is so small (on the order of a molecule free path) that any chemical reaction which requires a very large number of collisions for its realization is practically absent therein (14). The reaction occurs very rapidly in the combustion zone following the shockwave because of the high preheating; consequently, the size of this zone is also small in absolute value, although it exceeds the shockwave width by many hundreds and thousands of times.

Since the quantitative relations for all the waves as a whole remain the same as for just a single combustion zone, let us use (7-41) in order to show the reader unacquainted with shockwave theory (10) the basic laws required to comprehend the latter.

Let us transform in (7-41) from the ratio of the stagnation temperatures T_{*2}/T_{*1} to the quantity $\bar{q}_* = (T_{*2}/T_{*1}) - 1$

$$\bar{q}_* = \frac{\lambda_2^2(1+\lambda_1^2)^2}{\lambda_1^2(1+\lambda_2^2)^2} - 1 = \frac{(\lambda_2^2 - \lambda_1^2)(1-\lambda_1^2\lambda_2^2)}{\lambda_1^2(1+\lambda_2^2)^2} \qquad (7\text{-}47)$$

Equation (7-47) has been written for the process with heat supply; it is evidently suitable also for the particular case $q_* = 0$, the absence of heat supply. There follows from (7-47) for this condition ($\bar{q}_* = 0$, $T_{*2} = T_{*1}$)

$$\lambda_1 = \lambda_2$$

(that is, $T_2 = T_1$, $w_2 = w_1$, $p_2 = p_1$, etc., a trivial relation for the same gas state) or

$$\lambda_1\lambda_2 = 1; \qquad w_1 w_2 = a_{cr}^2 \qquad (7\text{-}48)$$

Expression (7-48) shows the possibility of adiabatic rearrangement of the flow, its jump-like transition from the supersonic flow region $\lambda_1 > 1$ to the subsonic $\lambda_2 = 1/\lambda_1 < 1$ or, apparently, conversely from the subsonic $\lambda_1 < 1$ into the supersonic $\lambda_2 = 1/\lambda_1 > 1$.

It is not difficult to show that the second case is thermodynamically impossible (10, 13c), since it contradicts the second law of thermodynamics. Without relying on a computation, let us show this by using the curve of the change of state of the gas moving along a "thermal nozzle" (10) shown on Figure 7-6 in the TS plane. Shown on Figure 7-11 schematically is the curve of the temperature and entropy change for a gas being rarefied with heat supply in subsonic flow in a pipe of constant cross section along the line A-M to the point M-1, and continuing to be rarefied with heat elimination along the line M-B.

Let us select a certain point 1 on the upper branch of the curve and let us find the point 2 on its lower branch which satisfies the condition $T_{*2} = T_{*1}$. Let us note that the quantity of heat supplied to the gas in the section 1-M is measured by the area crosshatched by vertical lines $(Q = - \int\limits_{1}^{M} T\,dS)$ and the quantity of heat liberated from the section $M - 2$ is, respectively, the area crosshatched by horizontal lines $(Q = - \int\limits_{2}^{M} T\,dS)$.

It is evident that the equality of these areas is possible if and only if the point 2 is to the left (in the region of lower values of the entropy) of the point 1. Therefore, a jump-like transition from the state 1 to 2 would mean a decrease in the entropy in an isolated system and the transition from 2 to 1, means an increase. The first case is evidently impossible.[14]

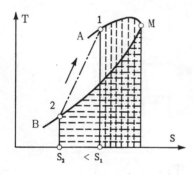

Fig. 7-11. Adiabatic shock in the TS diagram (temperature-entropy). $2 \rightarrow 1$—compression shock $(\Delta S = S_2 - S_1 > 0)$; $1 \rightarrow 2$—rarefaction shock (impossible; $\Delta S = S_1 - S_2 < 0)$.

Hence, the "spontaneous" rearrangement of the flow (which actually occurs under the influence of some kind of perturbation) is possible only with the transition from a supersonic flow region $(\lambda_1 > 1)$ to the subsonic $(\lambda_2 < 1)$. In particular, the latter means that the combustion zone in a detonation wave behind the shock-wave is the usual flame front in a subsonic flow.

The diagram of the detonation wave is shown on Figure 7-12. To be graphic, it is assumed that the wave is immobile and the gas flows

---

[14] The fact that the process of gas motion along a tube of constant cross section with heat supply and elimination is relied upon to prove the impossibility of adiabatic rarefaction shocks in a perfect gas is understandably inessential. We speak only of the comparison of the initial and final states of the gas, and the actual curve of the process plays no part at all here. In an adiabatic shock, just as in the transition from state 1 to state 2, or conversely in a thermal nozzle, three conservation equations are satisfied: matter ($\rho w = $ const), momentum ($p + \rho w^2 = $ const), and energy ($T_* = $ const); however, the transition toward the pressure drop (1-2), possible in a thermal nozzle in connection with the heat liberation to the surrounding medium, and the drop in the entropy in just one part of the system, contradicts the second principle for an isolated system, which is an adiabatic shock.

to it with the velocity λ_1 (equal to the wave propagation velocity relative to the fixed gas), is retarded to the value of the reduced velocity $\lambda_2 = 1/\lambda_1$ in the first layer of the wave, the shockwave 1-2, and is then again accelerated with the supply of heat in the subsonic flame front ($\lambda_2 < 1$) 2-3 to the value λ_3. In order to transform to the absolute values of the velocity with respect to the fixed gas the value of w_1, the wave propagation velocity (see Figure 7-12) should be subtracted from the quantities w_1, w_2, and w_3.

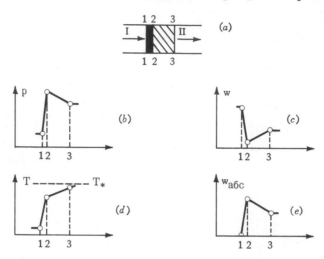

Fig. 7-12. Diagram of a detonation wave. (a) Diagram of the wave; I—fresh mixture; 1-2—shockwave; 2-3—combustion zone; II—combustion products; (b), (c), (d), (e) change in the pressure, velocity (relative to the wave), temperature, and absolute velocity of the gas (for propagation of the detonation in a fixed burning mixture) in the detonation wave.

Let us note that the formulas presented in section 7-3 are suitable to the computation of the change of state of a gas and the velocity over the whole wave; they are retained also for the computation of the second layer of the wave of the combustion zone 2-3. As regards the computational relations for the adiabatic shockwave 1-2, the latter can be derived without difficulty from the relations for the flame front by the substitution $\lambda_1 \cdot \lambda_2 = 1$ (7-48) into the latter.

For example, we have for the ratio of the values of the temperature on both sides of the adiabatic shock ($T_{*2} = T_{*1}$; $\lambda_2 = 1/\lambda_1$)

$$\frac{T_2}{T_1} = \frac{T_{*2}}{T_{*1}} \frac{1 - \dfrac{k-1}{k+1}\lambda_2^2}{1 - \dfrac{k-1}{k+1}\lambda_1^2} = \frac{1 - \dfrac{k-1}{k+1}\dfrac{1}{\lambda_1^2}}{1 - \dfrac{k-1}{k+1}\lambda_1^2}$$

where $T_2/T_1 = 11.6$ for $\lambda_1 = 2.35$ and $k = 1.4$, if $T_1 = 300°K$
$T_2 = 3500°K$.

Let us also present the formula for the change in the velocity
by substituting the following relation in (7-40)

$$\frac{w_2}{w_1} = \frac{1}{\lambda_1^2} \qquad (7\text{-}49)$$

(the velocity changes ~ 5.5 times in the example presented above).

Now, let us show[15] that the stationary propagation of detonation
occurs at a velocity corresponding to the limiting case at which
the value of the reduced velocity equals unity at the exit from the
combustion zone: $\lambda_3 = 1$.

Let us consider first the picture of the shockwave attenuation in
an inert medium (Figure 7-13 a).

As is seen from the graph, the value of the reduced velocity of
the wave λ_1 drops with distance from the location of the explosion
and the value $\lambda_2 = 1/\lambda_1$, the reduced gas velocity behind the wave
front, increases. In the limit, both values converge and the shockwave degenerates into a sound wave for $\lambda_1 = \lambda_2 = 1$.

If the shockwave is propagated in a burning mixture then a combustion zone can arise behind it. The quantity $[\bar{q}_* = q/(c_p T_{*1})] =$
$[q/(c_p T_1)][1 - (k-1)/(k+1)\lambda^2]$ is very small for a very high propagation rate $[\bar{q}_* = q = 0$ in the limit for $\lambda_1^2 = \lambda_{max}^2 = (k+1)/(k-1)]$.
In this case, the reduced velocity of the combustion products with
respect to the zone λ_3 is practically in agreement with the quantity
λ_2 behind the shock: $\lambda_3 \approx \lambda_2$.

Fig. 7-13. Diagram of stationary propagation of detonation.
(a) Shockwave attenuation in an
inert medium; (b) change in the
reduced velocity in a detonation
wave which occurs as a result
of an explosion.

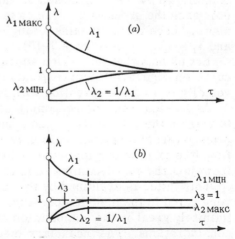

[15] Following the work of G. N. Abramovich and the author of this book (2);
see (10) for details.

As the shockwave weakens, i.e., the value of λ_1 is reduced and λ_2 is increased, the value of λ_3 also increases since the quantity $\bar{q}_*$ increases as λ_1 decreases. Quantitative relations are easily traced by (7-41) and (7-47) and Figure 7-8b for the subsonic flame front (the value of λ_1 on Figure 7-8b corresponds to λ_2 and the value of λ_2 corresponds to λ_3 for a detonation wave).

After the value λ_3 has become equal to unity ("thermal crisis," section 7-3), a further increase in the velocity of the combustion products with heat supply becomes impossible. In conformance with this, a further increase in the value of λ_2 ahead of the flame front and, therefore, a drop in the value of $\lambda_1 = 1/\lambda_2$, the reduced propagation velocity of a detonation wave, also becomes impossible. The wave motion proceeds at a constant velocity $\lambda_{1\,min}$ for $\lambda_3 = 1$ (see Figure 7-13b).

The explanation presented shows why the stationary propagation of detonation is impossible with a velocity λ_1 less than that which corresponds to the thermal crisis for the combustion products at the exit from the wave ($\lambda_3 = 1$, upper branch of the $\lambda_1 = \lambda(\bar{q})$ curve on Figure 7-10). As regards the impossibility of stabilizing the motion of a high-speed wave, it can be explained from purely mechanical considerations. The combustion zone, accompanying the adiabatic compression shock in the detonation wave, is a rarefaction wave (see Figure 7-12; heat supply in the subsonic zone leads to a pressure reduction). If the velocity λ_1 is larger than $\lambda_{1\,min}$ (7-44), but λ_3 is correspondingly less than unity, then the rarefaction wave 2-3 will reach the compression wave 1-2 and weaken it. Then the perturbations, being propagated at sonic speed, will be demolished by the combustion products in the $\lambda_3 = 1$ case and will not reach the shockwave. The case $\lambda_1 < \lambda_{1\,min}$ has been excluded above, hence there remains a single possible flow region for $\lambda_3 = 1$ and $\lambda_1 = \lambda_{1\,min}$ (see Figure 7-10).

Let us note that the region above the upper branch of the $\lambda(q)$ curve on Figure 7-10 corresponds to the nonstationary detonation velocity or to its propagation with forced ignition (14).

As is seen from the reasoning presented, the problem of determining the rate of flame-front propagation for the stationary propagation of a detonation is solved completely in a supersonic flow (the total detonation wave 1-3 on Figure 7-12) by starting from just the gas-dynamics equations.

This latter is explained by the fact that the reaction rate is very rapid in the high-temperature zone, i.e., it can be considered infinitely great in the computation and thus be eliminated from the considerations. The incendiary mechanism of a hot mixture in a detonation wave is of gas-dynamic nature and is related to the shockwave being propagated at a very high rate, in connection with

which, the considerably slower phenomena of molecular and turbulent transport can also be eliminated from the considerations.

An exact computation of the detonation velocity (taking into account changes in the specific heat, the phenomenon of combustion
product dissociation at high temperatures, etc.) yields complete
agreement with experiment (14, 46).

However, the part of the kinetic phenomena, transport and reaction rate, also becomes substantial for detonation if we speak of
the character of the phenomena near the propagation limits or of
the transformation of slow combustion into detonation. The research of K. I. Shchelkin on the occurrence of detonations in rough
pipes (56), the investigations of A. S. Sokolik (46, et al.), the theoretical computations of Ia. B. Zel' dovich (14) on the determination
of the limits of detonation combustion, etc., show that both the reaction rate and the transport phenomena: heat conduction, viscosity, diffusion, play a large part in all these cases. Intensification
of these processes in the turbulent motion of a hot mixture leads
to the earlier occurrence of detonation; the losses, friction and
heat elimination, lead to the collapse of detonation and to extinction, the combined effect of flow turbulization and losses makes
the occurrence of an intermediate form of rapid combustion (wave
propagation along a spiral from one or several incendiary points,
so-called "detonation spin" (56), rapid combustion with a propagation rate on the order of several hundred meters per second,
etc.) possible near the detonation limits. A theoretical analysis
of these phenomena is made considerably more complicated by
the necessity of taking into account the gas-dynamic structure of
the flow, the formation of oblique shocks, etc. The substantial
difficulties are related here to the impossibility of considering the
phenomenon as one-dimensional, in substance, one on whose progress the local values of the temperature, velocity, etc., have a
sharp effect. Just as in the case of turbulent combustion, it is
impossible to consider the reaction rate strictly as a function of
the mean temperature, the presence of local "hot spots" determines flame propagation.

A more detailed consideration of these questions is beyond the
scope of this book; it would require complete reliance on the conceptions and computing apparatus of gas dynamics. However, it
should be noted, and this is very essential, that the results of investigations of the mechanics of the phenomena are in agreement
with the general conclusions obtained in this book from an analysis
of the thermal-combustion region.

In particular, a computation shows that the reduction in the
temperature by a quantity of order of magnitude $R T^2 M/E$ corresponds to the limit of the propagation of detonation combustion,

just as for extinction in the simple combustion case (see section 3-3).

Just so long as the subject of investigation is the stable, stationary combustion process (in any of its forms) an approximate analysis of the phenomena is possible by relying only on the general equations of material transport and energy (motion, heat propagation, and diffusion). Here, the reaction rate can be eliminated from the considerations for an effective process with high completeness of combustion and for high temperatures, by setting it infinitely large. If the research problem reduces to a clarification of the limits of existence of such a stationary process, the conditions of its occurrence and collapse, etc., then it is always necessary to consider a finite reaction rate and its temperature and concentration dependences. A qualitative picture of the phenomenon, the peculiarities of ignition and extinction, etc., can be clarified from investigations of the thermal region of the process for simple exothermal reactions, as has been shown in this book. Use of the conceptions and conclusions obtained here in an analysis of a real furnace process is a problem of the future to a considerable degree; however, they can be of substantial assistance in interpreting experimental results and in correctly formulating experimental investigations.

Bibliography

1. Abramovich, G. N.: Doklady, *Akad. Nauk SSSR*, vol. 54, p. 579, 1946.
2. Abramovich, G. N., L. A. Vulis: Doklady, *Akad. Nauk SSSR*, vol. 55, p. 511, 1947.
3. Blinov, V. I.: *Izvest. VTI*, No. 7, 1934.
4. Blinov, V. I.: *Trudy Voronezh. Gosudarst. Univ.*, vol. 11, Issue 1, 1939.
5. Buben, N. Ia., D. A. Frank-Kamenetskii: *Zhur. Fiz. Khim.*, vol. 19, p. 250, 1945; Suppl. vol., p. 148, 1947.
6. Buben, N. Ia., D. A. Frank-Kamenetskii: *Zhur. Fiz. Khim.*, vol. 20, p. 225, 1946.
7. Vulis, L. A.: *Zhur. Tekh. Fiz.*, vol. 16, pp. 83, 89, 95, 1946.
8. Vulis, L. A.: *Zhur. Tekh. Fiz.*, vol. 10, p. 1959, 1940.
9. Vulis, L. A., L. A. Vitman: *Zhur. Tekh. Fiz.*, vol. 11, pp. 509, 1115, 1941.
10. Vulis, L. A.: Termodinamika gazovykh potokov (Thermodynamics of Gas Flows). GOSENERFOIZDAT, 1950; Doklady, *Akad. Nauk SSSR*, vol. 54, p. 773, 1946.
11. Vulis, L. A.: *Zhur. Tekh. Fiz.*, vol. 20, p. 97, 1950.
12. Vyrubov, D. N.: *Zhur. Tekh. Fiz.*, vol. 9, p. 1923, 1939.
13. Zel'dovich, Ia. B., et al.: Kurs teorii goreniia, detonatsii i vzryva, pod red. (Course in the Theory of Combustion, Detonation and Explosion) Ia. B. Zel'dovich, ed.
13a. Zel'dovich, Ia. B., V. V. Voevodskii: Teplovoi vzryv i rasprostranenie plameni v gazakh, ch. I (Thermal Explosions and Flame Propagation in Gases, Part I). MMI Press, 1947.
13b. Zel'dovich, Ia. B., D. A. Frank-Kamenetskii: Turbulentnoe i geterogennoe gorenie, ch. II (Turbulent and Heterogeneous Combustion, Part II). MMI Press, 1947.
14. Zel'dovich, Ia. B.: Teoriia goreniia i detonatsii gazov (Theory of Combustion and Detonation of Gases). Akad. Nauk SSSR Press, 1944.
15. Zel'dovich, Ia. B., Iu. A. Zysin: *Zhur. Tekh. Fiz.*, vol. 11, p. 493, 1941.
16. Zel'dovich, Ia. B., D. A. Frank-Kamenetskii: *Zhur. Fiz. Khim.*, vol. 12, p. 1008, 1938.
17. Zel'dovich, Ia. B.: *Zhur. Tekh. Fiz.*, vol. 14, p. 162, 1944.
18. Zel'dovich, Ia. B.: *Zhur. Fiz. Khim.*, vol. 22, p. 27, 1948.
19. Zel'dovich, Ia. B.: *Zhur. Tekh. Fiz.*, vol. 19, p. 499, 1949.
20. Zel'dovich, Ia. B.: *Zhur. Fiz. Khim.*, vol. 13, p. 169, 1939.
21. Kantarovich, B. V.: *Zhur. Tekh. Fiz.*, vol. 12, pp. 640, 647, 1942.
22. Katsnek'son, B. D., D. A. Timofeev: Trudy, TsKTI, Book 12, Mashgiz, 1949.
23. Klibanov, Ts. A., V. V. Pomerantsev, D. A. Frank-Kamenetskii: *Zhur. Tekh. Fiz.*, vol. 12, p. 14, 1942.
24. Kondrat'ev, V. N.: Uspekhi khimii, vol. 10, Issue 1, 1941; *Zhur. Fiz. Khim.*, vol. 13, p. 1260, 1939; vol. 14, p. 287, 1940.
25. Knorre, G. F.: Topochnye protssesy (Furnace Processes). GOSENERGOIZDAT, 1951; Kurs topochnykh protsessov, ch. I, ENERGOIZDAT,

1930; ch. II, ENERGOIZDAT, 1937 (Course in Furnace Processes, Part I, 1930; Part II, 1937).

26. Kolmogorov, A. N., I. G. Petrovskii, N. S. Piskunov: *Biull.* MGU, A, 1 (Mat.-Mekh.), Issue 6, 1937.

27. Landau, L. D.: *Zhur. Eksp. i Teoret. Fiz.*, vol. 14, p. 240, 1944.

28. Landau, L. D., E. M. Livshitz: Mekhanikha sploshnykh sred (Continuum Mechanics). GOSTEKHIZDAT, 1944.

29. Loitsianskii, L. G.: Aerodinamika pogranichnogo sloia (Aerodynamics of the Boundary Layer). GTTI, 1941.

30. Lewis, B., G. von Elbe: Combustion, Flames and Explosions in Gases. Translated from the English, with supplements by D. A. Frank-Kamenetskii, ed., GIIL, 1948.

31. Minskii, E. M., D. A. Frank-Kamenetskii: Doklady, *Akad. Nauk SSSR*, vol. 50, p. 353, 1945.

32. Mikhel'son, V. A.: Collected Works, vol. 1. "Novyi agronom" Press, Moscow, 1930.

33. Mikheev, M. A.: Teploperedacha (Heat Transmission). GOSENER-GOIZDAT, 1949.

34. Predvoditelev, A. S., L. N. Khitrin, O. A. Tsukhanova, Kh. I. Kolodtsev, M. K. Grodzovskii: Gorenie ugleroda (Carbon Combustion). Akad. Nauk SSSR Press, 1949.

35. Nabaldian, A. B., V. V. Voevodskii: Mekhanizm okisleniia i goreniia vodoroda (Mechanism of Oxidation and Combustion of Hydrogen). Akad. Nauk SSSR Press, 1949.

36. Predvoditelev, A. S., O. A. Tsukhanova: *Zhur. Fiz.*, vol. 9, p. 295, 1939; vol. 10, p. 1113, 1940.

37. Ravich, M. B.: Poverkhnostnoe gorenie (Surface Combustion). Akad. Nauk SSSR Press, 1946.

38. Rakipova, Kh. A., Ia. K. Troshchin, K. I. Shchelkin: *Zhur. Tekh. Fiz.*, vol. 17, p. 1397, 1947.

39. Rezniakov, A. B.: *Vestnik Akad. Nauk Kazakh. SSSR*, No. 2(59), p. 47, 1950.

40. Sbornik (Collection): Protsess goreniia uglia (Process of Coal Combustion). A. S. Predvoditelev, ed., ONTI, 1938.

41. Sokolik, A. S.: *Uspekhi Khim.*, vol. 7, p. 976, 1938.

42. Sbornik (Collection): Issledovanie protsessov goreniia naturalnogo topliva (Investigation of the Combustion Processes of Natural Fuel). G. F. Knorre, ed., GOSENERGOIZDAT, 1948.

43. Sbornik (Collection): "Kinetika tsepnykh reaktsii okisleniia" (Kinetics of Chain Reactions of Oxidation). A. B. Nabaldian, N. M. Emanual, eds., Akad. Nauk SSSR Press, 1950.

44. Semenov, N. N.: Tsepnye reaktsii (Chain Reactions). ONTI, 1934.

45. Semenov, N. N.: *Uspekhi Fiz. Nauk*, vol. 23, Issue 3; vol. 24, Issue 4, 1940.

46. Sokolik, A. S.: Gorenie i detonatsiia v gazakh (Combustion and Detonation in Gases). GTTI, 1934; *Zhur. Fiz. Khim.*, vol. 7, p. 571, 1936; vol. 13, p. 1031, 1939.

47. Todes, O. M.: *Zhur. Fiz. Khim.*, vol. 4, pp. 78, 81, 1933.

48. Todes, O. M.: *Zhur. Fiz. Khim.*, vol. 13, pp. 868, 1594, 1939; vol. 14, p. 1026, 1940.

49. Todes, O. M., Margolis: *Izvest. Akad. Nauk SSSR, Otdel. Khim. Nauk,*
     No. 1, p. 47; No. 3, p. 275, 1946.
50. Frank-Kamenetskii, D. A.: Diffuziia i teploperedacha v khimicheskoi
     kinetike (Diffusion and Heat Transmission in Chemical Kinetics).
     Akad. Nauk SSSR Press, 1947.
51. Frank-Kamenetskii, D. A.: *Zhur. Tekh. Fiz.,* vol. 9, p. 1457, 1939;
     Doklady, *Akad. Nauk SSSR,* vol. 30, p. 729, 1941.
52. Frank-Kamenetskii, D. A.: *Zhur. Fiz. Khim.,* vol. 13, p. 756, 1939.
53. Frank-Kamenetskii, D. A.: *Uspekhi Khim.,* vol. 7, No. 9, 1938;
     vol. 10, Nos. 4 and 5, 1941.
54. Khitrin, L. N.: *Zhur. Tekh. Fiz.,* vol. 7, pp. 30, 190, 194, 691, 704,
     1937.
55. Chukhanov, Z. F.: Doklady, *Akad. Nauk SSSR,* vol. 26, p. 354, 1940;
     vol. 44, p. 297, 1944; vol. 47, p. 190, 1945; *Izvest. Akad. Nauk SSSR,*
     O.T.N., No. 1, p. 3, 1948.
55a. Chukhanov, Z. F.: Doklady, *Akad. Nauk SSSR,* vol. 81, p. 821, 1951.
56. Shchelkin, K. I.: Doklady, *Akad. Nauk SSSR,* vol. 23, p. 636, 1940;
     Zhur. Tekh. Fiz., vol. 17, p. 613, 1947.
57. Shchelkin, K. I.: *Zhur. Tekh. Fiz.,* vol. 13, p. 520, 1943.

INDEX

9545